Piano WHITE PAGES

This publication is not authorised for sale in the United States of America and/or Canada

HAL LEONARD EUROPE
Distributed by Music Sales

Exclusive Distributors:

Music Sales Limited
14-15 Berners Street, London W1T 3LJ, UK.

Music Sales Pty Limited
120 Rothschild Avenue, Rosebery, NSW
2018, Australia.

Order No. HLE90003210
ISBN 1-84609-796-7

Printed in the EU.

Your Guarantee of Quality
As publishers, we strive to produce every
book to the highest commercial standards.
The book has been carefully designed to
minimise awkward page turns and to make
playing from it a real pleasure.
Throughout, the printing and binding have
been planned to ensure a sturdy,
attractive publication which should give
years of enjoyment.
If your copy fails to meet our high
standards, please inform us and we will
gladly replace it.

www.musicsales.com

ADIA

Words and Music by SARAH McLACHLAN
and PIERRE MARCHAND

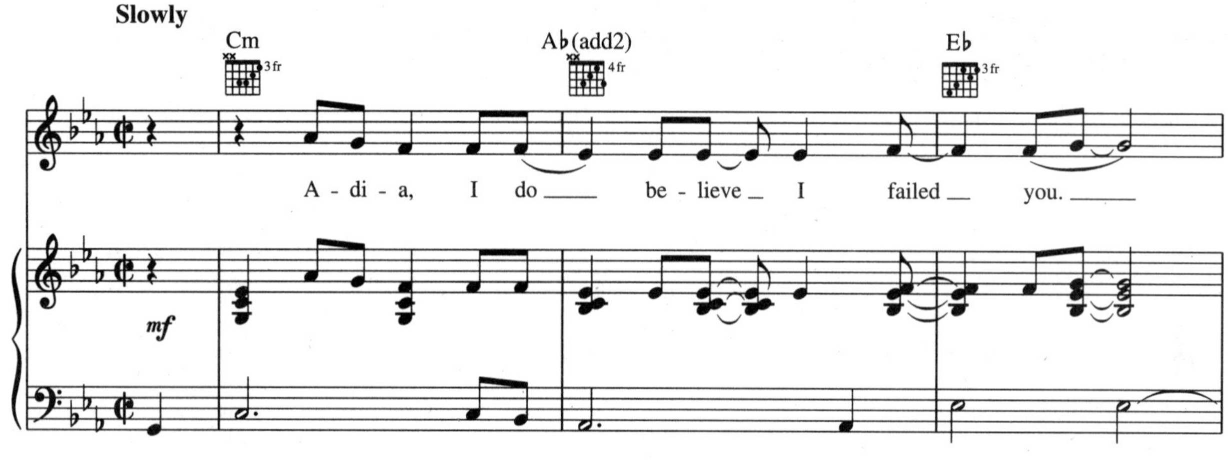

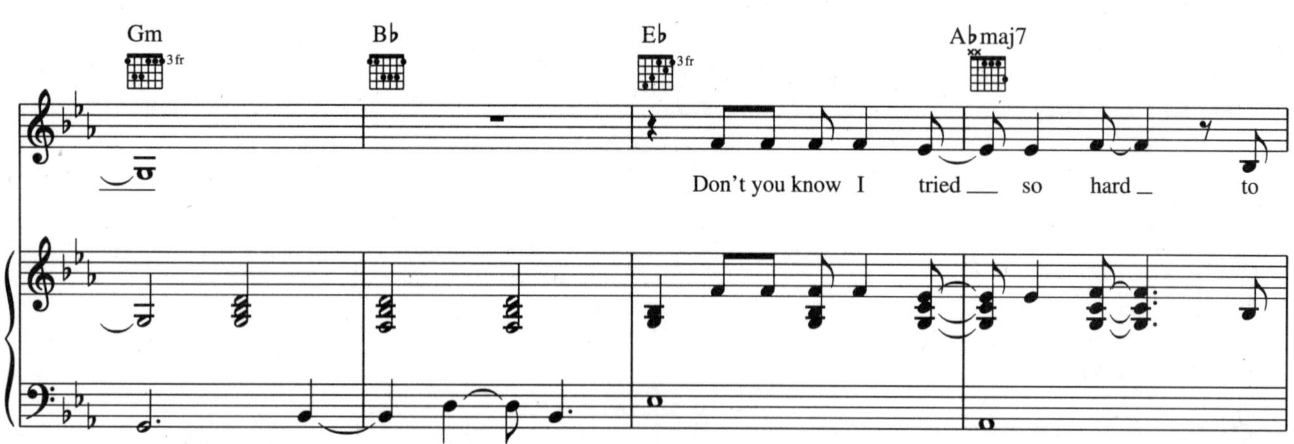

E♭
G/B
Cm
F7
love you in my way.
It's eas - y,
E♭
B♭
let it go.
Cm
A♭
A - di - a, I'm emp - ty since you left
A - di - a, I thought that we could make
E♭
Cm
A♭
me.
it.
Try-ing to find a way to car - ry on.
I know I can't change the way you feel.

Gm7
Bb
Eb
3fr
I search my - self and ev -
I leave you with your mis -
Abmaj7
Eb/G
Bb/F
- 'ry - one to see where we went wrong. There's
- er - y, a friend who won't be - tray.
Fm
Bbsus2
Bb
Eb
6fr
no one left to fin - ger. There's no one here to blame.
Pull you from your tow - er. I take a - way your pain.
Ab
Fm
Bbsus2
Bb
4fr
There's no one left to talk to, hon - ey, and there
I show you all the beau - ty you pos - sess

E♭
B♭m/D♭
A♭(add2)
ain't no one to buy our in - no - cence 'cause
if you'd on - ly let your - self be - lieve that
B♭
E♭
D♭dim7
we are born in - no - cent.
A♭
Fm7
Be - lieve me, A - di - a, we are still
B♭
Gm
D♭dim7
in - no - cent. It's eas - y,

Fm7
we all fal - ter.
And does it mat -
1
G7
- ter? __
2
G7
N.C.
- ter? __
F7/C
3 fr
E♭
3 fr
B♭
Cm
3 fr
F

B♭
B♭7
'Cause we are born
E♭
3fr
D♭dim7
in - no - cent.
Be - lieve me,
A♭
4fr
Fm7
B♭
A - di - a,
we are still in - no - cent.
Gm
3fr
D♭dim7
It's eas - y, we all fal -

Fm7
To Coda
ter.
Does it mat - ter?
Bbsus
Bb
Eb
Gm
Be - lieve me,
A - di - a,
we are still
Gm7
Abmaj7
Fm7
Bb7
D.S. al Coda
in - no - cent.
'Cause we are born
CODA
Bb
G7
- ter?

ALL NIGHT LONG
(All Night)

Words and Music by
LIONEL RICHIE

Ab
4fr
Gb
have some fun, Throw a - way the work to be done.
in their feet, Life is good, wild, and sweet.
Bbm
Ab
4fr
let the mu - sic play on (play on, play on.) Ev - 'ry - bod - y sing,
let the mu - sic play on (play on, play on.) Feel it in your heart
Gb
Bbm
Ab
4fr
ev - 'ry - bod - y dance, lose your - self in wild ro - mance, We're going to
and feel it in your soul, let the mu - sic take con - trol, We're going to
Gb
Bbm
par - ti' ka - ra - mu, fi - es - ta, for - ev - er. Come on and
par - ti' lim - ing, fi - es - ta, for - ev - er. Come on and

2nd time omit these bars
Ab
4fr
Gb
sing a - long: We're going to par - ty, ka-ra-mu, fi-es-ta, for-ev-er.
Bbm
Ab
4fr
Come on and sing a - long:
sing my song:
All night
Gb
Ab
4fr
long, (All night) all night, All night long, (All night) all night,
Gb
All night long, all night, All night

1
A♭
4 fr
2
A♭
4 fr
long,
Oh.
(All night)
long,
(All night)
Yeah!
N.C.
Once you get start - ed you can't sit down,
G♭
N.C.
Come join the fun, it's a mer-ry - go -
G♭
round,
N.C.
Ev - 'ry - one's danc-ing their trou-bles a -

G♭
N.C.
way,
Come join our par - ty, see how we play!
G♭maj7
Fm7
G♭maj7
Fm7
N.C.
G♭maj7
Fm7
G♭maj7
Fm7
N.C.
Tom bo li de say de moi ya
Yeah, Jam-bo Jum - bo
Way to par - ti' o we goin'
Oh, jam-ba-li.
Tom bo li de say de moi ya

G♭maj7
Fm7
G♭maj7
Fm7
G♭/A♭
4fr
Yeah, Jam-bo Jum-bo.
Oh
G♭maj7
Fm7
A♭
4fr
Yes
We're gon-na have a par-ty
All night
G♭
A♭
4fr
long, (All night) all night, All night long, (All night) all night,
G♭
All night long, all night, All night

A♭
4fr
long ___ (All night)
(All night)
G♭
Ev - 'ry - one _ you meet, _ they're jam - ming in ___ the street, _ All night
A♭
4fr
G♭
long. ___ (All night)
(All night)
A♭
4fr
Repeat and Fade
(All night)
(All night)

ALL SHOOK UP

Words and Music by OTIS BLACKWELL
and ELVIS PRESLEY

Eb7
F7
Bb
Eb7
mm oh, oh, yeah, yeah!
Bb
My hands are shak - y and my knees are weak, I
can't seem to stand on my own two feet.
Who do you thank when you
have such luck? I'm in love!
I'm all shook up! Mm

E♭7
F7
B♭
E♭7
mm oh, oh, yeah, yeah!
B♭
E♭7
Please don't ask what's on my mind, I'm a
tongue gets tied when I try to speak, my
B♭
lit - tle mixed up but I'm feel - in' fine. When I'm
in - sides shake like a leaf on a tree. There's
E♭7
near that girl that I love best, My
on - ly one cure for this soul of mine, that's to

F7
B♭
heart beats so it scares me to death!
have the girl that I love so fine!
She touched my hand, what a
chill I got, her kiss - es are like a vol - ca - no that's hot!
I'm
proud to say she's my but - ter - cup. I'm in love!
I'm
E♭7
F7
all shook up! Mm mm oh, oh, yeah,

1
B♭
E♭7
B♭
2
B♭
yeah!
My
yeah!
I'm
E♭7
F7
all shook up!
Mm
mm
oh,
oh,
yeah,
B♭
E♭7
yeah!
I'm
all shook up!
Mm
mm
oh,
F7
B♭
oh,
yeah,
yeah!
I'm
all shook up!

AMAZED

Words and Music by MARV GREEN,
CHRIS LINDSEY and AIMEE MAYO

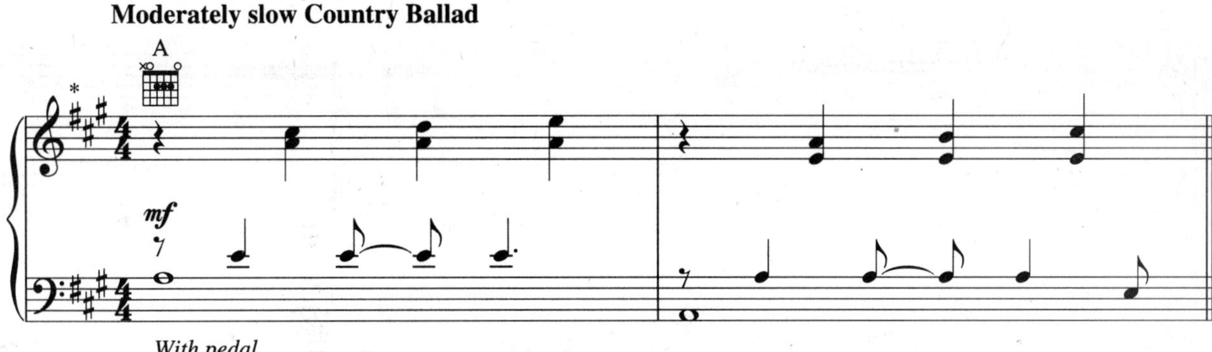

*Recorded a half step lower.

A
E
Ba - by, when you touch me,
I can feel how much you love me,
Your hair all a - round me;
ba - by, you sur - round me.
F♯m
D
and it just blows me a - way.
You touch ev - 'ry place in my heart.
C
G
I've nev - er been this close to an - y - one or an - y - thing.
Oh, it feels like the first time ev - 'ry time.
Am
Am7
F
I can hear your thoughts. I can see your dreams.
I wan-na spend the whole night in your eyes.

D
A
I don't know how you do what you do.
I'm so in love with you.
Bm
G
It just keeps get-tin' bet - ter.
D
A
Bm
I wan-na spend the rest of my life
with you by my side
for-ev-er and ev - er.
G
F
Ev-'ry lit-tle thing that you do,

1
G
A
baby, I'm amazed by you.
2
G
A
C
D
baby, I'm amazed by you.
A
C
G
Dsus
D
G
Ev'ry little thing that you do.
A
Bm
G
I'm so in love with you. It just keeps gettin' better.

D
A
I wan-na spend the rest of my life with you by my side
Bm
G
F
for-ev-er and ev - er.
Ev-'ry lit-tle thing that you do,
G
F/A
oh,
ev - 'ry lit - tle thing that you do,
Freely
Tempo I
G/B
G
N.C.
A
ba-by, I'm a-mazed by you.
rit.

AMANDA

Words and Music by
TOM SCHOLZ

Am
G
Dsus4
D
oth-er day
know-in' I love
you.
G
C/G
And I,
I'm get-tin' too close
a-
G
Em
Bm
gain.
I don't wan-na see it end.
If I
C
G/B
Am
G
tell you to-night,
will you turn out the light
and walk a-way
know-in' I love

D
C/D
3fr.
G/D
D
you?
I'm gon - na
cresc.
f
Em
Am7
D
take you by sur-prise and make you re - al - ize, A - man - da.
I'm gon - na
mp
f
Em
Am7
D
tell you right a - way; I can't wait an - oth - er day, A - man - da.
I'm gon - na
mp
f
Em
Am7
D
say it like a man and make you un - der-stand, A - man - da.
I

Csus2
G
C/G
love you.
And I feel like to-day's the
15ma
dim.
mp
G
Em
Bm
day. I'm look-in' for the words to say. Do you
C
G/B
Am
G
wan-na be free? Are you read-y for me to feel this way? I don't wan-na lose
D
D7sus4
G
C/G
ya. So, it may be too soon, I

G
Em
Bm
know. The feel-in' takes so long to grow. If I
C
G/B
Am
G
tell you to-day will you turn me a-way and let me go? I don't wan-na lose
D
C/D
3fr.
G/D
D
Bm
you.
cresc.
f
Em
Am7
D
mp
f

Em
Am7
D
I'm gon-na
mp
f
take you by sur-prise and make you re - al - ize, A - man - da.
I'm gon-na
tell you right a-way; I can't wait an-oth-er day, A - man - da.
I'm gon-na
say it like a man and make you un-der-stand, A - man - da. Oh, girl.

E
Bm7
E
Bm7
E
Bm7
You and I, I know that we can't wait. And I swear,
E
Bm7
I swear it's not a lie, girl. To - mor - row may be too late.

C
D
G
D/F#
Em
Em/D
You, you and I, girl, we can share a life to-geth - er. It's now or nev -
C
C/B
Am
Am/G
D
C/D
3fr.
G/D
D
er, and to-mor-row may be too late. Oh.
G
C/G
G
Em
And feel-in' the way I do, I don't wan-na wait my whole life
mp
Bm
Am
Am/G
D
through to say I'm in love with you.

AMERICAN TUNE

Words and Music by
PAUL SIMON

F C G G♯dim Am A7 D7 G
wea - ry to my bones, Still, you don't ex - pect to be
lived so well so long, Still, when I think of the
C G D G C F C G
1. E Am Dm
bright and bon vi - vant so far a - way from home, so
road we're trav - 'ling on, I won - der what's gone wrong,
C(Gbass) G C
far a - way from home. I don't know a
2. E Am Dm C (Gbass) G C
I can't help it, I won - der what's gone wrong.

C
And I dreamed I was dy - ing,
I dreamed that my soul
G
Am
E♭dim
G (D bass)
rose un - ex - pect - ed - ly,
And look - ing back down at me,
F
C
G
C
smiled re - as - sur - ing - ly.
And I dreamed I was fly - ing,
G
Am
E♭dim
And high up a - bove my eyes could clear - ly see the Sta - tue of

G (D bass) F C G C
Lib - er - ty sail - ing a - way to sea, and I dreamed I was fly - ing.
F C G C G E Am E7
We come on the ship they call the May - flower, We come on the ship that sailed the moon.
Am C F C G C G C B dim
We come in the a - ge's most un - cer - tain hours and
Am E Am C9 F G
sing an A - mer - i - can Tune. Oh, and it's al - right, it's

F
C
G
C
F
C
G
Am
A7
al - right, it's al - right. You can't be for - ev - er blessed.
D7
G
C
G
D
G
C
Still, to - mor - row's goin' to be an - oth - er work - ing day, And I'm
F
C
G
E
Am
Dm
C (G bass)
G
try - ing to get some rest, That's all I'm try - ing, to get some
C
F
C
G
F
C
G
C
rest.
ritard.

ANGIE

Words and Music by MICK JAGGER
and KEITH RICHARDS

C
Dm
C
G
here?
With no loving in our souls and no
Dm
Am
C
F
money in our coats,
you can't stay we're satisfied,
G
Am
but Angie,
E7
G
Bb/F
F
Angie,
you can't say we never tried.

C
Dm
C
Em/B
Am
An - gie, you're
E7
G
B♭/F
F
beau-ti-ful,
but ain't it time we said good-bye?
C
Dm
C
Am
An - gie,
E7
G
B♭/F
F
I still love you.
Re-mem-ber all those nights we cried?

C
Dm
C
G
All the dreams we held so close seemed to all
Dm
Am
C
F
go up in smoke.
Let me whis - per in your ear;
G
Am
"An - gie,
E7
G
B♭/F
F
An - gie,
where will it lead us from

C
Dm
C
Em/B
Am
here?"
E7
G
B♭/F
F
C
Dm
C
Em/B
Am
E7
G
B♭/F
F
C
Dm
C
Oh,

G
Dm
Am
An - gie, don't _ you weep, all your kiss - es still taste sweet.
C
F
G
I hate that sad - ness in _ your eyes, but
Am
E7
An-gie, An - gie,
G
B♭/F
F
C
Dm
C
Em/B
ain't it time _ we said good - bye? Oh,

Am
E7
yes.
G
B♭/F
F
C
Dm
C
With no
G
Dm
Am
lov-ing in our souls and no mon-ey in our coats,
C
F
G
you can't say we're sat-is-fied, but

Dm Am

An-gie, I still _ love you, ba - by.

Dm Am

Ev-'ry-where I ___ look I see your eyes. ____

Dm Am

There ain't a wom - an that _ comes _ close to you.

C F G

Come on, ba - by, dry _ your eyes. ___________ But

Am
E7
Angie,
An - gie,
G
B♭/F
F
C
Dm
C
ain't it good to be a - live?
Am
E7
An - gie,
An - gie,
G
B♭/F
F
Em
Dm
C
they can't say we nev - er tried.

ANGRY EYES

Words and Music by KENNY LOGGINS
and JIM MESSINA

D9
4fr
D
C
G
an - gry eyes,
well, I'll bet you wish you could
G7
1
cut me down with those an - gry eyes.
2
D
C
G
an - gry eyes.
What a shot you could be if you could
G7
F
G
shoot at me with those an - gry eyes.

D
C
You try to de-fend that you are not the one to blame,
Am7
D
C
but I'm find-ing it hard, my friend, when I'm
G
G7
D9
4fr
D
in the dead-ly aim of those an-gry eyes,
C
G
well, I'll bet you wish you could

G7
D9
4fr
D
cut me down with those an - gry eyes,
C
G
what a shot you could be if you could
G7
F
G
shoot at me with those an - gry eyes.
Dm7
Cmaj7
Dm7
Cmaj7
G
Em
D7sus
3fr
You and I must start to re - al - ize,

F
C
F
C
blind - ness binds us to - geth - er in a

D
F
Cmaj7
Dm7
false dis - guise.
Can you see

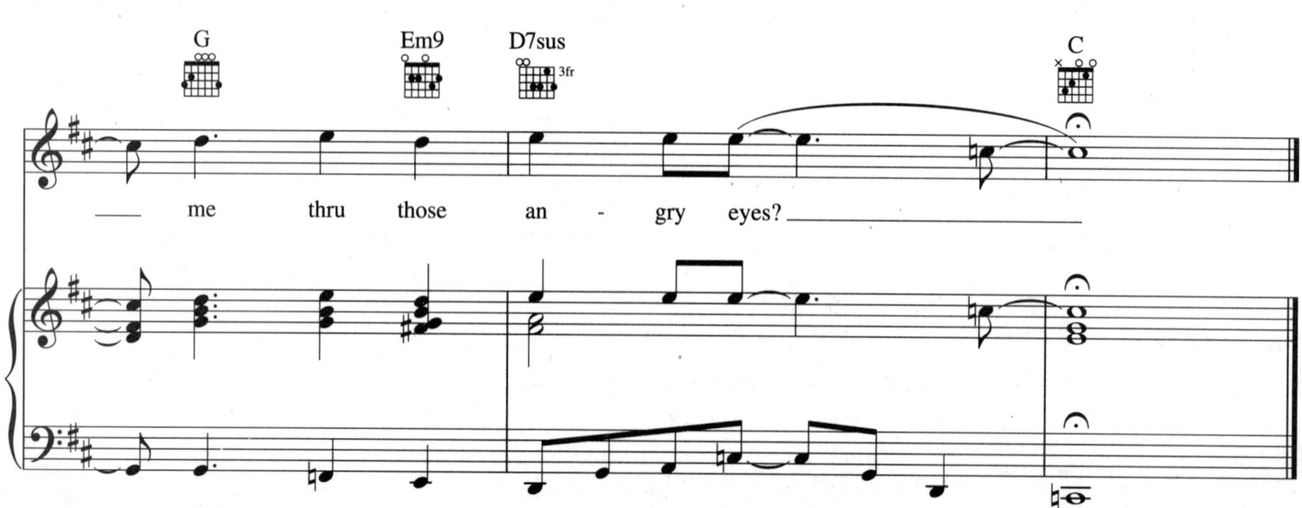
G
Em9
D7sus
3fr
C
me thru those an - gry eyes?

BABY, I LOVE YOUR WAY

Words and Music by
PETER FRAMPTON

Em7
D
C(add2)
3
far a - way
I can see them
Wish I could buy one
from the
un - der
out of
F9
Bm7
cit - y.
the pine.
sea - son.
But don't
hes - i - tate,
E7
Am7
'cause your
love
won't
D7
G
D
wait.
Ooh
ba - by, I love your way

Am7
C
G
D
ev-'ry day.
Wan-na tell you I love your way
Am7
C
G
D
ev-'ry day.
Wan-na be with you night and day.
Am7
C
To Coda
1
G
D/F♯
Em7
Cmaj9
Bm7
Am7
D7sus

2
G
D/F♯
Em7
Cmaj7
F9
G
D/F♯
Em7
Cmaj7
F9
Bm7
E7
But don't
hes-i - tate, __
'cause your
Am7
D7
D.S. al Coda
love ____
won't __ wait. ____

CODA
G
D
Am7
C
Ooh ba-by, I love your way ev-'ry day.
G
D
Am7
C
Wan-na tell you I love your way. Ooh.
G
D
Am7
C
Wan-na be with you night and day.
G
D
Em
Cmaj7
Bm7
Am7
G
3

ANOTHER DAY IN PARADISE

Words and Music by
PHIL COLLINS

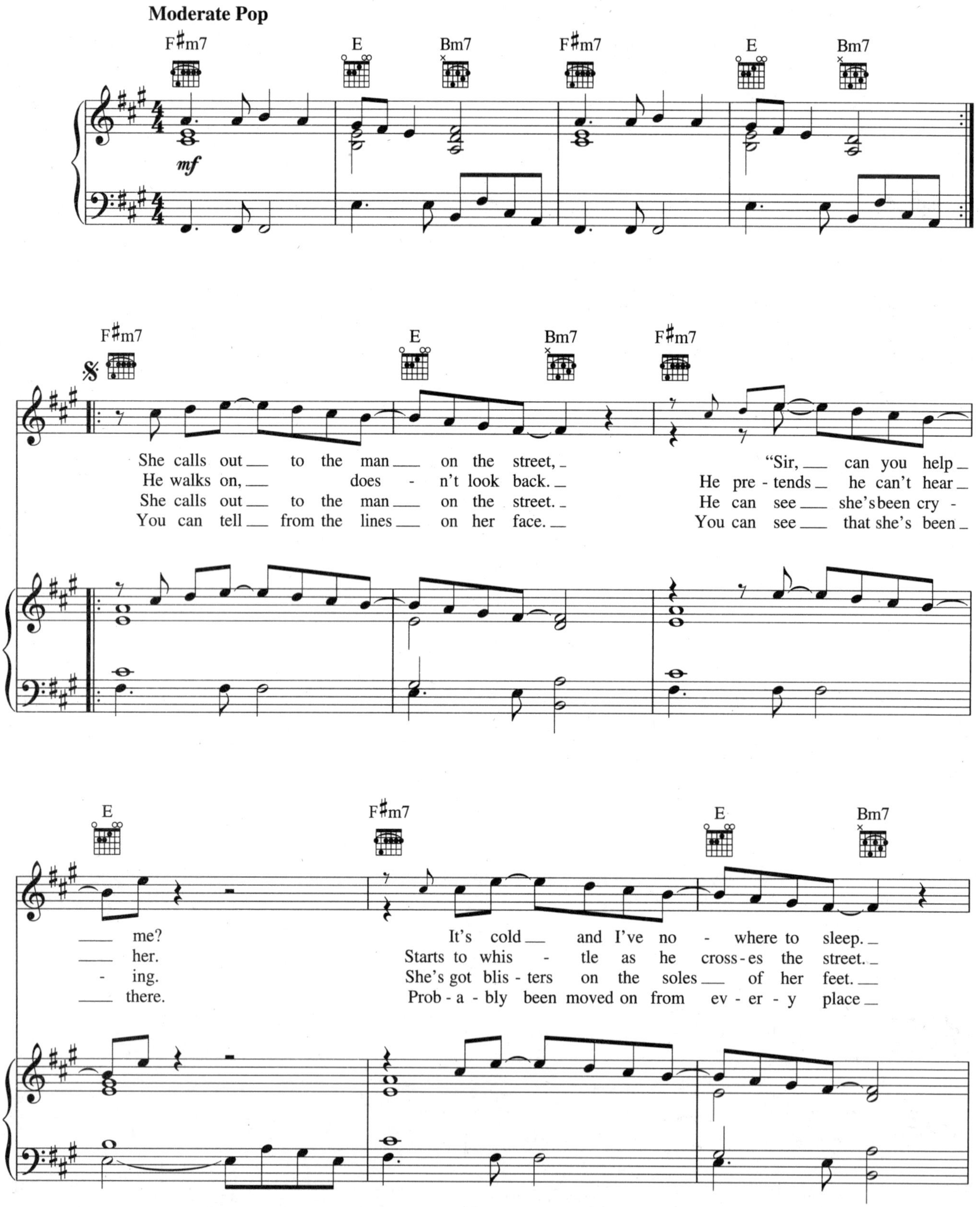

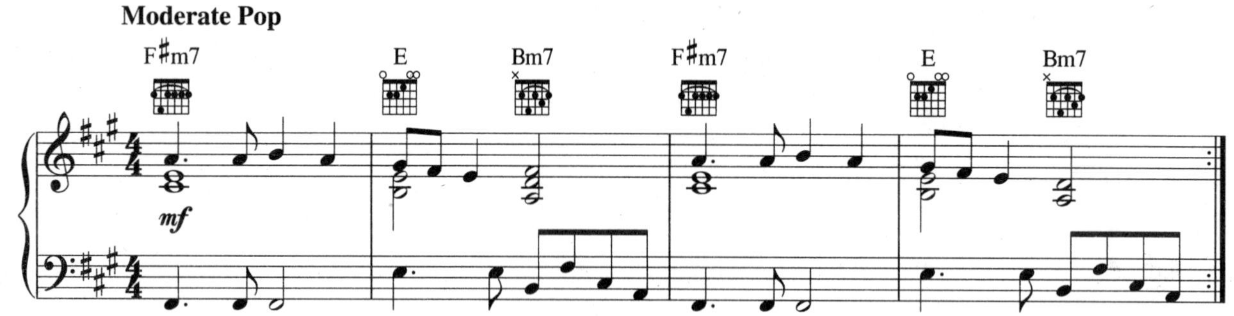

F♯m7 E Bm7 F♯m7

She calls out to the man on the street, "Sir, can you help
He walks on, doesn't look back. He pretends he can't hear
She calls out to the man on the street. He can see she's been cry-
You can tell from the lines on her face. You can see that she's been

E F♯m7 E Bm7

me? It's cold and I've nowhere to sleep.
her. Starts to whistle as he crosses the street.
ing. She's got blisters on the soles of her feet.
there. Probably been moved on from every place

F♯m7
1
E
2-4
E
Is there some-where you can tell me?"
Seems em-bar - rassed to be
there.
She can't walk, but she's try -
- ing.
'cause she did - n't fit in
there.
F♯m
E/F♯
Dmaj7/F♯
Oh, think twice, 'cause it's an - oth - er day for you and me in
E/F♯
F♯m
E/F♯
par - a - dise.
Oh, think twice, 'cause it's an -
Dmaj7/F♯
E
F♯m
E
D
F♯m7
oth - er day for you,
you and me in par - a - dise.

E
Bm7
F#m7
E
Bm7
(3.) Just think a - bout __ it.
(1. - 3.) Think a - bout __
F#m7
E
Bm7
F#m7
To Coda
__ it.
(3.) Think a - bout __ it.
1
E
Bm7
D.S.
2
E
Bm7
E/G#
F#m
Oh, Lord, __ is there
E
A
E/G#
noth-ing more an - y - bod - y can do? __
Oh, __ Lord, __

F#m
E
A
there must be some-thing you can say.
D.S. al Coda
CODA
E
Bm7
It's just an -
F#m7
E
Bm7
F#m7
oth - er day for you and me in par - a - dise.
Repeat and Fade
E
Bm7
It's just an -
Optional Ending
E
Bm7
F#m

BACK AT ONE

Words and Music by
BRIAN McKNIGHT

Amaj7 E(add2)/G♯ C♯/E♯

let me show you now that I'm for real. If
Nev - er would have made it ver - y far, 'cause you

Amaj7 E(add2)/G♯ C♯m7/F♯

all things in time, time will re - veal. Yeah,
know you've got the keys to my heart. 'Cause

B G♯m7 F♯sus

one, you're like a dream come true. Two, just wan - na be with you.

E(add2) C♯m7 D♯m7 E F♯

Three, girl, it's plain to see that you're the on - ly one for me. And

B
G♯m7
4fr
F♯sus
four, re - peat steps one through three.
Five, make you fall in love with me. If
E(add2)
1
C♯m7
4fr
C♯m7/F♯
9fr
ev - er I ___ be - lieve _ my work _ is done, ___
then I'll start ___ back ___ at one. ___
B
2
C♯m7
4fr
C♯m7/F♯
9fr
E
___ Yeah. ___
Say ___
___ then I'll start ___ back ___ at one. ___
B/D♯
4fr
E(add2)
___ fare - well _ to the dark _ of night; I see the com - ing of ___ the sun. ___ I ___

B/D#
G#sus
G#7#5
feel like a lit - tle child whose life has just be - gun. You
C#m7
D#m7
G#m7
came and breathed new life in - to this lone - ly heart of mine. You
C#m7
C#m7/F#
Dm7/G
G/B
N.C.
threw out the life - line, just in the nick of time.
C
Am7
Gsus
One, you're like a dream come true. Two, just wan - na be with you.

F(add2) C/E Dm7 Em7 F G

Three, girl, it's plain to see that you're the on - ly one for me. And

C Am7 Gsus

four, re - peat steps one through three. Five, make you fall in love with me. If

F(add2) Dm7 Dm7/G

ev - er I be - lieve my work is done, then I'll start back at one.

C F Am11 Dm11 Dm7/G Amaj9

rit.

BEAUTIFUL

Words and Music by
LINDA PERRY

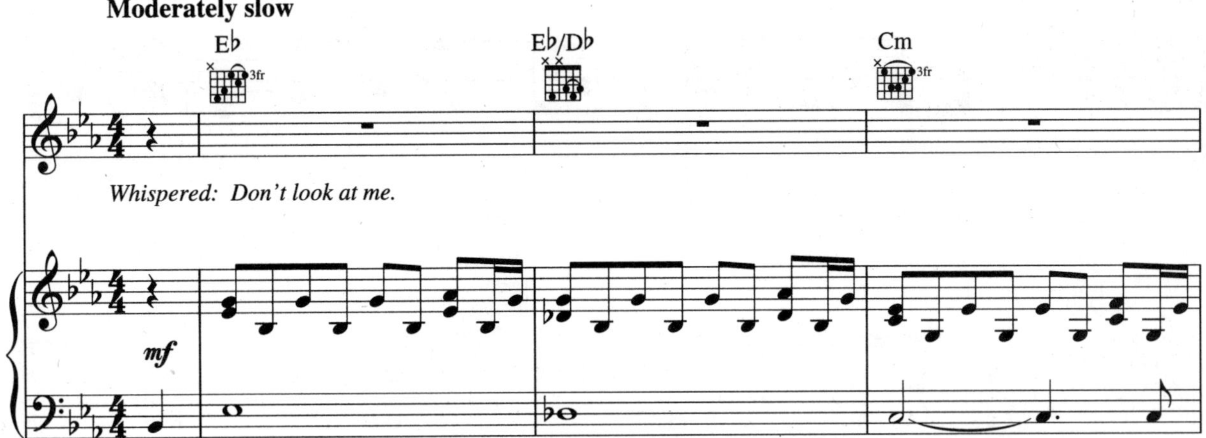

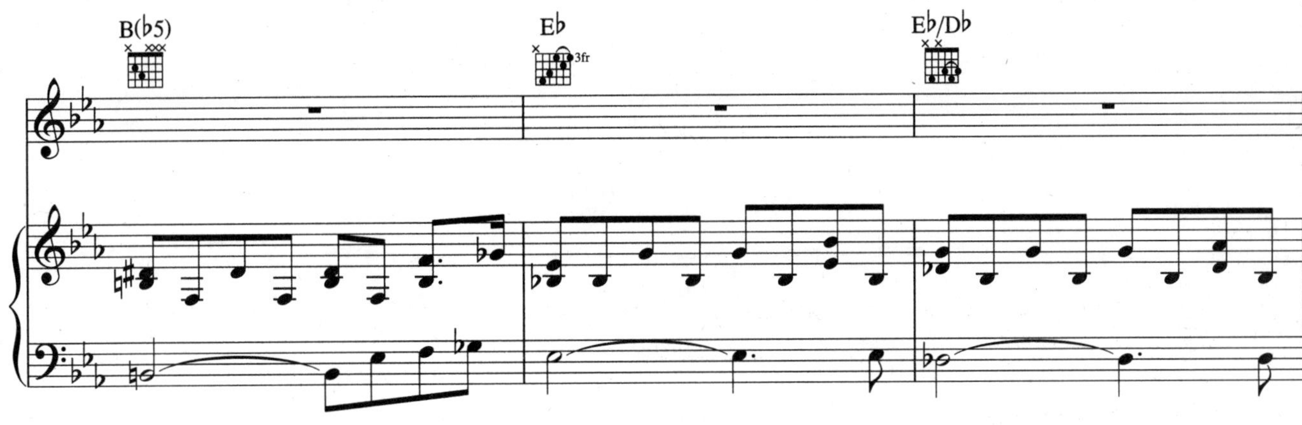

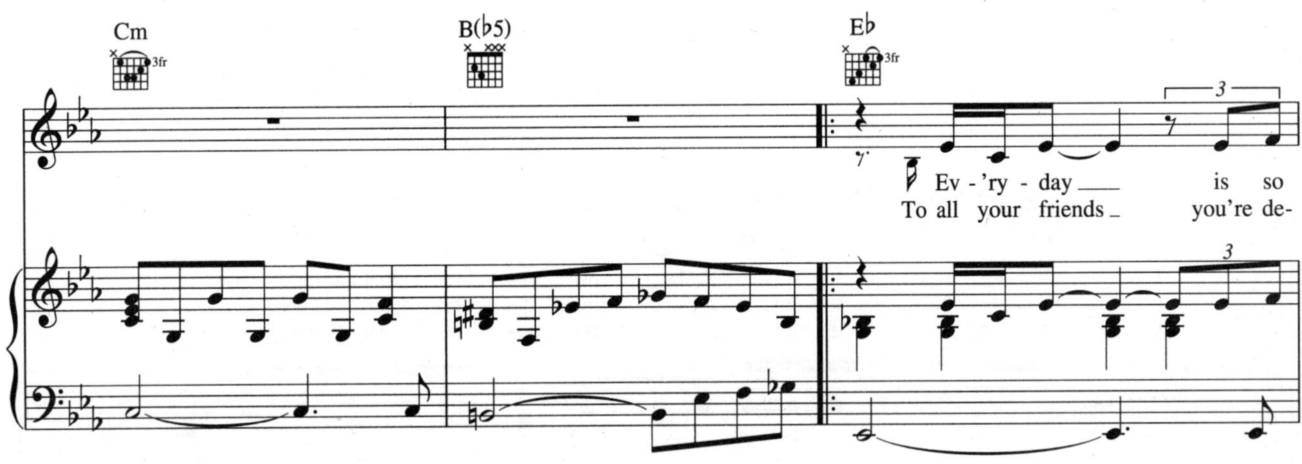

E♭/D♭
Cm
3fr
B(♭5)
won - der - ful, then sud - den - ly, it's hard to breathe.
lir - i - ous. So con - sumed in all your doom.
E♭
3fr
E♭/D♭
Now and then I get in - se - cure from all the pain,
Try - ing hard to fill the emp - ti - ness. The piec - es gone,
Cm
3fr
B(♭5)
feel so a - shamed.
left the puz - zle un - done. Ain't that the way it is?
A♭
4fr
Fm
I am beau - ti - ful no mat - ter what they say.
You are beau - ti - ful no mat - ter what they say.
'Cause we are beau - ti - ful no mat - ter what they say.

Eb
Eb/Db
Cm
Ab
3fr
4fr
Words can't bring me down.
Words can't bring you down.
Words won't bring us down.
I am beau - ti - ful in
You are beau - ti - ful in
We are beau - ti - ful in
Fm
Eb
Eb/Db
ev - 'ry sin - gle way. Yes, words can't bring me down,
ev - 'ry sin - gle way. Yes, words can't bring you down,
ev - 'ry sin - gle way. Yes, words won't bring us down,
Cm
1, 3
Fm7
To Coda
Eb
oh no.
oh no.
oh no.
So don't you bring me down to - day.
So don't you bring me down
Eb/Db
Cm
B(b5)

2
Fm7
E♭
3fr
So don't you bring me down to-day.
No mat-ter what we do.
E♭/D♭
Cm
3fr
No mat-ter what we say.
We're the song in-side the tune
B(♭5)
E♭
3fr
full of beau-ti-ful mis-takes.
And ev-'ry-where we go
E♭/D♭
Cm
3fr
the sun will al-ways shine.
And to-mor-row we might a-wake

B(♭5)
D.S. al Coda
(Take 1st Ending)
CODA
E♭
on the oth - er side.
to - day.
E♭/D♭
Cm
B(♭5)
Don't you bring me down
E♭
E♭/D♭
to - day,
yeah,
ooh.
Cm
B(♭5)
N.C.
E♭
Don't you bring me down
um
to - day.

BEHIND BLUE EYES

Words and Music by
PETE TOWNSHEND

G
D
C6/9
to be hat - ed, to be fat - ed
on their an - ger. None of my pain and woe
A(add2)
C
to tell - ing on - ly lies.
can show through.
But my dreams,
D
G
C
they aren't as emp - ty as my con - science
D
E
Bm
seems to be. I have hours

C
D
on - ly lone - ly.
My love is ven - geance
A(add2)
1
that's nev - er free.
free.
2
E
Bm
A
E
Bm
A
E
Bm
A
When my fist clench - es, crack it o - pen

E
Bm
G
D
before I use it and lose my cool. When I smile,
Bm
A
D
Bm
A
tell me some bad news before I laugh and act like a
E
Bm
A
E
fool. If I swal-
Bm
A
E
Bm
G
low anything evil, put your finger down my

D
Bm
A
D
throat. And if I shiv - er, please give me a blank - et. Keep me warm;
Bm
A
E
Em
let me wear your coat.
No one knows what it's like
G
D
to be the bad man,
to be the
C6/9
A
sad man
be - hind blue eyes.

BLAZE OF GLORY

Words and Music by
JON BON JOVI

G
Dm
old coat for a pil - low and the earth was last night's bed. I
look - ing for for - give - ness but be - fore I'm six feet deep, Lord,
F
C
To Coda
don't know where I'm go - ing, on - ly God knows where I've been. I'm a
I got to ask a fa - vor and I hope you'll un - der - stand. 'Cause I've
G
Dm
dev - il on the run, a six - gun lov - er, a can - dle in the wind, yeah!
D5
5fr

Dm
When you're brought in - to this world _ they
ask a - bout _ my con-science and I
C
G
say you're born in sin. Well, at least they gave me some - thing I did - n't have to
of - fer you my soul. You ask if I'll grow to be _ a wise _ man, well, I
Dm
F
steal or have _ to win. Well, they tell me that _ I'm want - ed, yeah,
ask if I'll _ grow old. You ask me if _ I've known love and what it's like to
C
G
I'm a want - ed man. _ I'm a colt in your sta-ble, I'm what Cain was to A-bel. Mis-ter,
sing songs in the rain. _ Well, I've seen love come, I've seen it shot down, I've

Dm
G
catch me if you can. I'm go - ing
seen it die in vain. Shot
down in a blaze of glo -
D
G
- ry. Take me now but know the truth.
D
G
I'm go - ing out
'Cause I'm go - ing down
I'm go - ing out
in a blaze of
D
C
To Coda II
glo - ry. Lord, I nev - er drew first but I drew first blood,
and I'm
I'm the
and I'm

G
1
D5
no one's son. Call me young - gun.
dev - il's son. Call me young -
You
2
D5
gun.
G
D
Play 3 times
Guitar solo ad lib.
F
G
N.C.
Solo ends

D5
5fr
D.S. al Coda
Each
CODA
G
lived life to the full-est, let this boy
Dm
die like a man.
G
Star - ing down a bul - let, let me make
Dm
my fi - nal stand.
rit.
a tempo
D.S.S. al Coda II
Shot
CODA II
G
no one's son, call me young

D
C
G
gun.
I'm a young gun.
D
C
Young gun,
yeah, yeah, yeah, young
G
D5
5fr
gun.

BLOWIN' IN THE WIND

Words and Music by
BOB DYLAN

D G G/F#

How many seas must a white
Yes, and how many years can some peo-
Yes, and how many ears must

A/E D

dove sail before she
ple exist before they're allowed
one man have before he can hear

G D/F# A/E

sleeps in the sand? Yes, and how
to be free? Yes, and how
people cry? Yes, and how

D G G/F# A/E

many times must the cannonballs fly
many times can a man turn his head
many deaths will it take 'til he knows

D
G
D/F#
be - fore they are for - ev - er banned?
and pre - tend that he just does - n't see?
that too man - y peo - ple have died?
D
G
G/F#
The an - swer, my friend,
A/E
A/C#
D
G
is blow - in' in the wind. The an -
G/F#
A/E
D
- swer is blow - in' in the wind.

G
D/F♯
A
D

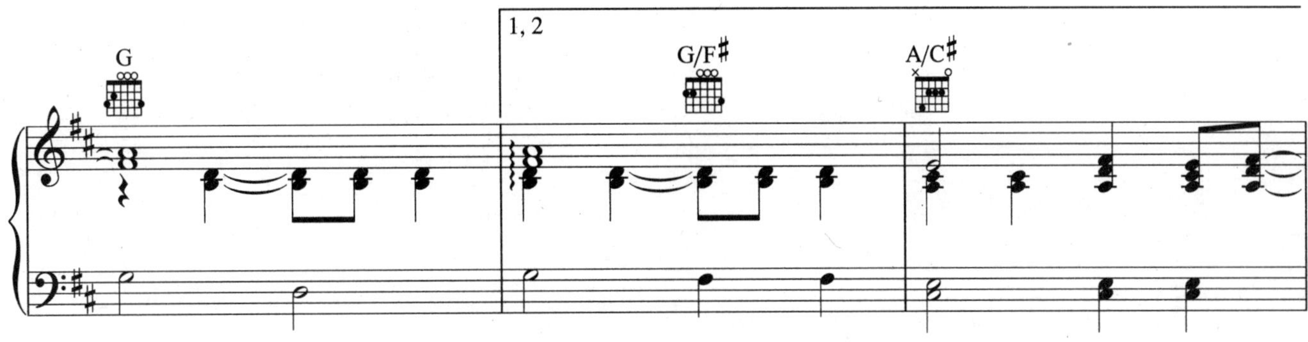
G
1, 2
G/F♯
A/C♯

D
3
Slower
G/F♯
Yes, and

A/E
D
rit.

BORDERLINE

Words and Music by
REGGIE LUCAS

D
C
G/B
D
- na be your pris-'ner, so ba - by, won't you set me free.
me in your arms you love me till I just can't see.
C
G/B
G/A
3fr
D
C
G/B
Stop play - in' with my heart. Fin - ish what you start when
But then you let me down. When I look a-round, ba -
D
C
G/B
G/A
3fr
D
you make my love come down. If you want me let me know. Ba -
- by, you just can't be found. Stop driv - in' me a - way. I
C
G/B
D
- by, let it show. Hon - ey, don't you fool a - round.
just wan-na stay. There's some-thin' I just got to say.

Bm7
B/D#
Em7
A/C#
Just try to un - der - stand, I've giv -
F#m7
Gmaj7
G/A
- en all I can, 'cause you got the best of me.
A
A/C#
F#/A#
Bor - der- line,
Bm
A
E/G#
feels like I'm go - in' to lose my mind. You just keep

Em7 D/F♯ D/A A D/A

— on push - in' my — love o - ver the bor - der - line.

A A/C♯ F♯/A♯ 4fr

Bor - der - line, feels like I'm go -

Bm A E/G♯ Em7 D/F♯

- in' to lose — my mind. — You just keep — on push - in' my —

D/A A D/A A

— love o - ver the bor - der - line.

A/C♯
F♯/A♯
4fr
Bm
A
E/G♯
Keep on push - in' me, ba - by. Don't you know you drive me cra -
Em7
D/F♯
D/A
- zy? You just keep on push - in' my love o - ver the bor -
To Coda
A
D/A
A
D.C. al Coda
CODA
A
- der line.
A/C♯
F♯/A♯
4fr
Bm
A
E/G♯
Look what your love has done to me. Come on, ba - by, set

Em7 D/F♯ D/A

me free. You just keep on push - in' my love o - ver the bor -

A D/A A A/C♯ F♯/A♯ 4fr

- der - line. You cause me so much pain

Bm A E/G♯

I think I'm go - in' in - sane. What does it take to make you see? You just keep

Em7 D/F♯ D/A A D/A A

on push - in' my love o - ver the bor - der - line.

THE BOXER

Words and Music by
PAUL SIMON

Am
G
F
All lies and jest, still a man hears what he wants to hear, And
dis - re-gards the rest.
C
G
C
When I left my home and my fam - i - ly, I was

Am
G
no more than a boy in the com - pa - ny___ of stran - gers in the
Dm7
C
qui - et of a rail - way sta - tion run - ning scared,___
Am
C
F
Lay - ing low, seek - ing out the poor - er quar - ters where the
G
F
Em
Dm
rag - ged peo - ple go, Look-ing for the plac - es on - ly they would

C
Am
know. Lie - la - lie, Lie - la -
G
Am
G
lie la lie - la - lie lie - la - lie Lie - la -
F
G
C
lie la la la la Lie - la la la la lie.
Ask - ing on - ly work - man's wag - es I come

Am
G
look - ing for a job, but I get no of - fers, Just a
Dm7
C
come-on from the whores on Sev-enth Av - e - nue.
Am
Dm7
G
F
I do de - clare, there were times when I was so lone-some I
C
G
took some com-fort there. Ooo - la - la la - la la la.

C
C
Then I'm lay - ing out my
G7
C
Am
G
win - ter clothes and wish - ing I was gone, go - ing home
Dm7
G7
G
C
Where the New York Cit - y win - ters are - n't bleed - ing me,
Em
Am
Lead - ing me,

G
C
going home.
C
In the clear-ing stands a box-er, and a fight-er by his
Am
G
G7
trade, And he car-ries the re-mind-ers of ev-'ry glove that
C
Dm7
G7
C
laid him down Or cut him till he cried out in his an-ger and his shame,

Am
G
F
C
"I am leav - ing, I am leav - ing." But the fight - er still re-mains.
G
C
G
F
C
Lie - la
Fade
Am
G
Am
lie, Lie - la - lie la lie - la - lie Lie - la - lie
G
F
C
Lie - la lie la la la la lie - la la la la lie. Lie - la

BRICK

Words and Music by BEN FOLDS
and DARREN JESSEE

G6/9
D
G6/9
am
numb.
D
G6/9
D
Up the stairs
They call her name
Driv-ing back
G6/9
D
to her a - part - ment,
at sev - en thir - ty.
to her a - part - ment,
she is balled up on
I pace a - round the park -
for the mo - ment we're
G6/9
D
G6/9
the couch.
ing lot,
a - lone.
Her mom and dad
and I walk down
Well, she's a - lone
went down to Char-lotte,
to buy her flow - ers
and I'm a - lone.

To Coda
D
G6/9
they're not home to find us out.
and sell some gifts that I got.
Now I know it.
Bm7
G6/9
Bm7
And we drive.
Can't you see
Now that I
it's not me
G6/9
D
G6/9
have found some-one, I'm feel-ing more a - lone
you're dy - ing for? Now she's feel-ing more a - lone
than I
than she
Bm7
E7sus
E7
E7sus
G
A
ev - er have be - fore.
ev - er has be - fore.
She's a brick and I'm

A/D
G6
A
A/D
D6/9
4fr
drown - ing slow - ly off the coast and I'm head - ed no - where.
G6
A
A/D
1
G
A
G
She's a brick and I'm drown - ing slow - ly.
D
2
G
A
G
A
D/F♯
G
D
G
A
G
A
D/F♯
G

E7sus
E7
G6/9
D
Dsus
D
As weeks went by they showed that she was not fine.
They told me, "Son, it's time to tell the truth," and
she broke down and I broke down 'cause I was
Gsus2
D.S. al Coda
tired of ly - ing.

CODA
G6/9
G
A
She's a brick and I'm
A/D
G6
A
A/D
D6/9
4fr
drown - ing slow - ly off the coast and I'm head - ed no - where.
G6
A
Bm7
A/C♯
She's a brick and I'm drown - ing slow - ly.
G
A
G
A
D/F♯
G
D
rit.

BROWN EYED GIRL

Words and Music by
VAN MORRISON

Eb
Ab
Eb
Bb7
3fr
4fr
In the mist - y morn - ing fog with our hearts a - thump - in', and
Ab
Bb7
Eb
Cm
you, my brown eyed girl.
Ab
Bb7
Eb
Bb7
You, my brown eyed girl. Do you re - mem -
Eb
Chorus
- ber when we used to sing: sha la la la

Additional Lyrics

2. Whatever happened to Tuesday and so slow
Going down the old mine with a transistor radio
Standing in the sunlight laughing
Hiding behind a rainbow's wall
Slipping and a-sliding
All along the water fall
With you, my brown eyed girl
You, my brown eyed girl.
Do you remember when we used to sing:
Chorus

3. So hard to find my way, now that I'm all on my own
I saw you just the other day, my, how you have grown
Cast my memory back there, Lord
Sometime I'm overcome thinking 'bout
Making love in the green grass
Behind the stadium
With you, my brown eyed girl
With you, my brown eyed girl.
Do you remember when we used to sing:
Chorus

CANDLE IN THE WIND

Music by ELTON JOHN
Words by BERNIE TAUPIN

E
A
wood-work
died,
and they whis-pered
in - to your brain.
oh, the
press still hound-ed you.
E/G♯
They set you on the tread - mill
and they made you change your name.
All the pa - pers had to say
was that Mar - i - lyn was found in
A
D/A
A
B
B7
the nude.
It seems to me you lived your life like a
E
A
E
can - dle in the wind,
nev - er know-ing who to cling to when the

B
Bsus
2fr
B
A
rain set in.
I would have liked to have known
C♯m
4fr
you, but I was just a kid.
Your can - dle burned out
B
Bsus
2fr
B
A
long be - fore
your leg - end ev - er did.
A/G♯
F♯m7
E
3

B
A
A/G#
F#m7
E
Esus
E
1
B
B7
2
B
B7/A
E
Good-bye Nor - ma Jean,
A
though I nev - er knew you at all you had the grace to
E/G#
A
D/A
hold your - self while those a - round you crawled.

A
E
Good-bye Nor-ma Jean, from a young man in the
A
E/G#
twen-ty sec-ond row who sees you as some-thing more than sex-ual, more than
A
Asus
A
just our Mar-i-lyn Mon-roe. It
B
B7
E
E7
seems to me you lived your life like a can-dle in the wind,

A
E
never knowing who to cling to when the rain
B
Bsus
2fr
B
A
set in.
And I would have liked to have known
C♯m
4fr
you, but I was just a kid.
Your candle burned out
B
Bsus
2fr
B
A
long before
your legend ever did.

A/G#
F#7
E
E7/G#
I
A
C#m
4fr
would have liked to have known you, whoa, but I was just a kid.
B
Your can - dle burned out long be - fore
Bsus
2fr
B
A
A/G#
F#m7
E
your leg - end ev - er did.
rit.

CALIFORNIA DREAMIN'

Words and Music by JOHN PHILLIPS
and MICHELLE PHILLIPS

Medium Rock beat

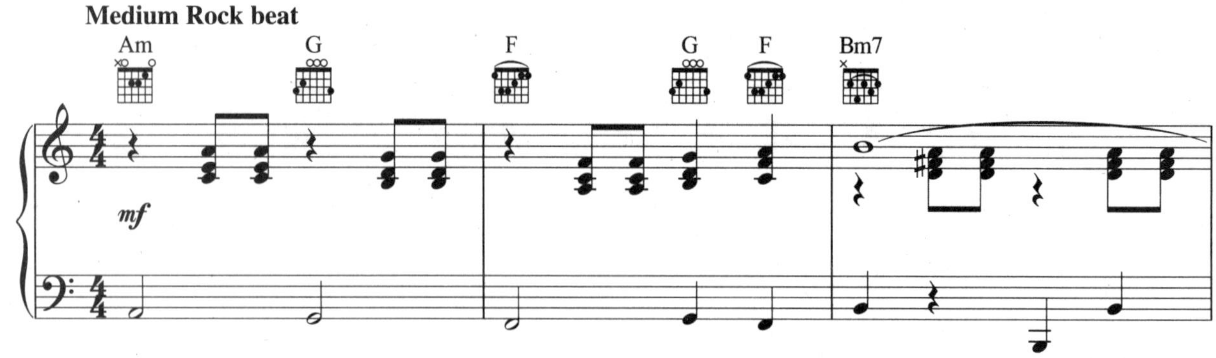

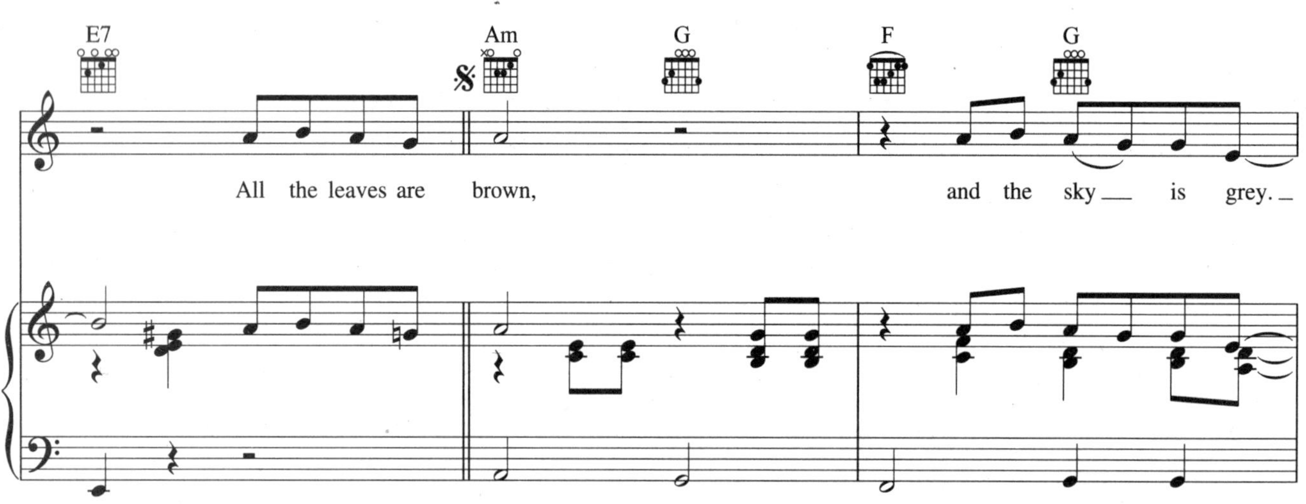

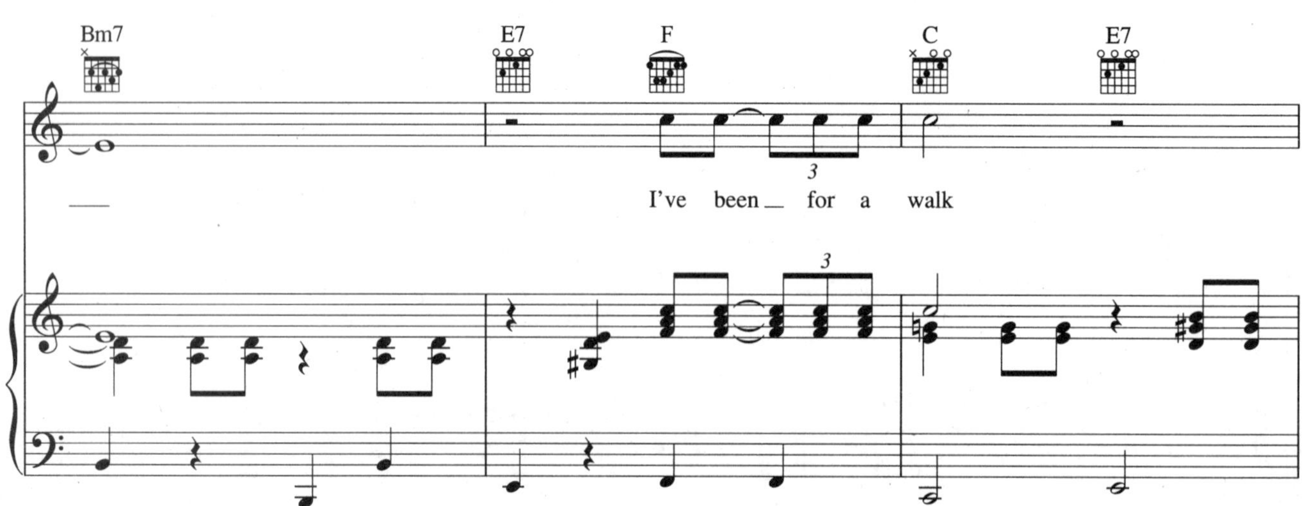

Am
F6
E
Dm6
E7
on a win - ter's day.
I'd be safe and
If I did - n't
Am
G
F
G
Bm7
warm,
tell her
if I was in L. A.
I could leave to - day.
E7
Am
G
To Coda
F
G
Cal - i - for - nia dream - in'
on such a win - ter's
Bm7
E7
Am
G
day.
Stopped in - to a church,

F G Bm7 E7 F
I passed a - long the way. Oh, I got down on my
C E7 Am F E Dm6
knees, and I pre - tend to pray.
E7 Am G F G
You know the preach - er likes the cold. He knows I'm gon - na
Bm7 E7 Am G
stay. Cal - i - for - nia dream - in'

F
G
Bm7
E7
D.S. al Coda
on such a win-ter's day.
All the leaves are
CODA
Am
on such a win-ter's day. (Cal-i-for-nia dream-in') on such a win-ter's
day. (Cal-i-for-nia dream-in') on such a win-ter's day.
Fmaj7

CALIFORNIA GIRLS

Words and Music by BRIAN WILSON
and MIKE LOVE

*Recorded one half step higher.

E♭
and the South - ern girls with the
I dig a French bi - ki - ni on Ha -
F7
way they talk they knock me out when I'm down there. The
wai - ian is - land dolls by a palm tree in the sand. I've
B♭
A♭/B♭
Mid - west farm - er's daugh - ters real - ly make you feel al - right.
been all a - round this great big world, and I've seen all kinds of girls.
E♭
And the North - ern girls with the
Yeah, but I could - n't wait to get

F7
way they kiss, they keep their boy - friends warm at night.
back in the States, back to the cut - est girls in the world.
B♭
Cm7
I wish they all could be Cal - i - for - nia, I
A♭
B♭m
G♭
wish they all could be Cal - i - for - nia, I wish they all could be
A♭m
1
B♭
Cal - i - for - nia girls. The

2
B♭
L.H.
B♭
I wish they all could be Cal - i - for - nia, I
Cm7
wish they all could be Cal - i - for - nia, I
Repeat and Fade
Optional Ending
B♭
Cal - i - for - nia girls.

CAN'T BUY ME LOVE

Words and Music by JOHN LENNON
and PAUL McCARTNEY

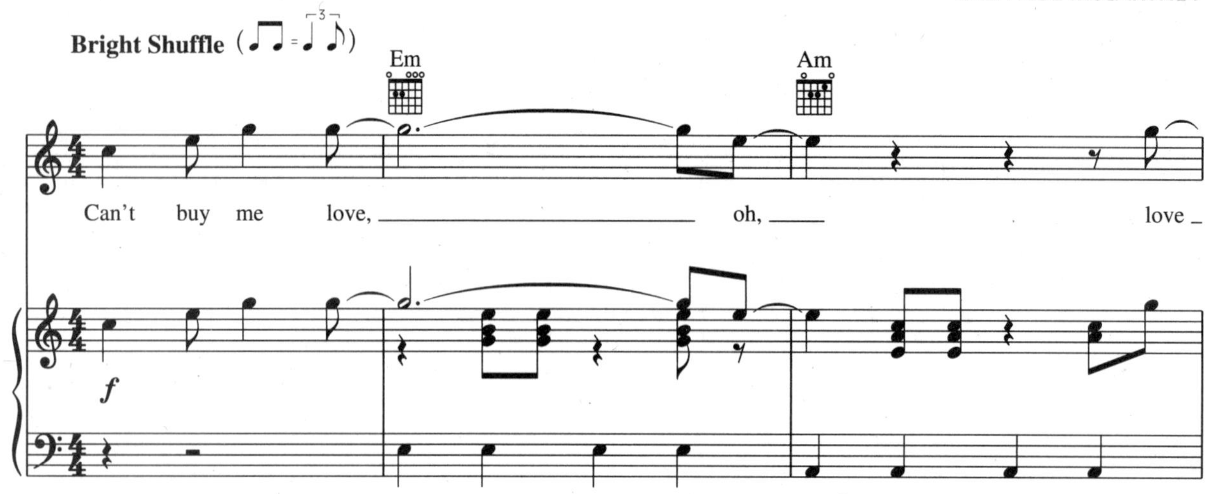

F7
I'll get you an - y - thing, my friend, if it
I may not have a lot to give but what I've
C
G
makes you feel al - right.
got I'll give to you.
'Cause I don't care too
F7
1
C
much for mon - ey, for mon - ey can't buy me love.
I'll
End solo
2, 3
C
Em
Am
C
Can't buy me love, oh, ev - 'ry-bod - y tells me so.

Em
Am
Dm7
Can't buy me love, oh, no no no
G
C
no! Say you don't need no dia - mond rings and I'll be sat - is - fied,
F7
Tell me that you want the kind of things that
C
G
F7
To Coda
mon - ey just can't buy. I don't care too much for mon-ey,

C
D.S. al Coda
mon - ey can't buy me love.
(Scream)
CODA
C
Em
mon - ey can't buy me love.
Can't buy me love
Am
Em
Am
love
can't buy me love.
Dm7
G
C

CARIBBEAN QUEEN
(No More Love On The Run)

Words and Music by KEITH VINCENT ALEXANDER
and BILLY OCEAN

Dm
C
And all heads turned 'cause she was the cream.
And I get so ex - cit - ed just from her per - fume.
In the blink of an eye
E - lec - tric eyes
I knew her num - ber and her name.
that you can't ig - nore;
She said I was the
and pas - sion burns

Dm
C
Dm
C
To Coda
ti - ger she want - ed to tame.
you like nev - er be - fore.
Dm
C
Dm
Car - ib - bean queen,
now we're shar -
C
B♭maj7
- ing the same dream,
and our hearts
Dm/A
Gm7
they beat as one.

B♭
Dm
C
Dm
C
D.S. al Coda
No more love on the run.
CODA
Dm
C
B♭
I was in search
of a good time,
just run - ning my game,
C
B♭
yeah.
Love was the fur - thest,
fur - thest from my
C
B♭
C

Dm
mind.
Car - ib - bean
Dm
C
queen,
now we're shar - ing the same dream,
B♭maj7
Dm/A
Gm7
and our hearts they beat as one.
B♭
C
Dm
C
Dm
C
Repeat ad lib. and Fade
No more love on the run.
Car - ib - bean

THE CLOSER I GET TO YOU

Words and Music by JAMES MTUME
and REGGIE LUCAS

Amaj7
Dmaj9
C♯m7
A
your love has cap - tured me.
Dmaj7
C♯m7
Em7
A7
Boy: O - ver and o - ver a - gain, I try to tell my - self that
Dmaj7
C♯m7
Em7
A7
we could nev - er be more than friends, and all the while in - side I
Dmaj7
C♯m7
Bm7
E7sus
To Coda
knew it was real, the way you make me feel.

Amaj7
Dmaj9
C♯m7
F♯m7
Amaj7
Girl: Ly-ing here next to you, time just seems to
Dmaj9
C♯m7
F♯m7
Amaj7
Dmaj9
C♯m7
F♯m7
fly. Need-ing you more and more:
Amaj7
Dmaj9
C♯m7
A
Dmaj7
let's give love a try.
Boy: Sweet-er than sweet - er love
C♯m7
Em7
A7
Dmaj7
grows, and heav - en's there for those who fool the tricks of

C♯m7
Em7
A7
Dmaj7
C♯m7
time, with the hearts of love they find true love in a
Bm7
E7sus
D.S. al Coda
spe - cial way. Girl: The clos - er I get to
CODA
Amaj7
Dmaj9
C♯m7
F♯m7
Girl: The clos - er I get to you,
Amaj7
Dmaj9
C♯m7
F♯m7
the more you make me see.

Amaj7
Dmaj9
C#m7
F#m7
By giv - ing you all I've got,
your love has cap - tured me.
Repeat ad lib. and Fade
Optional Ending
rall.

CHAMPAGNE SUPERNOVA

Words and Music by
NOEL GALLAGHER

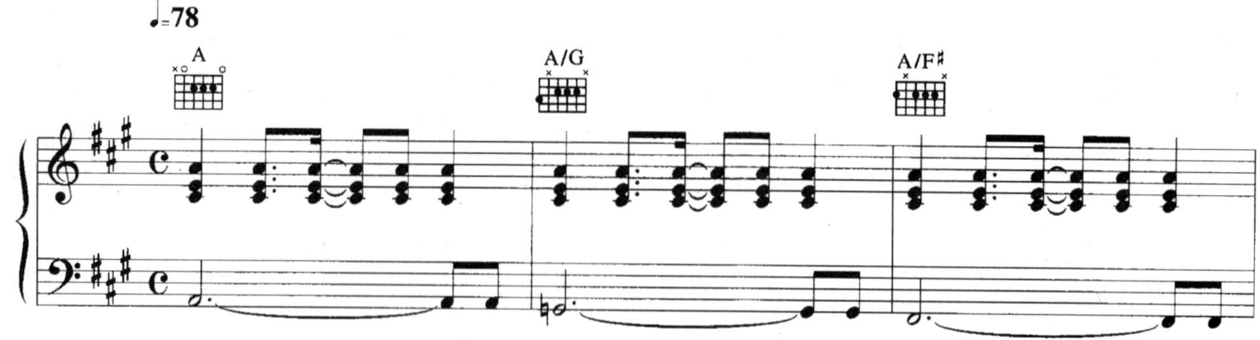

A/E
A
A/G
slow-ly walk-ing down the hall fast-er than a can-non ball,
A/F♯
A/E
where were you while we were get-ting high.
Some day you will
A
A/G
find me caught be-neath the land - slide,
in a cham-
A/F♯
A/E
A
- pagne su-per-no - va in the sky.
Some day you will find me caught be-neath the land-

A/G
A/F♯
slide, in a cham - pagne su - per - no - va, a
A/E
A
A/G
cham - pagne su - per - no - va in the sky.
A/F♯
A/E
A
1. Wake up the dawn and ask her why, a
(Verse 2 see block lyric)
A/G
A/F♯
dream - er dreams she ne - ver dies, wipe that tear a - way now from your eyes.

A/E
A
A/G
Slow-ly walk-ing down the hall, fast-er than a can-non ball,
A/F♯
E
where were you while we were get-ting high.
Some day you will
A
A/G
find me caught be-neath the land - slide, in a cham-
A/F♯
A/E
A
- pagne su-per-no - va in the sky.
Some day you will find me caught be-neath the land-

A/G
A/F♯
E
- slide, in a cham - pagne su-per-no - va, a cham-pagne su-per-no - va. 'Cause
D
peo - ple be - lieve that they're gon - na get a - way for the sum -
A
G
- mer but you and I we live and die the
D
E
E7
world's still spin - ning round, we don't know why, why, why, why, why.

1.
A
A/G
A/F♯
A/E
A
A/G
A/F♯
A/E
2.
A
A/G
A/F♯
Fmaj7
G
play 4 times

Fmaj7
G
Fmaj7
G
A
A/G
A/F♯
A/E
A
A/G
A/F♯
A/E
A
A/G
How ma - ny spe - cial peo - ple change—
how ma - ny lives are liv - ing strange,—

Verse 2:
How many special people change
How many lives are living strange
Where were you while we were getting high?
Slowly walking down the hall
Faster than a cannon ball
Where were you while we were getting high?

CHANGES

Words and Music by
DAVID BOWIE

C
Em7
Fmaj7
ev - 'ry time I thought I'd got it made, it seemed the taste was not so sweet.
G
C
Dm7
Em7
E♭m7
6fr
Dm7
So I turned my - self to face me, but I've nev - er caught a glimpse
G
Cmaj7
Dm7
Em7
E♭m7
6fr
of how the oth - ers must see the fak - er. I'm much too
Dm7
G7
F
C
Em/B
fast to take that test. (Ch - ch - ch - ch-chang - es) Turn and face the strange.

Am
C/G
F
Am/E
D
Don't want to be a rich-er man.
(Ch-ch-chang-es)
G7
F
C
Em/B
Am
C/G
(Ch-ch-ch-ch-chang-es) Turn and face the strange.
(Ch-ch-chang-es)
F
Am/E
D
Am
G
B♭
Just gon-na have to be a dif-'frent man. Time may change
F
E+
D6
Dm7
1
C
N.C.
me, but I can't trace time.

2
C
Dm7
Em7
F
time. Strange fas - ci - na - tion, fas -
C
F/C
C
F
ci - nat - ing me. Chang - es are
G13
3fr
G7
F
tak - ing the pace I'm go - ing through. (Ch - ch - ch - ch-chang - es)
C
Em/B
Am
C/G
F
Am/E
Turn and face the strange.
(Ch - ch-chang - es)
Oh, look out, you rock 'n'

D
G7
F
C
Em/B
roll - ers.
(Ch - ch - ch - ch - chang - es) Turn and face the strange. _
Am
C/G
F
Am/E
D
(Ch - ch - chang - es) ___
Pret - ty soon now __ you're gon - na get old - er.
Am
G
B♭
F
E+
D6
Dm7
C
Time may change me, but I can't trace time. I said that
Am
G
B♭
F
E+
D6
Dm7
C
Time may change me, but I can't trace time.

Additional Lyrics

2. I watch the ripples change their size, but never leave the stream
   Of warm impermanence and so the days flowed through my eyes
   But still the days seem the same.
   And these children that you spit on as they try to change their worlds
   Are immune to your consultations, they're quite aware of what they're going through.

   (Ch-ch-ch-ch-Changes) Turn and face the strange.
   (Ch-ch-changes) Don't tell them to grow up and out of it.
   (Ch-ch-ch-ch-Changes) Turn and face the strange.
   (Ch-ch-changes) Where's your shame? You've left us up to our necks in it.
   Time may change me, but you can't trace time.

CLOCKS

Words and Music by GUY BERRYMAN, JON BUCKLAND, WILL CHAMPION and CHRIS MARTIN

Fm
Eb
3fr
Oh I beg, I beg and plead. Sing - in', come out of
could not stop that you now know. Sing - in', come out up -
Bbm
Fm
things un - said. Shoot an ap - ple off my head. And a
on my seas, curse missed op - por - tu - ni - ties. Am I
Eb
3fr
Bbm
trou - ble that can't be named. A tig - er's wait - ing
a part of the cure or am I part of
Fm
Eb
3fr
Bbm
to be tamed.
the dis - ease?
Sing - in', you

Fm
E♭
3fr
are.
You
B♭m
Fm
are.
1
E♭
3fr
B♭m
A♭6
3fr
E♭
3fr
B♭m
A♭6
3fr

2
E♭
3fr
B♭m
Fm
You
are.
E♭
3fr
B♭m
Fm
are.
E♭
3fr
B♭m
A♭maj7
E♭
3fr
B♭m
A♭maj7
To Coda
You
are.

G♭maj7
D♭
1, 2
A♭
And noth - ing else com - pares.
3
A♭
G♭maj7
E♭/G
B♭m/F
1
Fm
2
Fm
D.S. al Coda
(with repeats)

CODA
E♭
3fr
B♭m
Home, home, where I want - ed to
A♭6
3fr
E♭
3fr
B♭m
go. Home, home, where I
A♭6
3fr
E♭
3fr
B♭m
want - ed to go.
Fm
Repeat and Fade
Optional Ending
E♭
3fr

THE COLOUR OF LOVE

Words and Music by BILLY OCEAN, JOLYON SKINNER,
BARRY EASTMOND and WAYNE BRATHWAITE

Eb/Bb
6fr
F/Bb
col - ours to cre - ate a
sea - sons. You're the rea - son it
Eb
3fr
F
Gm
3fr
vi - sion of har - mo - ny. It would be
hap - pens that way. What you see are
Dm7
Fm/Bb
Bb7
a re - al - i - ty 'cause it's on - ly what's in - side of my
col - ours of e - mo - tion re - flect - ing what I feel deep in -
Eb
3fr
Dm
Cm7
3fr
heart. You would see I've al - ways loved you right
side. Now I'd like to take a look at e -

E♭/F
B♭
Dm7
from the very - y start. Tell me,
mo - tions that you hide. Tell me,
what is the col - our of love?
Cm
E♭/F
Gm
Dm7
What do you see?
Is it warm, is it
Cm
E♭/F
B♭
Dm7
ten - der when you think of me?
I see the col - our of love
Cm7
E♭/F
E♭
B♭/D
when I'm think - ing of you
as a pic - ture per - fect
3fr

C7
E♭/F
1
B♭
E♭/B♭
6fr
paint ing of love for-ev - er true.
F
E♭
3fr
F
2
B♭
true. And,
G♭(add9)
A♭/G♭
4fr
Fm7
oh, though man - y may try to keep us a - part
B♭m
E♭m
6fr
D♭/F
Oh, the col - our that I see in you will

G♭
D♭/F
shine a light to see us through. No mat - ter what the world will do,
Cm7
F7sus
B♭
Dm7
I'll al - ways love you.
Cm7
E♭/F
Gm
Dm
Cm
E♭/F
B♭
Dm
Cm
E♭/F
E♭
B♭/D

C#m
E/F#
B
D#m7
C#m
E/F#
4fr
6fr
What is the col - our of love?
true.
What do you see?
G#m
D#m7
C#m
E/F#
Is it warm, is it ten - der when you think of me?
B
D#m7
C#m7
E/F#
I see the col - our of love when I'm think - ing of you
E
B/D#
C#7
E/F#
Repeat ad lib. and Fade
as a pic - ture per - fect paint - ing of love for - ev - er

COME SAIL AWAY

Words and Music by
DENNIS DeYOUNG

Am
G
Am
On board I'm the cap - tain, so climb a - board. We'll search for to - mor - row,
G
C
Em/B
Am
Am/G
on ev - 'ry shore. And I'll try, oh Lord, I'll try
3
3
F
G
C
Dm
Em
Dm
to car - ry on.
C
G7
C
Em/B
Am
Am/G
I look to the sea.
tr
f

F
G
Re - flec-tions in the waves spark my mem - o - ry,
C
Em/B
Am
Am/G
F
some hap - py, some sad.
I think of child-hood friends and the
G
Am
G
dreams we had.
We lived hap - p'ly for - ev - er so the sto - ry goes.
Am
G
But some - how we missed out on the pot of gold.
But we'll

C
Em/B
Am
Am/G
F
G
try best that we can,
to car - ry
C
F/C
G5/C
F/C
C
F/C
on.
G5/C
F/C
C
F/C
G5/C
F/C
A gath-er-ing of an-gels ap-peared a-bove my head. They
ff
C
F/C
G5/C
F/C
sang to me this song of hope and this is what they said. They said

C
F/C
G5/C
F/C
come sail a - way, come sail a - way, come sail a - way with me, lads.
C
F/C
G5/C
F/C
Come sail a - way, come sail a - way, come sail a - way with me.
C
F/C
G5/C
F/C
To Coda
Come sail a - way, come sail a - way, come sail a - way with me.
C
F/C
G5/C
A♭
4fr
Come sail a - way, come sail a - way, come sail a - way with me.

C
F/C
G5/C
I
thought that they were an - gels but much to my sur - prise, we
climbed a - board their star - ship and head - ed for the skies. Sing - in'
D.S. al Coda
CODA
Optional Ending
Repeat and Fade
Come sail a - way, come sail a - way, come sail a - way with me.

COME TO MY WINDOW

Words and Music by
MELISSA ETHERIDGE

C(add9)
G
D
I would dial the num - bers just to lis - ten to your breath. And
Keep - ing my eyes o - pen, I can - not af - ford to sleep.
C(add9)
G
D
I would stand in - side my hell and hold the hand of death.
Giv - ing a - way prom - is - es I know that I can't keep.
C(add9)
G
D
You don't know how far I'd go to use this pre - cious ache. And
Noth - ing fills the black - ness that has seeped in - to my chest. I
C(add9)
G
D
you don't know how much I'd give or how much I can take.
need you in my blood, I am for - sak - ing all the rest.
Just to reach

Em
C(add9)
D
you. Just to reach you. Oh, to
Em
C(add9)
D
G
C(add9)
reach you, oh. Come to my win -
Am
D
G
C(add9)
dow. Crawl in - side, wait
Am
D
G
C(add9)
by the light of the moon. Come to my win -

Am
Dsus
1
G
C(add9)
Am7
D
Dsus
D
- dow, I'll be home soon.
2
G
C(add9)
Am7
D
Dsus
D
soon.
Em
D/E
I don't care what they think.
C
C/B
I don't care what they say.

Am
Am7
What do they know a - bout this love
D
Dsus
D
G
C(add9)
an - y - way?
Am7
D
Dsus
D
G
C(add9)
Am7
D
Dsus
Come,
C(add9)
G
D
come to my win - dow, I'll be home, I'll

C(add9) G D
be home, I'll be home. I'm com - ing home.
G C(add9) Am D G C(add9)
Come to my win - dow, Crawl in - side, wait
Am D G C(add9) Am Dsus
by the light of the moon. Come to my win - dow, I'll be home
G C(add9) Am7 D
soon. I'll be home, I'll be home. I'm com - in' home.
Repeat and Fade
Optional Ending
G

COULD IT BE MAGIC

Inspired by "Prelude In C Minor" by F. Chopin

Words and Music by BARRY MANILOW
and ADRIENNE ANDERSON

Dsus
D
E♭maj7
Dm7
E♭maj7
- sa, an - gel of my life - time, an - swer to all an -
you; build my world a - round you, nev - er leave you till
D7sus
Dm7
Gsus (add2)
G
G7/F
Cm/E♭
G7/D
swers I can find; ba - by, I love you.
my life is done. Ba - by, I love you.
Cm
A♭/C
Bm7
G/B
B♭maj7
B♭6
(1., 3.) Come, come, come in - to my arms.
(2., 4.) Now, now, now and hold on fast.
Am7
A♭7
G
To Coda
Let me know the won - der of all of you.
Could this be the mag - ic at last?

1, 3
G7/F
Cm/E♭
G/D
2
Dm7/F
C(add2)/E
C/E
Cm/E♭
Ba - by, I want _ you.
Am(add9)
Bm7/E
Am(add9)
Bm7/E
Am(add9)/E
Gsus
D.S. al Coda
(with repeats)
CODA
G7/F
Cm/E♭
G/D
Cm
A♭/C
Could it be mag - ic?
1. Come,
2., 3. Now,
come,
now,

Bm7
G/B
B♭maj7
B♭6
Am7
come in - to my arms.
now and hold on fast.
Let me know the won -
Could this be the mag -
A♭7
Gsus
G
1, 2
G7/F
Cm/E♭
G/D
- der of all of you.
- ic at last?
Ba - by, I want you.
Could it be mag - ic?
3
G/F
Cm
Fm
G7
Cm
A♭
D♭
G7♯5
G7
Cm

CRUCIFY

Words and Music by
TORI AMOS

A#5
6fr
F#5
Fig-ures that my cour - age would choose to sell out now.__ I've been
B
F#
G#m
4fr
E
F#
G#m
4fr
look-ing for a sav-ior in these dirt-y streets,_ look-ing for a sav-ior__ be
E
F#
B
F#
neath these dirt - y sheets._ I've been rais - ing up my hands,_ drive an - oth - er

G♯m
G♯m/F♯
G♯m/E♯
E
4fr
nail_ in.___ Just what God_ needs,_ one more vic - tim.___ Why do
G♯m
C♯m7
F♯
C♯m7
G♯m
C♯m7
we cru-ci-fy___ our selves? Ev - 'ry day___ I cru-ci-fy___ my
mf
F♯
C♯m7
G♯m
C♯m7
self. Noth-ing I do___ is good e-nough for you.___ I cru - ci - fy___ my -

F♯
C♯m7
G♯m
C♯m7
F♯
4fr
self, ev - 'ry day I cru-ci-fy my - self. My
C♯m
E
heart is sick of be-ing, I said my heart is sick of be - ing in
G♯m
B
E
C♯m
chains. Oh, oh,

To Coda
1.
2.
G#m
B
E
C#m
E
C#m
4fr
chains.
Oh, oh.
Oh, oh.
G#
A#m
B
F#
G#
A#m
Please
be,
save
me,
B
F#
G#
A#m
B
F#
I
cry.

G♯
A♯m
B
F♯
4fr
Ah,
ah.
B
F♯
G♯m
E
F♯
G♯m
mp
Look-ing for a sav-ior in these dirt-y streets,
look-ing for a sav-ior be
E
F♯
B
F♯
neath these dirt-y sheets.
I've been rais-ing up my hands,
drive an-oth-er
mf

Additional lyrics

(Verse 2)
Got a kick for a dog, beggin' for love
Gotta have my suffering so that I can have my cross
I know a cat named Easter, he says "Will you ever learn?"
You're just an empty cage girl if you kill the bird.

I've been looking for a savior in these dirty streets
Looking for a savior beneath these dirty sheets
I've been raising up my hands, drive another nail in
Got enough guilt to start my own religion.

CRYING

Words and Music by ROY ORBISON
and JOE MELSON

C
G7
wished me well; _ you could-n't tell ________ that I'd been
don't love me and I'll al - ways be ________
C
Em
C
cry - ing o - ver you, cry - ing
cry - ing o - ver you, cry - ing
Em
F
o - ver you. When you said, "So
o - ver you. Yes, now you're _
G7
F
G7
long;" left me stand - ing ________ all a - lone, a - lone and
gone and from this ________ mo - ment on I'll be

C
C+
F/C
cry - ing, cry - ing, cry - ing,
cry - ing, cry - ing, cry - ing,
Fm/C
C
cry - ing. It's hard to un - der - stand, but the
cry - ing. Yeah, cry - ing,
G7
1 C
touch of your hand can start me cry - ing.
cry - ing o - ver
2 C
I thought that you.

DANCING QUEEN

Words and Music by BENNY ANDERSSON,
BJORN ULVAEUS and STIG ANDERSON

Bm7
E7/B
A
D/A
Watch that scene, diggin' the danc - ing queen.
A
D/A
A
D/A
A
D/A
Fri-day night and the lights are low.
A
F♯m
E
A/E
Look-ing out for a place to go,
oh,
where they play the right mu - sic.
E
A/E
E
F♯m
E
F♯m
Get-ting in the swing,
you come to look for a king.

A
D/A
A
An - y-bod - y could be that guy.
You're a teas - er. You turn 'em on,
Night is young and the mu - sic's
leave 'em burn - ing and then you're
F♯m
E
A/E
E
A/E
E
high.
gone,
With a bit of rock mu - sic,
look ing out for an - oth - er.
ev - 'ry - thing is fine.
An - y - one will do.
You're in the
F♯m
E
F♯m
Bm7
mood for a dance,
and when you get the chance,
E7
A
you are the danc - ing queen,

D/A
A
D/A
young and sweet, only seventeen.
A
D/A
A
E/G♯
Dancing queen, feel the beat from the tambourine.
F♯m7
A/E
E
C♯7
You can dance. You can jive,
F♯m
B7/D♯
D
having the time of your life. Oh, see that girl.

Bm7
E7/B
A
Watch that scene, dig - gin' the danc - ing queen.
D/A
A
1
D/A
A
D/A
A
D/A
2
D/A
Dig - gin' the
A
D/A
A
Repeat and Fade
danc - ing queen.

DANCING WITH MYSELF

Words and Music by BILLY IDOL
and TONY JAMES

A5
5fr
mir - ror's re - flec - tion, I'm a - danc - in' with my - se -
pass me by, and leave me danc - in' with my - se -
E5
elf. Oh, when there's no one else in si - ight, and in the
elf. So let's sink an - oth - er dri - ink, 'cause it - 'll
A5
5fr
To Coda
B5
crowd - ed, lone - ly ni - ight, well, I wait so long for my
give me time to thi - ink. If I had the chance, I'd ask the
A5
5fr
love vi - bra - tion, and I'm danc - in' with my - se -
world to dance, and I'd be danc - in' with my - se -

E5
elf. elf. Oh, oh, oh, danc - in' with my - se - elf. Oh, oh, oh,
A5
5fr
B5
danc - in' with my - se - elf. Well, there's no - thin' to lose, and there's
A5
5fr
no - thin' to prove, when I'm danc - in' with my - se -
1
E
elf, oh, oh, oh, oh. If I

2
E
A
oh.
Oh, oh, oh, oh, oh.
E
Oh, oh, oh, oh,
oh, oh, oh,
3
B
B5
oh.
E5
Play 3 times

B5
CODA
D. S. al Coda
B5
Well, ___ if I
had ___ the chance, _ I'd ask the
A5
5fr
world _ to dance, _ and I'd be danc - in' with my - se - elf. Oh, oh, oh,
E5
A5
5fr
danc - in' with my - se - elf. Oh, oh, oh, danc - in' with my - se -

B5
elf.
If I had the chance, I'd ask the
world to dance, and if I had the chance, I'd ask the
world to dance, if I had the chance, I'd ask the
world to dance.
Oh, oh, oh,

E5
A5
5fr
oh.
Oh, oh, oh, oh.
Oh, oh, oh,
vocal ad lib to end
(Danc - in' with my - se -
elf. Oh, oh, oh, danc - in' with my - se -
Repeat and Fade
Optional Ending
elf. Oh, oh, oh)
elf. Oh, oh, oh, oh.)

DANIEL

Words and Music by ELTON JOHN
and BERNIE TAUPIN

G7
E7
Am
I can see the red tail - lights heading for Spain.
Well, Dan - iel says it's the best place he's ev - er seen.
G
F
G
Oh, and I can see Dan - iel wav - ing good-bye.
Oh, and he should know; he's been there e - nough.
Am
F
God, it looks like Dan - iel.
Lord, I miss Dan - iel.
G7
F/G
To Coda
Must be the clouds in my eyes.
Oh, I miss him so much.

1
C
G7
2,3
C
End instrumental
Oh,
F
Dan - iel, my broth - er, you are old - er than me.
C
F
Do you still feel the pain of the scars

C
Am
that won't heal? Your eyes have died, but
G
F
A♭6
3 fr
you see more than I. Dan - iel, you're a
C
A7
Dm7
star in the face of the sky.
1
G7
2
G7
D.S. al Coda
CODA
C

F
Oh God, it looks like Dan - iel.
G7
F/G
C
Must be the clouds in my eyes.
F
G
C
F
C

DON'T DO ME LIKE THAT

Words and Music by
TOM PETTY

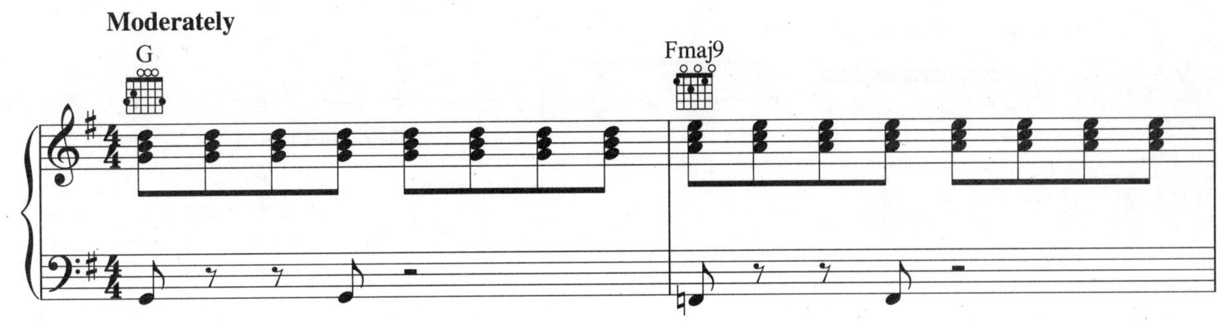

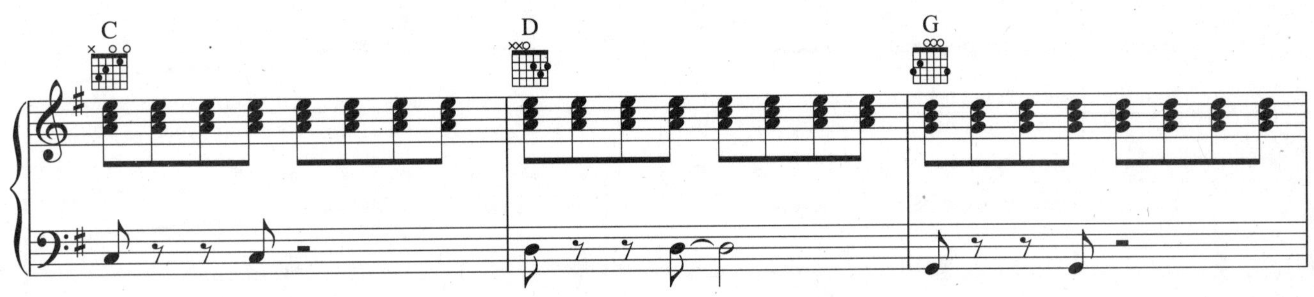

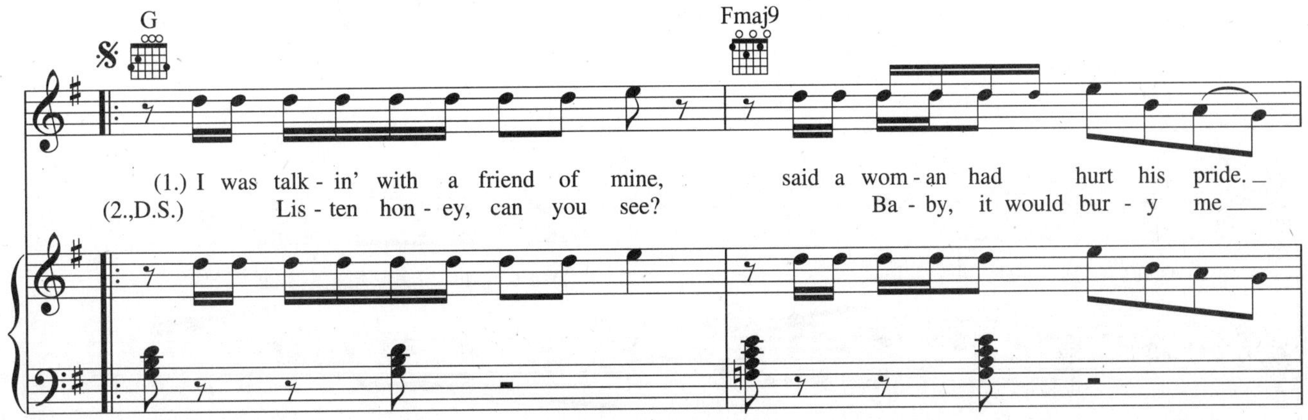

C
D
told him that she love him so and
if you were in the pub - lic eye
turned a - round and let him go.
giv - in' some - one else a try.
G
Fmaj9
Then he said, "You bet - ter watch your step
And you know you bet - ter watch your step
or you're gon - na get hurt your - self.
or you're gon - na get hurt your - self.
C
D
To Coda
Some - one's gon - na tell you lies,
Some - one's gon - na tell you lies,
cut you down to size."
cut you down to size."
G
Fmaj9
Don't do me like that.
Don't do me like that.

Em
C
D
What if I loved you, ba - by?
Don't do me like that.
Don't, don't, don't, don't.
G
Fmaj9
Don't do me like that.
Don't do me like that.
1
Em
C
D
Some - day I might need you, ba - by.
Don't do me like that.
2
Em
C
D
What if I need you, ba - by?
Don't do me like that, 'cause

G7 C7

some - where deep, down in - side, ___ some - one is say - in', "Love ___

G7 C7

___ does - n't last ___ that ___ long." ___

G7 C7

I've had this feel - in' in - side ___ night out and day ___ in, and

Cm D

D.S. al Coda

ba - by I can't take ___ it no more. ___

CODA
G
Fmaj9
Don't do me like that.
Don't do me like that.
Em
C
D
What if I loved you, ba - by?
Don't, don't, don't, don't.
G
Fmaj9
Don't do me like that.
Don't do me like that.
Em
C
D
Repeat and Fade
Optional Ending
G
I just might_ need you, hon - ey.
Don't do me like that.

DON'T KNOW WHY

Words and Music by
JESSE HARRIS

Gm7
C7
F7sus
B♭
Gm7
C7
I don't know why I did - n't come, I don't know why I did-n't
F7sus
B♭
F7sus
B♭maj7
B♭7
E♭maj7
3fr
D+
come. When I saw the break of day,
Gm7
C7
F7sus
B♭
B♭maj7
B♭7
I wished that I could fly a - way 'stead of kneel - ing in
E♭maj7
3fr
D+
Gm7
C7
the sand catch - ing tear - drops

F7sus B♭ Gm7 C7
in my hand. My heart is drenched in wine,
F7 Gm7
but you'll be on
C7 F7 F7/E♭ B♭/D F/C
my mind for - ev - er.
B♭maj7 B♭7 E♭maj7 D+ Gm7 C7
Out a - cross the end - less sea, I would die in ec -

F7sus
B♭
B♭maj7
B♭7
E♭maj7
3fr
D+
sta - sy.
But I'll be
a bag
of bones
Gm7
C7
F7sus
B♭
Gm7
driv - ing
down
the road
a - lone.
My heart
is
drenched
C7
F7
in
wine,
but
Gm7
C7
F7
you'll
be
on
my
mind
for
-
ev -

B♭maj7
B♭7
E♭maj7
D7♯5
er.
Gm7
C7
F7sus
B♭maj7
B♭7
E♭maj7
D+
Gm7
C7
F7sus
B♭maj7
B♭7
E♭maj7
D+
Some - thing has to make you run.

Gm7 C7 F7sus B♭

I don't know why I did - n't come. I

B♭maj7 B♭7 E♭maj7 D+

feel as emp - ty as a drum.

Gm7 C7 F7 B♭ Gm7 C7

I don't know why I did - n't come, I don't know why I did-n't

F7 B♭ Gm7 C7 F7sus B♭

come. I don't know why I did - n't come.

DON'T SPEAK

Words and Music by ERIC STEFANI
and GWEN STEFANI

Fm
B♭
E♭
3fr
B♭
let - ting go,
and if it's real, well, I don't want - to know.
you and I,
with my head in my hands I sit and cry.
C
Fm
B♭m
Don't speak, I know just what you're say -
E♭
3fr
C7
B♭m
C7
- ing, so please stop ex - plain - ing. Don't tell me 'cause it hurts.
Fm
B♭m7
C7
Fm
B♭m
Don't speak, I know what you're think -
No, no, no.

Eb
C7
Bbm
C7
To Coda
- ing. I don't need your rea - sons. Don't tell me 'cause it hurts.
Fm
Db
Eb
Cm
Our mem - o - ries,
Gm
Fm
Bb
Gm
Fm
Bb
D.S. al Coda
they can be in-vit - ing, but some are al-to-geth - er might - y fright - 'ning.
CODA
Fm
Db
Ab/C
It's all end - ing, I got - ta

C♭
G♭/B♭
6fr
A
A(♭5)/D♯
A♭
4fr
stop pre - tend - ing who we are.
Cm
3fr
Gm
3fr
Fm
B♭
Play 3 times
Instrumental solo
Gm
3fr
Cm
3fr
Fm
Cm
3fr
Gm
3fr
Solo ends
You and me,
Fm
B♭
Fm
B♭
I can see us dy - ing... Are we?

Fm
B♭m
E♭
3 fr
C7
Don't speak, I know just what you're say - ing, so please stop ex - plain -
B♭m
C7
Fm
B♭m7
C7
- ing. Don't tell me 'cause it hurts, No, no, don't
Fm
B♭m
E♭
3 fr
C7
speak, I know what you're think - ing, and I don't need your rea -
Repeat and Fade
B♭m
C7
Fm
B♭m7
C7
- sons. Don't tell me 'cause it hurts. Don't tell me 'cause it hurts.

DON'T TALK TO STRANGERS

Words and Music by
RICK SPRINGFIELD

no chord
C♯m11
C♯m
G♯m7
A/B
4fr
Why don't you tell me some - one is - n't lov - in' you, _ 'cause you're my
Now who's this, Don Juan I've been hear - in' of? _
girl, some say it's no long - er true. _ You're see - in' some slick con - tin -
Love hurts when on - ly one's in love. _ Did you fall at first sight or did you
ent - al dude. _____
need a shove? _____
I'm beg - gin' you, please
G♯m/B
B/E
E
B/C♯
C♯m7
Don't talk to stran - gers, (Ba - by don't you talk _) Don't talk to stran -

C♯m7
B/A
E/A
B/A
E/A
C♯m
(You know he'll on - ly use you up)
- gers Don't talk, don't talk, don't talk, _
B/C♯
C♯m7
B/C♯
C♯m7
B/A
E/A
_ don't talk, Don't talk to them Don't talk,
To Coda
B/A
E/A
C♯m7
no chord
Don't talk. Now tell me,
C♯m11
C♯m
G♯m7
A/B
C♯m11
C♯m
G♯m7
how's life in the big ci - ty? _ I hear the com - pe - ti - tion's tough, ba - by,

A/B
C#m11
C#m
G#m7
that's a pit - y, and ev - 'ry man's an ac - tor, ev - 'ry
A/B
G#m7
D.S. al Coda
girl is pret - ty. I don't like what's get - tin' back to me.
CODA
B
A
E/G#
Fais l'a - mour a - vec moi
B
A
E/G#
B
(What she say?) Vien dor - mir mon a - mour Don - nes moi

A E/G♯ A B B/E E B/C♯
ton coeur ce soir I'm beg-gin' you: Don't talk to stran-
C♯m7 B/E E B/C♯ C♯m7
gers, (Ba-by don't you talk) Don't talk to stran - gers
(You know he'll on-ly
B/A E/A B/A E/A C♯m B/C♯ C♯m7
use you up)
Don't talk, don't talk, don't talk, don't talk,
B/C♯ C♯m7 B/A E/A B/A E/A
Repeat and Fade
Don't talk to, Don't talk, Don't talk.
4fr

DONNA

Words and Music by
RITCHIE VALENS

F
B♭
C7
love my girl, Don - na where can you
1 F
B♭
C7
be, where can you be?
2 F
B♭
F
F7
be, where can you be? Oh,
B♭
F
dar - lin' now that you're gone I don't know what I'll

B♭
do. All my smiles and all my love for
C7
you.
F
B♭
C7
I had a girl, Don - na was her name,
F
B♭
C7
since she left me I've nev - er been the same. 'Cause I

F
B♭
C7
love my girl. Don - na where can you
be, where can you be?
Oh, Don - na, oh, Don - na.
Repeat and Fade
Oh, Don - na, oh, Don - na.

DREAM WEAVER

Words and Music by
GARY WRIGHT

Moderately fast

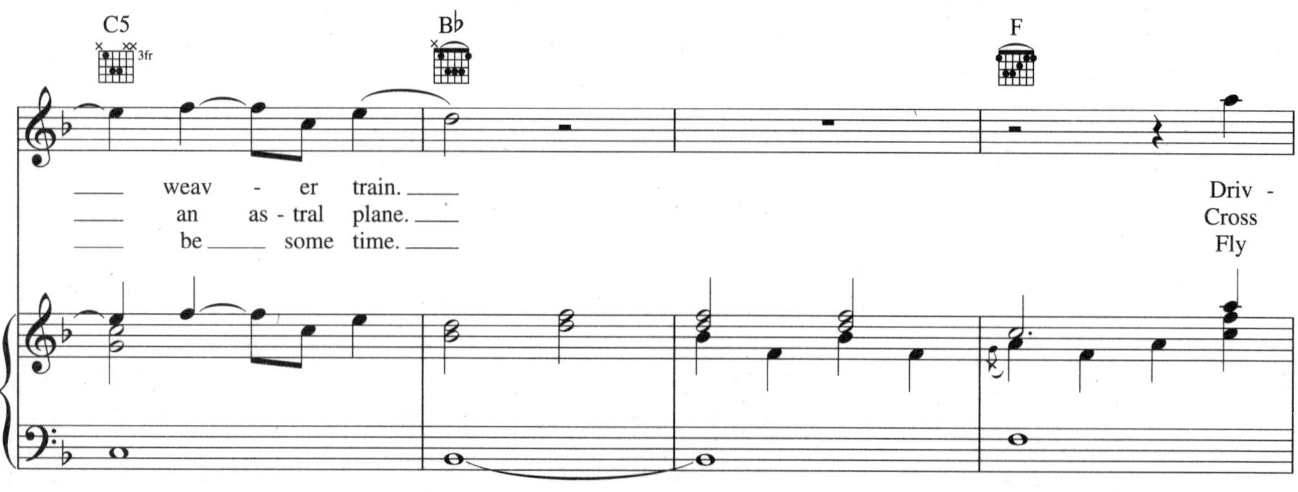

C
Eb/Bb
6fr
Bb
er, take a - way my wor - ries of to - day
the high - ways of fan - ta - sy,
me a - way to the bright side of the moon
F
C
Bb
and leave to - mor - row be - hind.
help me to for - get to - day's pain.
and meet me on the oth - er side.
F
F7/A
3fr
Bb
Ooh, dream weav - er,
3
3
F
F7/A
3fr
Bb
F
F7/A
3fr
I be - lieve you can get me through the night.

B♭
F
F7/A
3fr
B♭
F
F7/A
3fr
Ooh, _ dream
B♭
F
F7/A
3fr
B♭
To Coda
weav - er, I be - lieve _ we can reach _ the morn - ing light. _
F
F7/A
3fr
1 B♭
C
2 B♭
C
D.S. al Coda
CODA
F
F7/A
3fr
B♭
F
F7/A
3fr

B♭
F
F7/A
3fr
B♭
F
F7/A
3fr
Dream
weav-er,
B♭
F
F7/A
3fr
B♭
F
F7/A
3fr
B♭
F
F7/A
3fr
B♭
C/B♭
B♭
C/B♭
B♭
C/B♭
dream
weav-er.
B♭
C/B♭
B♭
C/B♭
B♭
C/B♭
B♭
C/B♭
Dm(♯4)
5fr
rit.

DREAMER

Words and Music by RICK DAVIES
and ROGER HODGSON

D
A7sus
A7
C
dream - er. Well, can you put your hands in your head, oh
Fmaj7
G
Fmaj7
G
A♭
no! I said "Far
B♭(add9)
Gm
C
out, what a day, a year, a laugh it is."
A♭
B♭(add9)
Gm
You know, well you know you had it

C
Gm
3fr
C
com - in' to you, now there's not a lot I can do.
D
A7sus
A7(add4)
3fr
D
Dream - er, you stu - pid lit - tle dream - er;
A7sus
A7(add4)
3fr
C
Fmaj7
G
so now you put your head in your hands, oh no. Whoo!
D
A7sus
A7
D

A7sus
A7
C
Fmaj7
G
I said
A♭
B♭(add9)
Gm
"Far out, what a day, a year, a
C
A♭
B♭(add9)
laugh it is." You know, well you
Gm
C
Gm
know you had it com - in' to you, now there's not a

C
lot I can do.
mp
B♭/C
C
(Work it out some - day.)
B♭/C

If
C
B♭/C
C
I could see some - thing... (You can see an - y - thing you want, boy.)
B♭/C
If I could be some - one. (You can be an - y - one.
C
Cel - e - brate, boy.) Well, if I can do some - thing... (Well,

you can do some - thing.) If I could do an - y - thing... _
(But can you do some - thing
B♭/C
out of this world?)
C
Gm7/C
Take a dream on a Sun - day.
cresc. little by little

I'll take a life, take a
C
hol - i - day.
Gm7/C
Take a lie, take a dream - er.
C
F/C
C
F/C
Dream, (dream,) dream, (dream,) dream, (dream,) dream, dream a - long...
mf

C
F/C
C
F/C
C
B♭maj7
C/B♭
B♭
C/B♭
B♭
C/B♭
B♭
C/B♭
B♭
C
Dream - er. (Dream - er, dream a - long.
Come on, you dream - er, dream a - long.) Roll it on. (Come on, you dream - er,
B♭maj7

dream _ a - long. _
Come on, you dream - er,
dream _ a - long.) _
cresc.
D
A7sus
A7
D
Dream - er,
you know you are a dream - er.
f
A7sus
A7
C
Fmaj7
G
Can you put your hands in your head, oh no! I said,
D
A7sus
A7
D
dream - er,
you're noth - ing but a dream - er.

A7sus
A7
C
Fmaj7
G
Can you put your hands in your head, oh no! Oh
Fmaj7
G
N.C.
no!
8va
(8va)
Fade out
(8va)
Optional Ending
rit.

ELEANOR RIGBY

Words and Music by JOHN LENNON
and PAUL McCARTNEY

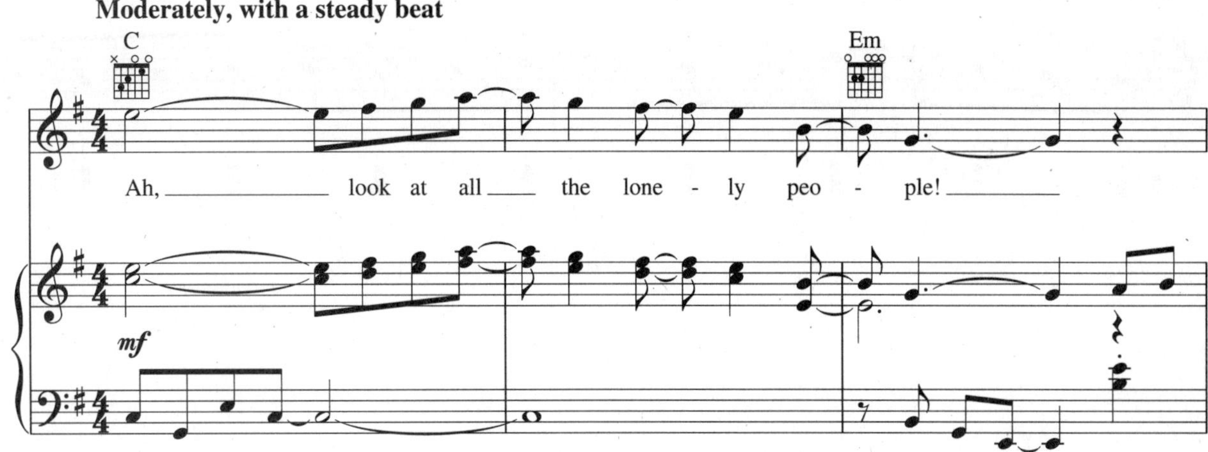

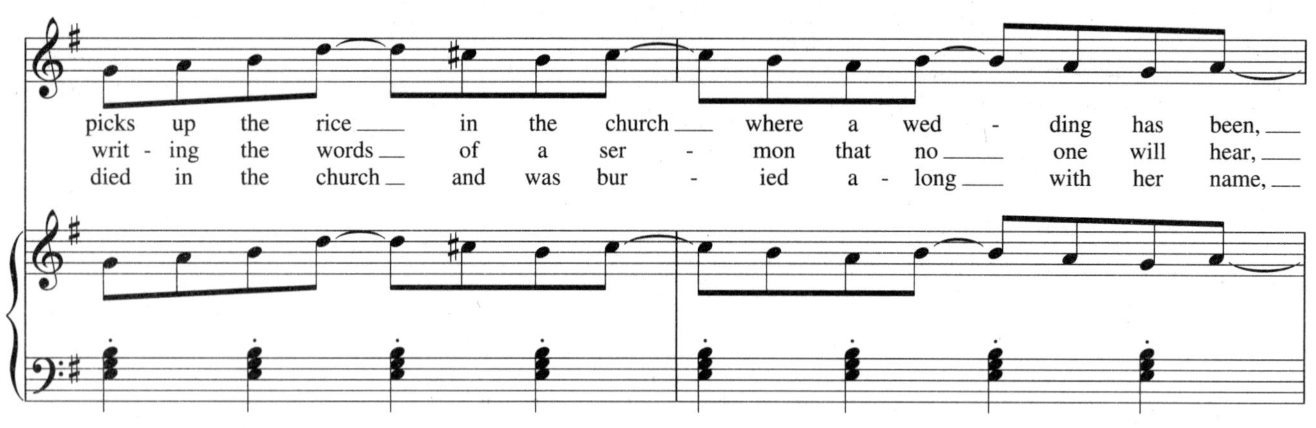
picks up the rice in the church where a wed - ding has been,
writ - ing the words of a ser - mon that no one will hear,
died in the church and was bur - ied a - long with her name,

C
Em
lives in a dream. Waits at the win - dow,
no one comes near. Look at him work - ing,
no - bod - y came. Fa - ther Mc - Ken - zie,

C
wear - ing the face that she keeps in a jar by the door,
darn - ing his socks in the night when there's no - bod - y there,
wip - ing the dirt from his hands as he walks from the grave,

Em
Em7
Em6
who is it for?
what does he care?
no one was saved.
All the lone - ly peo - ple, where do
C/E
Em
Em7
they all come from?
All the lone - ly peo -
Em6
C/E
To Coda
1
Em
- ple, where do they all be - long?
2
Em
D.C. al Coda
CODA
Em

EVERY ROSE HAS ITS THORN

Words and Music by BOBBY DALL, BRETT MICHAELS,
BRUCE JOHANNESSON and RIKKI ROCKETT

D
C
tried not to hurt you, __ though I tried. But I guess that's why __ they say,
G
C(add9)
G
ev - 'ry rose has its thorn, just like ev - 'ry night has its
C(add9)
G
D
C
G
dawn. __ Just like ev - 'ry cow - boy __ sings his sad, sad __ song,
C
G
ev - 'ry rose has its thorn.
yea it does

C(add9)
G
C(add9)
I
G
C(add9)
lis - ten to our favo - rite song play - ing on the ra - di - o, ___ hear the
G
C(add9)
D. J. say love's a game of ea - sy come and ea - sy go. ___ But I
G
C(add9)
G
C(add9)
won - der does ___ he know, has he ev - er felt ___ like this? And I

D
C
G
know that you'd be here right now if I could-'ve let you know some-how. I guess ev - 'ry rose has its
C(add9)
G
C(add9)
thorn, just like ev - 'ry night has its dawn. Just like
G
D
C
G
ev - 'ry cow- boy sings his sad, sad song, ev - 'ry rose has its
C(add9)
Em
D
C
G
thorn. Though it's been a - while now I can still feel so much pain.

Em
D
C
G
Like the knife that cuts _ you, the wound heals, but the scar, that scar re - mains.
C(add9)
G
C(add9)
G
I know I could have saved our love that night _ if I'd
C(add9)
G
known what to say._
In - stead of mak - ing love _ we both
C(add9)
G
C(add9)
made our sepa - rate ways._
Now I
hear you've found some - bod - y new___ and

G
C
D
that I nev- er meant that much to you.___ To hear that tears me up in - side___ and to
C
G
C(add9)
see you cuts me like a knife. I guess ev - 'ry rose has its thorn, just like
G
C(add9)
G
D
ev - 'ry night has its dawn.___ Just like ev - 'ry cow- boy ___ sings his
C(add9)
G
C(add9)
D
G
sad, sad___ song, ev - 'ry rose has its thorn.

EVERYBODY'S CHANGING

Words and Music by TIM RICE-OXLEY,
RICHARD HUGHES and TOM CHAPLIN

F
- - der your own land.
Dm7
But when I think a - bout it I
Gsus4
3fr
C
3fr
don't see how you can.
You're
C
3fr
F
ach - ing, you're break - ing and I can see the pain in your eyes.
(2.) gone from here, soon you will dis - ap - pear, fad - ing in - to beau - ti - ful light.

Dm7
Says ev - 'ry - bo - dy's chang - ing and
'Cause ev - 'ry - bo - dy's chang - ing and
G
Am
I don't know why.
I don't feel right.
F
G
So lit - tle time,
Csus4
3fr
C
3fr
F
Dm7
try to un - der - stand that I'm
try - ing to make a move just to

G
Em
stay in___ the game, I'm try - ing to stay___ a - wake___ and___ re -
A7
Dm
G
To Coda
-mem - ber___ my name but ev - 'ry - bo - dy's chang - ing and___ I don't feel___ the same.___
C
1.
Em7
G7
2. You're

2.
Fmaj7
Dm7
G7
Am
D.S. al Coda
Coda
Am
Oh,
Dm
G
rit.
C
ev - 'ry - bo - dy's chang - ing and I don't feel the same.

FEELIN' ALRIGHT

Words and Music by
DAVE MASON

C
F
C
I've got to leave here 'fore I start to scream,
'cause some-one's locked the door and
Got-ta stop be-liev-in' in all your lies,
'cause there's too much to do be-
till some-one comes a-long and takes my place,
with a dif-f'rent name and
F
C
took the key.
fore I die.
yes, a dif-f'rent face.
You feel-in' al-right?
F
C
I'm not feel-in' too good my-self.
F
C
Well, you feel-in' al-right?

F
C
I'm not feel - in' too good _ my - self. _
1,2 F
3 F
You feel-in'
C
F
al - right? _
I'm not feel - in' too good _
C
F
Repeat and Fade
_ my - self. _
Well, _ you feel-in'

EVERYTHING IS BEAUTIFUL

Words and Music by
RAY STEVENS

F
Dm7
G7sus
beau - ti - ful in its own way.
G7
C9
C7
Gm7
C9
Like a star - ry sum - mer night, or a snow - cov - ered win - ter's
F
B♭
F
C7
F
day. Ev - 'ry - bod - y's beau - ti - ful
Dm7
G7sus
G7
in their own way, un - der God's

C9
C7
Gm7
C9
F
B♭
heav - en the world's gon - na find a way.
F
C7
F
C
B♭
1. There is none so blind as he who will not
2. (See additional lyrics)
F
C
B♭
see. We must not close our minds, we must let our thoughts be
F
C
free. For ev - 'ry hour that pass - es by

Additional Lyrics

2. We shouldn't care about the length of his hair or the color of his skin,
Don't worry about what shows from without but the love that lies within,
We gonna get it all together now and everything gonna work out fine,
Just take a little time to look on the good side, my friend, and straighten it out in your mind.

FEEL

Words and Music by ROBBIE WILLIAMS
and GUY CHAMBERS

A7
Gm
3fr
Not sure I un - der - stand
Be - fore I fall in love
Dm/F
A/E
this role I've been giv - en.
I'm pre - par - ing to leave her.
A7
Dm
I sit and talk to God,
I scare my - self to death,
Am/C
A/C♯
and he just laughs at my plans.
that's why I keep on run - ning,

A7 Gm

My head speaks a lan - guage
be - fore I've ar - rived,

Dm/F A/E A7

I don't un - der - stand.
I can see my - self com - ing.
I just wan - na

B♭ F C

feel real love, feel the home that I live in.

B♭

'Cause I got too much life run - ning through my veins

F C 1. A/C♯

— going to waste. 2. I don't wan-na

2. B♭ F

And I need to feel real love and a life ever af-

C A/C♯ Dm Am/D

-ter. I can-not give it up.

F/D G/D Dm Am/D F/D G/D

Dm
Am
F
G
Dm
Am
Guitar
F
G
Dm
Am
F
G
Dm
Am/E
F
G
I just wan - na
B♭
F
C
feel real love, feel the home that I live in.

B♭
F
I got too much love
run - ning through my veins
to go to waste.
C
B♭
I just want to feel
real
love
F
C
and a life ev - er - af - ter.
There's a hole in my soul,
B♭
F
C
you can see it in my face,
it's a real big place.

A/C♯
Dm
Am/D
F/D
G/D
Dm
Am/D
F/D
G/D
Come and hold my
Dm
Am
F
G
hand,
I want to con - tact the
Dm
Am
F
G
Dm
Am
liv - ing.
Not sure I un - der - stand

F G Dm Am/E F G

this role I've been giv - en. Not sure I un - der - stand.

Dm Am F G Dm Am

Not sure I un - der - stand.

F G Dm Am F G

Not sure I un - der - stand. Not sure I un - der - stand.

Dm Am/E F G Dm

FIRE AND ICE

Words and Music by TOM KELLY,
SCOTT SHEETS and PAT BENATAR

G
F5 G5 A♭5
3fr
4fr
cry - in' for more.
pas - sion play.
I've seen you burn 'em be - fore.
Cm
3fr
A♭maj7
Fire and ice,
you come
B♭
Cm
3fr
on like a flame, then you turn a cold shoul - der.
Fire and ice,
A♭maj7
B♭
To Coda
I wan - na give you my love, but you'll just take a lit - tle piece of my heart.

1
F
A♭
4fr
Cm
3fr
You'll just tear it a - part.
N.C.
2
A♭
4fr
B♭
G
G/B
So you think you got it all fig - ured out, you're an ex -
E♭(add4) A♭
4fr
G
G/B
- pert in the field with - out a doubt. But I know your meth - ods

A♭
4fr
B♭
in - side and out and I won't be tak - en in by fire and ice.
Cm
3fr
A♭maj7
B♭
Cm
3fr
A♭maj7
B♭
A♭maj7
B♭
D.S. al Coda

CODA
Cm
Abmaj7
Bb
You come on like a flame, then you
turn a cold shoul - der. Fire and ice, I wan - na
give you my love, but you'll just take a lit - tle piece of my heart.
Repeat and Fade
Optional Ending
You come

FOOLIN'

Words and Music by JOE ELLIOTT, STEVE CLARK, PETER WILLIS, RICHARD SAVAGE, RICHARD ALLEN and ROBERT LANGE

Am(add2)
Fmaj7
On and on, we rode the storm.
Close your eyes, don't run and hide.
The flame has died, and the fire has gone. Oh,
Eas - y love is no eas - y ride.
this emp - ty bed is a night a - lone. I
Just wak - in' up from what we had could
Am
F
re - al - ized that long a - go.
stop good love from go - in' bad.
Is an - y - bod - y out there?

C5
G5
Am
G5/D
F5/C
3fr
An - y - bod - y there?
Does
Am
C5
G5
A5
E5
F5
5fr
an - y - bod - y won - der,
an - y - bod - y care?
G5
A5
B♭
Oh,
I just got - ta know
C
B♭(add2)/D
if you're real - ly there,

C(add2)/E
C5
3fr
and you real - ly care.
'Cause ba - by, I'm
D5
C5
D5
5fr
3fr
5fr
F5
B♭5
D5
C5
D5
not
f - f - f - fool - in'.
Ah, f - f - fool -
F5
G5
D5
C5
D5
To Coda
F5
B♭5
- in'.
F - f - f - fool - in'.
1
D5
C5
D5
F5
G5
D5
Ah, f - f - fool - in'.
Won't you

Am(add2)
Fmaj7
stay with me a - while?
Oh, oh.
Am(add2)
Fmaj7
2
D5 C5 D5
5fr 3fr 5fr
Ah, f - f - fool-
F5 G5 D5 C5 D5
3fr 5fr 3fr 5fr
F5 B♭5
- in'.
Guitar solo
D5 C5 D5
5fr 3fr 5fr
F5 G5
3fr
Dsus Csus Dsus
5fr 3fr 5fr

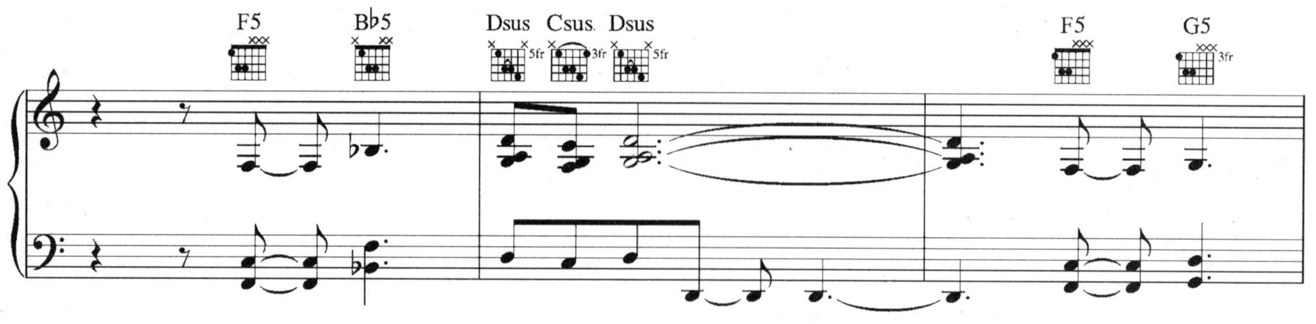
F5
B♭5
Dsus
Csus
Dsus
F5
G5

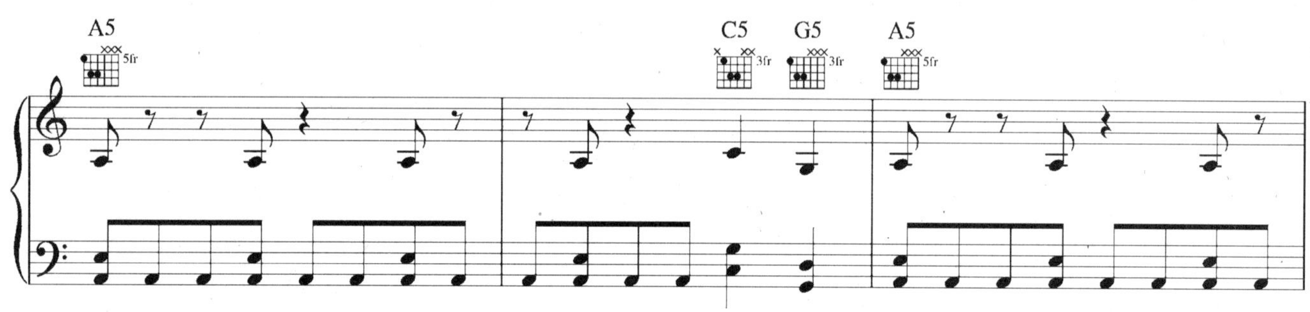
A5
C5
G5
A5

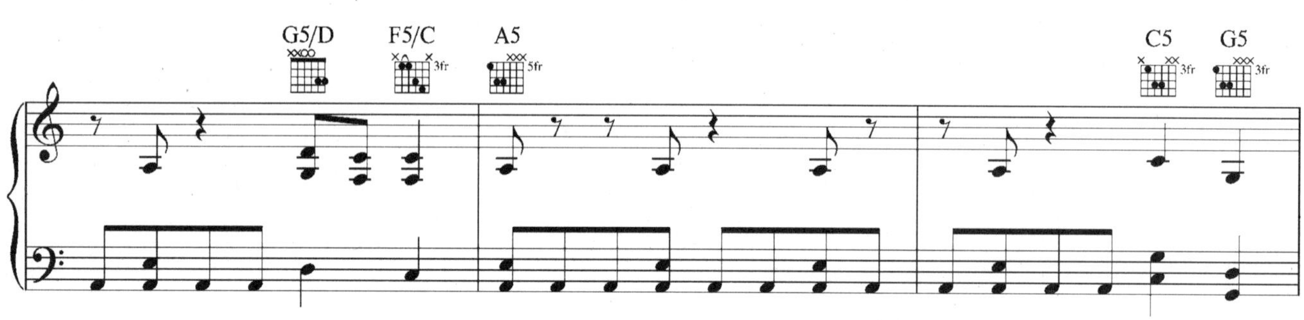
G5/D
F5/C
A5
C5
G5

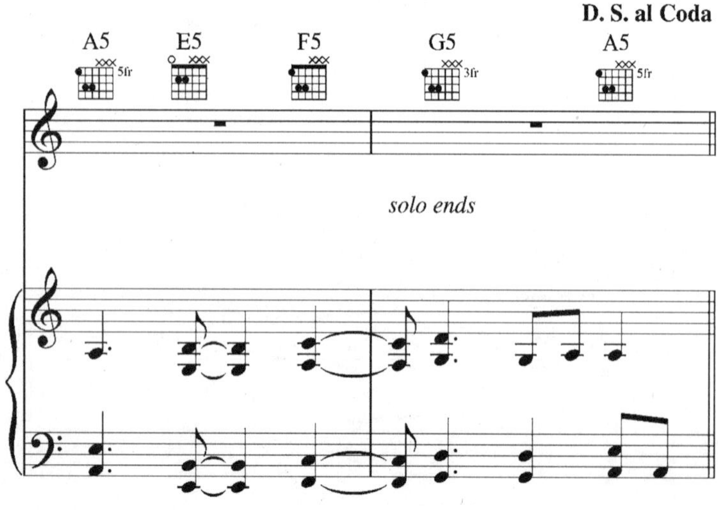
D. S. al Coda
A5
E5
F5
G5
A5
solo ends

CODA
D5
C5
D5
Oh, __ no,

F5
G5
Dm
F5
B♭5
I'm not fool - in' my - self.
(I'm not fool - in' my - self.)
No, no, no.
Dm
F5
G5
Dm
(I'm not fool - in' my - self.)
Oh, no, no.
(I'm not fool - in' my - self.)
F5
B♭5
Dm
F5
G5
I'm not fool - in'.
(I'm not fool - in' my - self.)
D5
C5
D5
5fr
3fr
5fr
D5
C5
D5
5fr
3fr
5fr

THE FIRST CUT IS THE DEEPEST

Words and Music by
CAT STEVENS

F
G
C
G
F
G
To Coda
but if you want, I'll try to love again. Baby, I'll try
and if you want, I'll try to love again. Baby, I'll try
C
F
G
C
G
to love again, but I know:
to love again, but I know:
The first cut is the deep-
F
G
C
G
F
G
-est. Baby, I know the first cut is the deep - est. When it
C
G
F
G
1
C
F
comes to bein' lucky, she's cursed; when it comes to lovin' me, she's he's worst.

G
I still
2
C G F G C F
comes to lov - in' me, she's / he's worst.
G
Play 3 times
C F G
D.S. al Coda
(take 2nd lyric)
I still
CODA
C F G
to love a - gain but I know:

C
G
The first cut is the deep -
F
G
C
G
F
G
- est. Ba - by, I know the first cut is the deep - est. When it
C
G
F
G
C
G
comes to be - in' luck - y, she's cursed; when it comes to lov - in' me, she's he's worst.
F
G
C
F
G
Repeat and Fade
Optional Ending
C

FOOLISH HEART

Words and Music by RANDY GOODRUM
and STEVE PERRY

*Recorded a half step lower.

C7
C9
Am7
Am7add4
Am7
D7sus
D7
pass - ing hour, some - one, some - how will be there
F/G
Fmaj9
G/F
Fadd9
G/F
read - y to share. I need a love that's strong. I'm so
Feel-ing that feel - ing a - gain. I'm
Fmaj9
G/F
Fadd9
G/F
C7
C9
ti - red of be - ing a - lone. But will my lone - ly heart
play - ing a game I can't win. Love's knock-ing on the door of my
Am7
Am7add4
Am7
D7sus
D7
F/G
play the part of the fool a - gain be - fore I be - gin?
heart once more. Think I'll let her in be - fore I be - gin.
Fool - ish heart,

Fsus2
G/B
C
Fmaj9
hear me call - ing. Stop be - fore you start
G/B
C
Fsus2
G/B
C
G/B
fall - ing. Fool - ish heart heed my warn - ing. You've been
1.
Am7
D7sus4
D7
F/G
Fmaj9
G/F
wrong be - fore; don't be wrong an - y - more.
F
G/F
Fmaj9
G/F
F
G/F
3fr

2.
Am7
D7sus
D7
F/G
Fmaj9
3fr
wrong be - fore; don't be wrong an - y - more. Fool - ish heart.
G/B
C
Fmaj9
G/B
C
Fool - ish, fool - ish heart.
Fmaj9
G/B
C
G/B
Am7
D7sus
D7
You've been wrong be - fore.
F/G
N.C.
mp

cresc.
Fool - ish
Fmaj9
G/B
C
Fmaj9
3fr
heart, hear me call - ing. Stop be - fore you start
mf
G/B
C
Fsus2
G/B
C
G/B
fall - ing. Fool - ish heart, heed my warn - ing. You've been

Am7 D7sus D7 F/G Fsus2
wrong be - fore; don't be wrong an - y - more. Fool - ish heart.
G/B C Fmaj9 3fr G/B C Fsus2
Oh, fool - ish, fool - ish heart.
G/B C G/B Am7 D7sus D7 F/G
You've been wrong be - fore.
Repeat and fade
Fsus2 G/B C Fmaj9 3fr G/B C
Vocal ad lib…

FOR THE GOOD TIMES

Words and Music by
KRIS KRISTOFFERSON

B♭
C7
F
glad we had some time to spend to - geth - er.
word a - bout to - mor - row or for - ev - er.
F7
B♭
Gm
3fr
There's no need to watch the bridg - es that we're
There'll be time e - nough for sad - ness when you
C7
N.C.
F
burn - ing.
leave me.
Lay your head up - on my
C7
pil - low, hold your warm and ten - der bod - y close to

F
F/E
Dm7
F/C
mine.
Hear the whis - per of the rain - drops blow - ing
B♭
B♭/A
Gm7
B♭/F
C7
soft a - gainst the win - dow,
and make be - lieve you
Gm7
C7
3
love me one more time
for the good
1
2
times.
I'll get a -
times.
rall.

FREE BIRD

Words and Music by ALLEN COLLINS
and RONNIE VAN ZANT

F
C
D
'cause there's too man - y plac - es I've got to see.
'cause the Lord knows I'm to blame.
G
D/F♯
Em
F
C
But if I stayed here with you, girl,
things just could-n't be the
D
G
D/F♯
Em
same.
'Cause I'm as free as a bird now.
F
C
Dsus
D
Dsus
D
F
C
And this bird you'll nev - er change.
And this bird you can - not

D
F
C
D
change.
And this bird you can - not
change.
F
C
D
G
D/F♯
To Coda
Lord
knows I can't
change.
Em
F
C
1
D
2
D
D.S. al Coda
CODA
F
C
D
Lord, help me, I can't
change.

GIMME SOME LOVIN'

Words and Music by STEVE WINWOOD,
MUFF WINWOOD and SPENCER DAVIS

E
A/E
E
A/E
Twen - ty peo - ple knock - in' 'cause they're want - ing some more.
Bet - ter take it eas - y, 'cause the place is on fire.
Bet - ter take it eas - y, 'cause the place is on fire.
E
A/E
E
A/E
Let me in, ba - by, I don't know what you've got. But you'd
Been a hard day ___ and I don't know what to do.
Been a hard day, ___ noth - in' went too good. Now I'm
E
A/E
E
A/E
bet - ter take it eas - y. This ___ place is hot.
Wait a min - ute, ba - by. It could hap - pen to you.
gon - na re - lax, hon - ey. Ev - 'ry - bod - y should. _
E
G
So glad ___ we made ___ it,

A
C
E
A/E
so glad_ we made_ it. You got-ta gim-me some
E
A/E
To Coda
lov - in', gim-me some lov - in',
E
A/E
E
gim-me some lov - in' ev - er - y day.
D/E
A/E D/E A/E
3

E7
E
A/E
Hey!
1
E
A/E
Well, I
2
E
A/E
D.S. al Coda
Well, I
CODA
E
A/E
gim - me some lov - in,'
E
A/E
Repeat and Fade
gim - me some lov - in,'

GIVE ME THE NIGHT

Words and Music by
ROD TEMPERTON

Chorus
Am7
C/D
To Coda II
Em7
Am7
mu - sic in the air, and lots of lov - in' ev' - ry - where, so give me the night.
Bm7
Cmaj7
Em7
Am7
1
Bm7
Cmaj7
2,3
Bm7
Cmaj7
Give me the night.
2. You need the
So come on
Gm7
F
Dm7
C
Gm7
F
Dm7
C
out to - night and we'll lead the oth - ers on a ride through par - a - dise.
And if you
Gm7
F
Dm7
C
Gm7
F
E♭maj7
C7
3
feel all right, then we can be lov - ers 'cause I see that star - light look in your eyes.
Well, don't you

Verse 2. You need the evenin' action, a place to dine.
A glass of wine, a little late romance.
It's a chain reaction.
We'll see the people of the world comin' out to dance.
'Cause there's. . . Chorus

Verse 3. (Instrumental)
'Cause there's. . . Chorus

Verse 4. And if we stay together,
We'll feel the rhythm of evening takin' us up high.
Never mind the weather.
We'll be dancin' in the street until the morning light.
'Cause there's. . . Chorus

GOOD VIBRATIONS

Words and Music by BRIAN WILSON
and MIKE LOVE

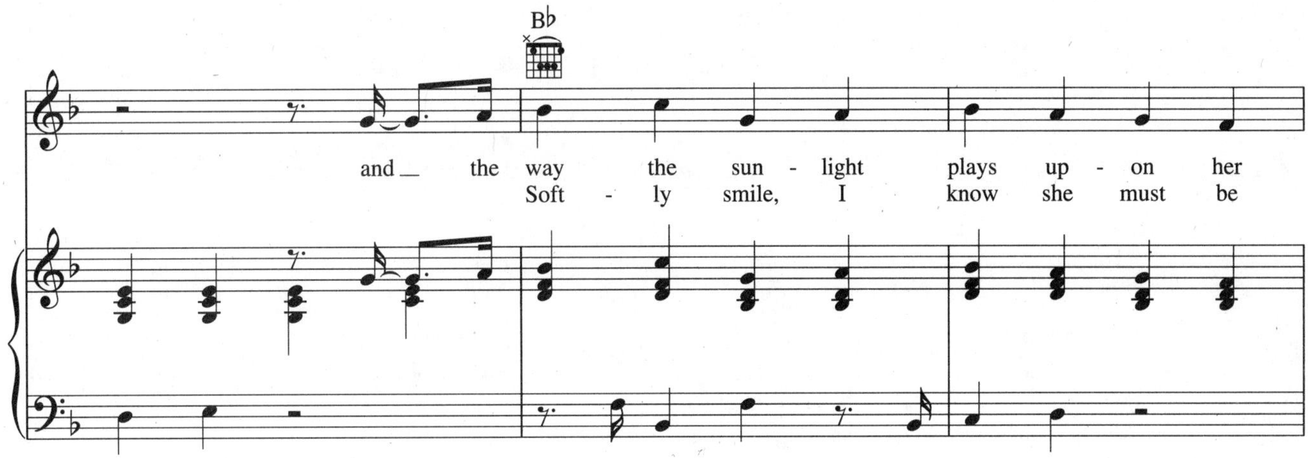

C
B♭
gen - tle word on the wind that lifts her
in her eyes, she goes with me to a
A
C7
per - fume through the air.
blos - som world.
F
Cm7
I'm pick - ing up good vi - bra - tions, she's giv - ing me ex - ci - ta - tions.
I'm pick - ing up good vi - bra - tions, she's giv - ing me ex - ci - ta - tions.

G
Dm7
G
Dm7
G
Dm7
I'm pick - ing up good vi - bra - tions, she's giv - ing me
G
Dm7
A
Em7
A
Em7
ex - ci - ta - tions. I'm pick - ing up good vi - bra - tions,
1
A
Em7
A
Em7
2
A
Em7
she's giv - ing me ex - ci - ta - tions. she's giv - ing me
A
Em7
A
ex - ci - ta - tions.

GOLDEN BROWN

Words and Music by JEAN-JACQUES BURNEL,
JET BLACK, HUGH CORNWELL
and DAVID GREENFIELD

E♭m
D♭
Gold - en Brown, tex - ture like sun, lays me down,
(Verses 2 & 3 see block lyric)
with my mind she runs through - out the night. No need to fight,
To Coda
1.
nev - er a frown with Gol - den Brown.

2.
D.C. al Coda
CODA
E♭m
D♭
B♭m
Fm
G♭
A♭
4fr
with Gol- den Brown._
1st time — Instrumental
2nd time — Ad lib. vocal

Repeat to fade

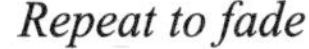

Verse 2:
Every time just like the last.
On her ship, tied to the mast
To distant lands, takes both my hands.
Never a frown with Golden Brown.

Verse 3:
Golden Brown, finer temptress
Through the ages she's heading west
From far away, stays for a day.
Never a frown with Golden Brown.

GOOD TIMES

Words and Music by NILE RODGERS and BERNARD EDWARDS

A13
Em7
Em7sus
Good times, these are the good times.
A7sus
A13
Em7
Our new state of mind.
Em7sus
A7sus
A13
To Coda
These are the good times.
Em7
A7sus
Hap - py days are here a - gain. The time is right for
A ru - mor has it that it's get - ting late. Time march - es on;

A13
Em7
mak - in' friends.
just can't wait.
Let's get to - geth - er. How 'bout a
The clock keeps turn - in'. Why
A7sus
quar - ter to ten?
hes - i - tate?
Come to - mor - row, let's
You sil - ly fool, you
A13
Em7
all do it a - gain.
can't change your fate.
Boys will be boys. Bet - ter
Let's cut the rug; lit - tle
A7sus
A13
let them have their toys.
jive and jit - ter - bug.
Girls will be girls.
We want the best.
Cute po - ny - tails and curls.
We won't set - tle for less.

Em7
A7sus
Must put an end to this stress and strife. I think I want to live the
Don't be a drag. Par - tic - i - pate. Clams on the half - shell __ and
1
A13
5fr
2
A13
5fr
D.S. al Coda
sport - ing life. __ Good times __ roll - er skates, roll - er skates. Good times __
CODA
Em7
Em7sus
A7sus
A13
5fr
Repeat and Fade
Optional Ending
Em7

GOODBYE YELLOW BRICK ROAD

Words and Music by ELTON JOHN
and BERNIE TAUPIN

C
F
B♭
- er. I did - n't sign up with you. I'm
- ment. There's plen - ty like me to be found,
E♭
3fr
C
F
not a pres - ent for your friends to o - pen. This boy's too young to be
mon - grels who ain't got a pen - ny sniff -ing for tid - bits like
B♭m7
E♭7
sing - ing the blues.
you on the ground.
A♭
4fr
D♭
B♭m7
Ah
Ah.

C
F
A7
So good-bye yel-low brick road, where the
B♭
F
D7
dogs of so-ci-e-ty howl.
You can't plant me in your pent-
Gm
3fr
C
F
C/E
-house. I'm go-ing back to my plough,
Dm
A
B♭
back to the howl-ing old owl in the woods,
hunt-ing the horn-y-backed

D♭
E♭
F
C/E
toad.
Oh, I've fin - 'ly de - cid - ed my
Dm
B♭
B♭/C
C
B♭m7
fu - ture lies
be - yond
the yel - low brick
road
E♭
A♭
D♭
B♭m7
Ah
Ah
C
1
F
2
F

HALLELUJAH

Words and Music by
LEONARD COHEN

C
F
G
Am
goes like this: the fourth, the fifth, the mi - nor fall, the
F
G
Em
ma - jor lift, the baf - fled king com - pos - ing Hal - le -
Am
Chorus
F
lu - jah. Hal - le - lu - jah,
Am
Hal - le - lu - jah, Hal - le -

F
1.2.3.4.
C
lu - jah, Hal - le - lu -
G
C
G
- jah.
2. Your
5.
C
G
F
lu - jah. Hal - le - lu - jah.
Am
Hal - le - lu - jah. Hal - le -

Additional Lyrics

2. Your faith was strong, but you needed proof.
You saw her bathing on the roof.
Her beauty and the moonlight overthrew you.
She tied you to a kitchen chair.
She broke your throne; she cut your hair.
And from your lips she drew the Hallelujah. *(To Chorus)*

3. Maybe I have been here before.
I know this room; I've walked this floor.
I used to live alone before I knew you.
I've seen your flag on the marble arch.
Love is not a victory march.
It's a cold and it's a broken Hallelujah. *(To Chorus)*

4. There was a time you let me know
What's real and going on below.
But now you never show it to me, do you?
And remember when I moved in you,
The holy dark was movin' too,
And every breath we drew was Hallelujah. *(To Chorus)*

5. Maybe there's a God above,
And all I ever learned from love
Was how to shoot at someone who outdrew you.
And it's not a cry you can hear at night.
It's not somebody who's seen the light.
It's a cold and it's a broken Hallelujah. *(To Chorus)*

HAPPY TOGETHER

Words and Music by GARRY BONNER
and ALAN GORDON

2
B
geth - er.
E
Bm7
2fr
E
I can see me lov - in' no - bod - y but you for all my life.
G
E
Bm7
2fr
When you're with me, ba - by, the skies - 'll be
E
G
Em
blue for all my life.
Me and you, and you and

D
me, no mat - ter how they toss the dice, it had to be. The on - ly one for
C
To Coda
B
me is you, and you for me, so hap - py to - geth - er.
E
Bm7
Ba ba ba ba ba ba
Instrumental
E
G
E
ba ba ba ba ba.
Ba ba ba ba

Bm7
2fr
E
Bm7
2fr
D.S. al Coda
(no repeats)
ba ba ba ba ba ba ba.
Instrumental ends
CODA
B
Em
B
geth - er, so hap - py to - geth - er.
Em
B
Em
B
Repeat ad lib.
And how is the weath - er? So hap-py to - geth - er.
Em
B
E
So hap - py to - geth - er.

HAVE I TOLD YOU LATELY

Words and Music by
VAN MORRISON

Cm7
3fr
Bb
Eb/F
ease my trou-bles that's what you do.
For the
Instrumental solo
Bb
Dm7
Eb
3fr
Eb/F
morn - in' sun in all its glo - ry greets the
Bb
Dm7
Eb
3fr
Eb/F
day with hope and com-fort, too.
Ebmaj7
3fr
Dm7
You fill my life with laugh - ter and some-how you make it bet - ter,

Cm7
3fr
Eb/F
Bb
Cm7
3fr
Bb/D
ease my trou - bles that's what you do.
Solo ends
Ebmaj7
3fr
There's a love that's di - vine
and it's yours and it's mine
Dm7
like the sun.
Cm7
3fr
Dm7
Ebmaj7
3fr
And at the end of the day
Dm7
we should give thanks and pray to the one,
1
Eb/F
to the one.
Have I

2
Eb/F
Bb
Dm7
to the one. And have I told you late - ly that I
Eb
3fr
Eb/F
Bb
Dm7
love you? Have I told you there's no one else a -
Eb
3fr
Eb/F
Ebmaj7
3fr
bove you? You fill my heart with glad - ness,
Dm7
Cm7
3fr
Eb/F
take a - way my sad - ness, ease my trou-bles that's what you

Bb
Cm7
Bb/D
Ebmaj7
do.
Take a - way all my sad - ness,
Dm7
Cm7
Bb
Cm7
Bb/D
fill my life with glad - ness,
ease my trou - bles that's what you do.
Ebmaj7
Dm7
Take a - way all my sad - ness,
fill my life with glad - ness,
Cm7
Eb/F
Bb
ease my trou - bles that's what you do.
rall.

HEART OF GLASS

Words and Music by DEBORAH HARRY
and CHRIS STEIN

C♯m
4fr
E5
mu-cho mis - trust,
love's gone be - hind.
E
C♯m
4fr
Once I had a love and it was di - vine.
Once I had a love and it was a gas.
3
3
E
Soon found out, I was los - in' my mind.
Soon turned out to be a pain in the ass.
Seemed
Seemed

C♯
like the real thing, but I was so blind.
like the real thing, on - ly to find
C♯m
4fr
E5
Mu-cho mis - trust, love's gone be - hind.
mu-cho mis - trust, love's gone be - hind.
A
In be - tween, what I find is pleas - ing and I'm
E
feel - ing fine. Love is so con - fus - ing; there's no

A
peace of mind, yet I fear I'm los - ing you. It's
F♯
B
To Coda
just no good, you teas - ing like you do.
A
E
A

F♯
B
E5
E
Once I had a love and it was a
3
C♯m
4fr
gas.
Soon turned out, had a heart of glass.
E
Seemed like the real thing, on - ly to

C#
C#m
4fr
find
mu-cho mis-trust, love's gone be-hind.
E5
A
Lost in-side a-
dor-a-ble il-lu-sion and I
E
can-not hide.
I'm the one you're us-ing; please don't
A
push me a-side. We

E
could've made it cruis - ing, yeah.
A
E
A
E

A
E
A
1
E
2
Yeah, _
F♯
B
rid - ing high on love's _ true _ blu - ish light. _

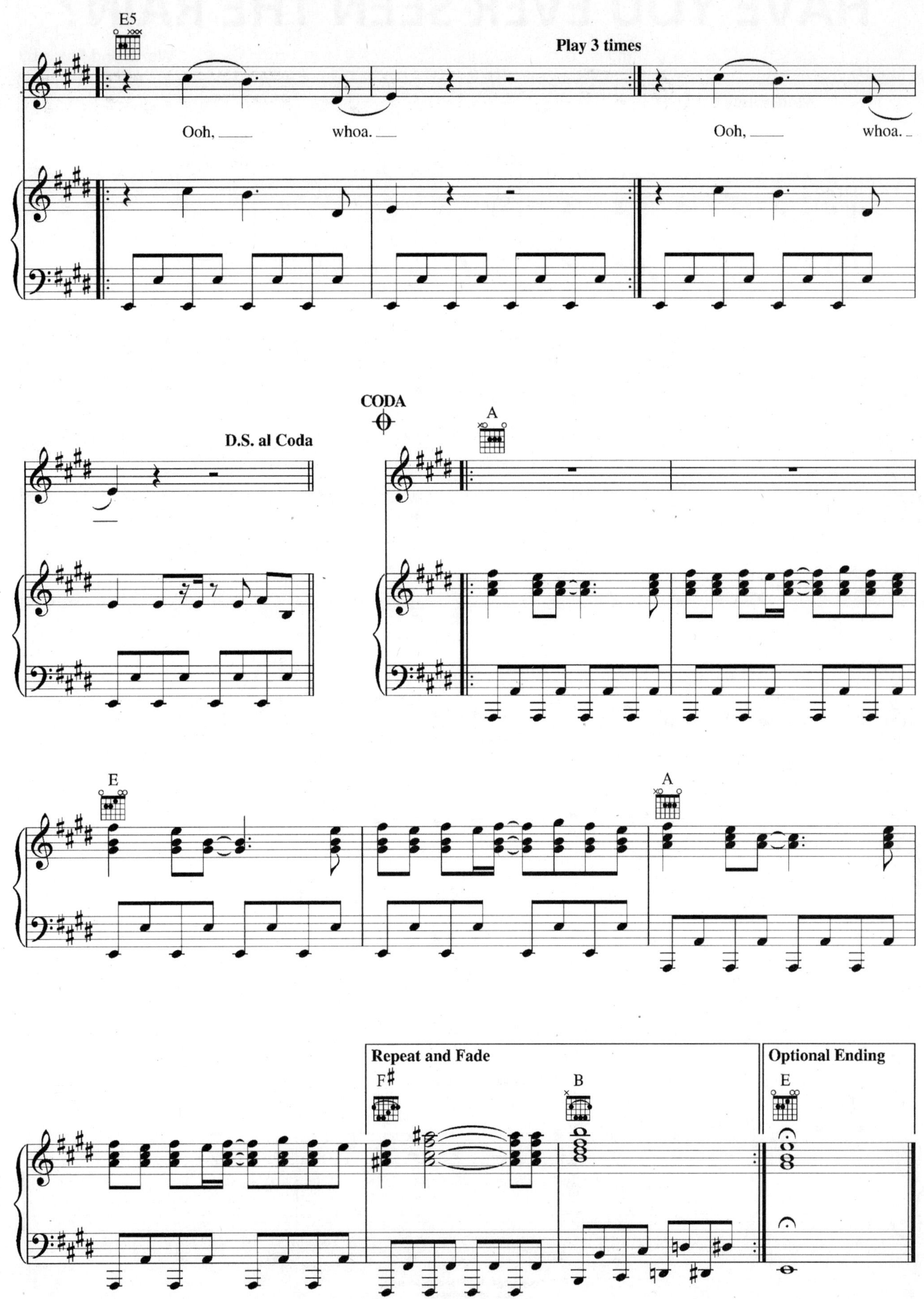
E5
Play 3 times
Ooh, whoa.
Ooh, whoa.
D.S. al Coda
CODA
A
E
A
Repeat and Fade
F♯
B
Optional Ending
E

HAVE YOU EVER SEEN THE RAIN?

Words and Music by
JOHN FOGERTY

When it's o - ver, so they say, it - 'll rain a sun -
G
C
- ny day. I know; shin - in' down like wa - ter.
F
G
I want to know, have you
C
Am
F
ev - er seen the rain? I want to

G
C
Am
know, have you ev - er seen the rain
F
Gsus
3fr
To Coda
C
com - in' down on a sun - ny day?
Yes - ter - day, and days be - fore, sun is cold and rain
G
is hard. I know; been that way for all

C
my time.
'Til for - ev - er, on
it goes
through the cir - cle, fast
and slow.
I know;
G
C
and it can't stop,
I won - der.
D.S. al Coda
CODA
C
G
C

THE HEAT IS ON

from the Paramount Motion Picture BEVERLY HILLS COP

Words by KEITH FORSEY
Music by HAROLD FALTERMEYER

C7
And the beat's a - live,
deep in - side.
The pres - sure's high,
B♭maj7/C
6fr
C
F7
just to stay a - live.
'Cause the heat is on.
C7

C
F/A
Oh oh oh oh, oh oh oh oh, caught
Bb
Bb/D
Eb
3fr
F
C
up in the ac-tion, I'll be look-ing out for you. Oh oh oh oh,
Gm7
3fr
oh oh oh oh, tell me you can feel it; tell me you can feel it; tell
To Coda
N.C.
C7
me do you feel it? The heat is on.

The heat is on, on the street. The heat is
on. The heat is on.
F7
N.C.
C7
The heat is... on!
Vocal 1st time only
1-3

4
C
F/A
Oh oh oh oh, oh oh oh oh, caught
Bb
Bb/D
Eb
3 fr
F
C
up in the ac-tion, I'll be look-ing out for you. Oh oh oh oh,
Gm7
3 fr
oh oh oh oh, tell me you can feel it; tell me you can feel it; tell
N.C.
C7
D.S. al Coda
me do you feel it?
The heat is

CODA
N.C.
C7
The heat is on, on the street.
on. The heat is on.
The heat is
on, in-side your head.
on, the pres-sure's high.
The heat is on, on ev-'ry beat.
The heat is on, the pres-sure's high.
1
F7
The heat is on.
The heat is
2
F7
The heat is on.
The heat is...

C7
N.C.
on!
Vocal tacet 1st time only
1
2
The heat is
on.
The heat is
Repeat ad lib. and Fade
on.
The heat is

HOLD ON LOOSELY

Words and Music by DON BARNES,
JEFF CARLISI and JAMES MICHAEL PETERIK

C
D
And my mind goes back to a girl that I left some years a - go,
E
E/D♯
who told me: Just hold on loose - ly,
E/D
A/C♯
D
E
E/D♯
but don't let go. If you cling too tight-
E/D
A/C♯
- ly, you're gon - na lose con - trol.

F♯m
B
F♯m
A
Your ba - by needs some - one to be-lieve in
and a whole lot of space
1
2
to breathe in.
to breathe in.
G/A
3fr
D/A
G/A
3fr
Don't let her slip a - way.
Sen-ti-men-tal fool.
D/A
B
D.S. and Fade
Don't let your heart get in the way.

HELPLESSLY HOPING

Words and Music by
STEPHEN STILLS

Am
C
Gasp - ing at glimp - ses of gen - tle true spir - it, he
G
D
runs, wish-ing he could fly, on - ly to
Am7
C
G
trip at the sound of good - bye.
D
Am
Word - less - ly watch - ing, he
Stand by the stair - way, you'll

C
G
waits by the win - dow and won - ders at the emp - ty place in - side.
see some - thing cer - tain to tell you con - fu - sion has its cost.
D
Am
Heart - less - ly help - ing him -
Love is - n't ly - ing, it's
C
G
self to her bad dreams, he wor - ries, did he hear a good - bye,
loose in a la - dy who lin - gers, say - in' she is lost
D
Am7
C
or e - ven hel - lo?
and chok - ing on hel - lo.

G
Am/G
G
They are one per - son, they are two
a - lone, they are three to - geth -
- er, they are for each oth - er.
Dm/F
C
G
C/G
1
G
2
G

HIGHER LOVE

Words and Music by WILL JENNINGS
and STEVE WINWOOD

E♭
F
E♭
B♭
wast - ed time.
real to me.
Look in - side your heart, I'll
There must be some - one who's
F
C
look in - side mine.
feel - ing for me.
Things look so bad
Dm
C
ev - 'ry - where.
In this whole world,
Am
B♭
C
what is fair?
We walk blind and we

B♭
F
C
try to see,
fall - ing be - hind in what
Am
Dm
B♭
F
could be.
Bring me a high - er love,
C
Dm7
B♭
F
bring me a high - er love,
C
Dm7
B♭
F
woah.
Bring me a high - er love.

1
C
Dm7
B♭
F
Where's that high - er love I keep
I could
Dm7
C
2
B♭
F
think - ing of? World's are turn - rise a - bove on a
Dm7
C
B♭
C
Dm7
high - er love. I will wait for
C
B♭
C
Dm7
it. I'm not too

C
B♭
C
Dm7
late for it.
Un - til then, I'll
C
B♭
C
Dm
sing my song
to cheer the
C
B♭
Dm
night a - long.
Bring it.

C
I could light the night up with my
soul on fire.
I could make the sun - shine from
Bb
Dm7
pure de - sire.
Let me feel that
Eb
3fr
Bb
Dm
Bb
love come o - ver me.
Let me feel how

F
C
N.C.
strong it could be.
Oh.
Repeat and Fade
B♭
F
Bring me a high - er love,
C
Dm7
B♭
F
bring me a high - er love,

C
Dm7
B♭
F
woah.
Bring me a high - er love,

C
Dm7
B♭
F
bring me a high - er love.

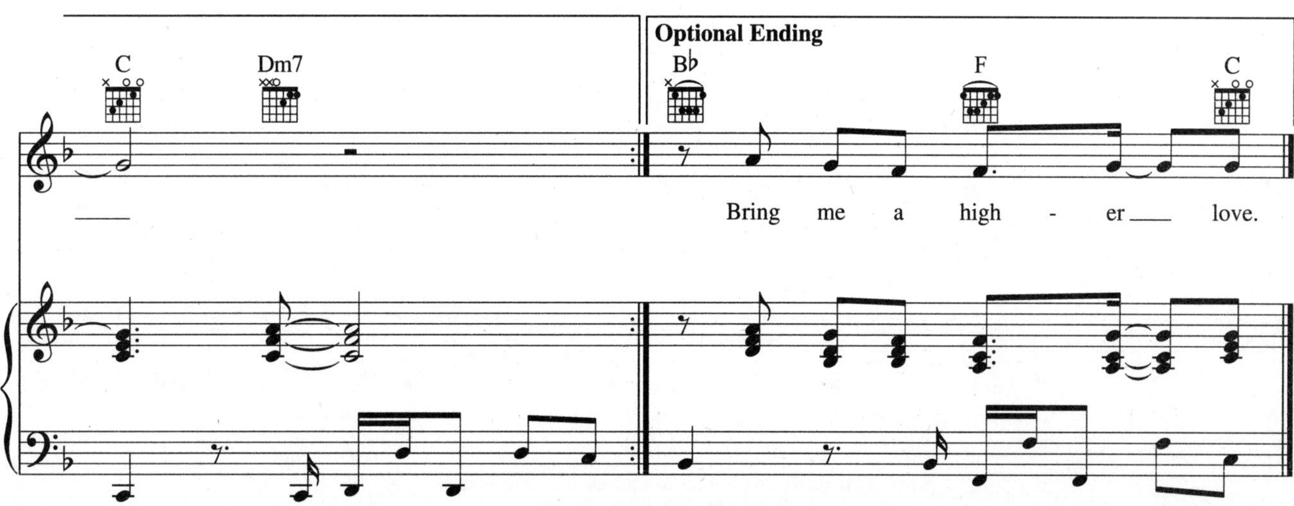
Optional Ending
C
Dm7
B♭
F
C
Bring me a high - er love.

HOT HOT HOT

Words and Music by
ALPHONSUS CASSELL

Moderate Latin Dance

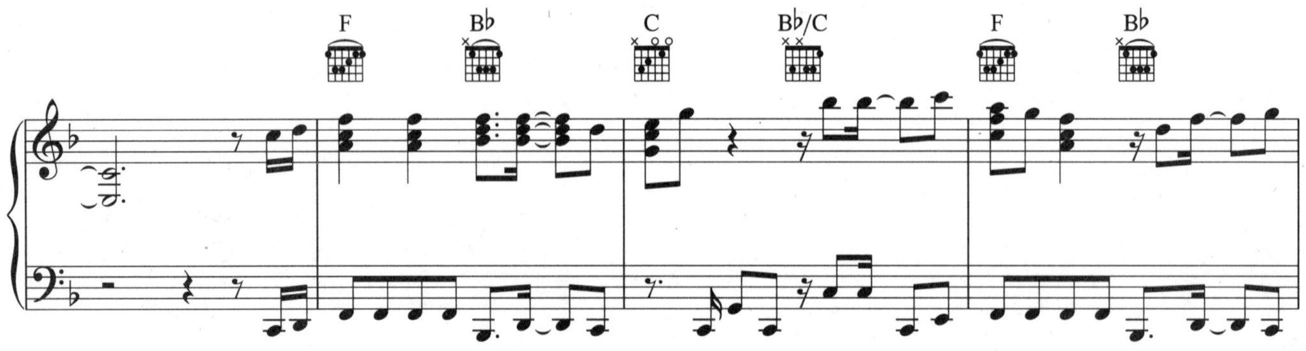

C
B♭/C
F
B♭
C
B♭/C
F
B♭
C
B♭/C
F
B♭
Me mind on fi - re,
See peo - ple rock - ing,
C
B♭/C
F
B♭
C
B♭/C
me soul on fi - re, feel - ing hot, hot, hot!
hear peo - ple chant - ing, feel - ing hot, hot, hot!
F
B♭
C
B♭/C
All the peo - ple, all a - round me, feel - ing
Keep up the spir - it, come on let's hear it, feel - ing

F
B♭
C
B♭/C
hot, hot, hot!
hot, hot, hot!
A - what to do on a night like
It's in the air, cel - e - bra - tion
this? Is it sweet? I can't re - sist! We
time. Is it sweet? Cap - ti - vate your mind. We
need a par - ty sound, a fun - da - men - tal
need this par - ty sound, this fun - da - men - tal
charm.
charm.
So we can rhum - bum - bum - bum.
Yeah,

F Bb C Bb/C F Bb
rhum - bum - bum - bum. Feel - ing hot, hot, _ hot!
C Bb/C F Bb 1 C Bb/C
Feel - ing hot, hot, _ hot!
2 C Bb/C F Bb C Bb/C
Feel - ing hot, hot, _ hot! Feel - ing
F Bb C Bb/C F Bb
hot, hot, _ hot!

C
N.C.
1-3
O - lé, o - lé, o - lé, o - lé. O -
4
F
B♭
C
B♭/C
lé, o - lé.
Feel - ing
Repeat and Fade
Optional Ending
hot, hot, hot!

I CAN'T GO FOR THAT

Words and Music by DARYL HALL,
JOHN OATES and SARA ALLEN

F
G
Am7
A♭
B♭
Cm7
dare me to draw the line? You got the bod - y now you
peat - ing the same old lines. Use the bod - y now you
D
Am7
F
Cm7
want my soul, Don't e - ven think a - bout it,
want my soul, Ooo for - get a - bout it, now,
F
G
A
Amaj7
A♭
B♭
C
Cmaj7
say no go.
say no go.
instrumental ends
And I'll, I'll do an - y -
A7
Dmaj7
D6
C7
Fmaj7
F6
thing that you want me to. And

A
Amaj7
C
Cmaj7
I'll do al - most an - y -
A7
Dmaj7
D6
C7
Fmaj7
F6
thing that you want me to, Yeah, but
Dm9
Am11
Fm9
Cm11
I can't go for that, no, no can do, I
Dm9
Am11
Fm9
Cm11
can't go for that, no, no can do. I

Dm9
3fr
Fm9
Am11
3fr
Cm11
can't go for that, no,
no can do. I

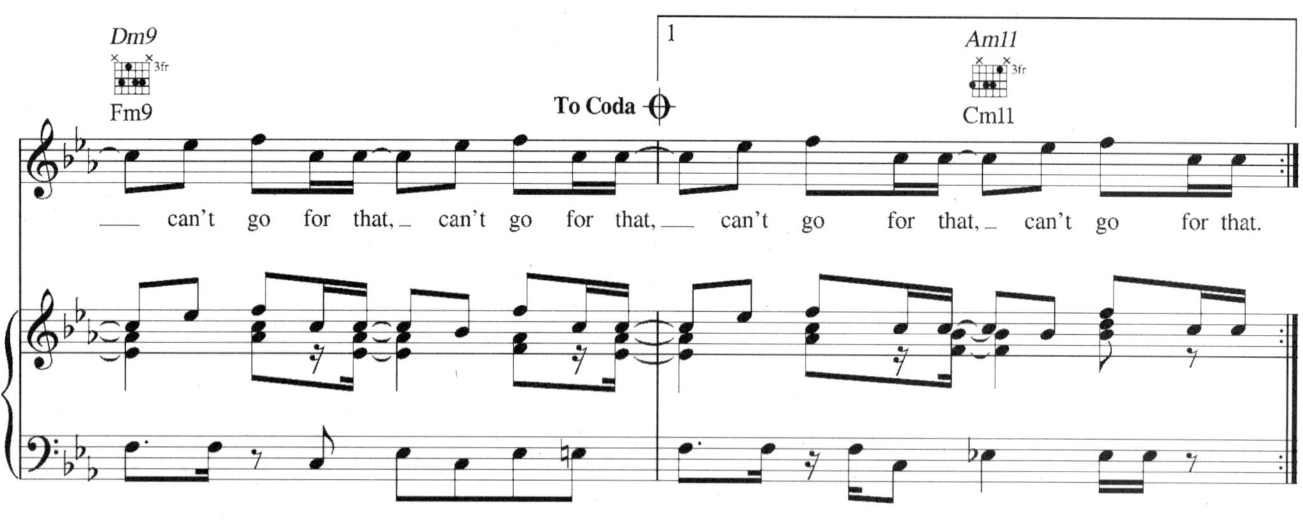
Dm9
3fr
Fm9
To Coda
1
Am11
3fr
Cm11
can't go for that, can't go for that, can't go for that, can't go for that.

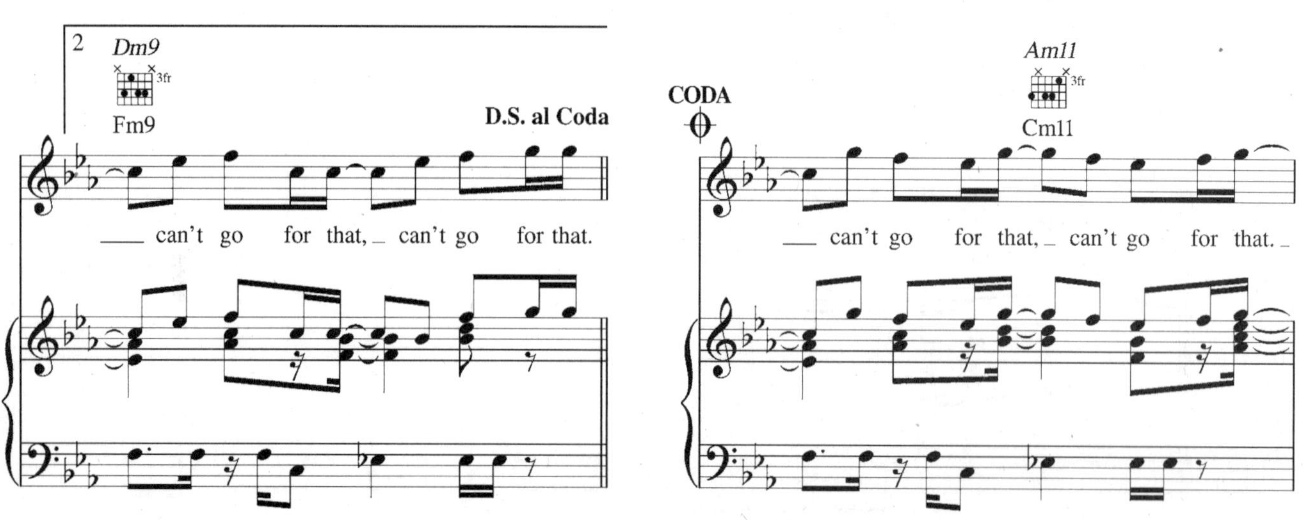
2
Dm9
3fr
Fm9
D.S. al Coda
can't go for that, can't go for that.
CODA
Am11
3fr
Cm11
can't go for that, can't go for that.

Dm9
3fr
Fm9
Am11
3fr
Cm11

Dm9
3fr
Fm9
Am11
3fr
Cm11

Dm9
3fr
Fm9
Am11
3fr
Cm11
Repeat and Fade

HURT

Words and Music by
TRENT REZNOR

Am
C
Dsus2
Am
C
Dsus2
real. The nee - dle tears a hole, the old fa - mil - iar sting.
pair. Be - neath the stains of time the feel - ings dis - ap - pear.
Am
C
Dsus2
Am
C
D
Try to kill it all a - way but I re - mem - ber ev - 'ry - thing.
You are some - one else, I am still right here.
G
Am7
Fadd9
What have I be - come
C
G
Am7
my sweet - est friend? Ev - 'ry - one I know

Fadd9
C
G
— goes a - way___ in the end.___ And
Am7
Fadd9
G
you could have___ it all,___ my em - pire of dirt.
Am7
Fadd9
I will let___ you down,___
1.
G
Am
C
D
I will make___ you hurt.___

2.
Am
C
Dsus2
G
I will make you hurt.
Am7
Fadd9
If I could start again, a
G
Am7
mil-lion miles a-way,
I would keep my-self,
Fadd9
G
I would find a way.

I BELIEVE I CAN FLY

Words and Music by
ROBERT KELLY

C
Dm7♭5/C
now I know the mean - ing of ture love. I'm
mir - a - cles in life I must a - chieve, but
C
Dm7♭5/C
E7♯5
lean - ing on the ev - er - last - ing arm. If I can
first I know it starts in - side of me.
Am7
Dm7♭5/A♭
C/G
see it, then I can do it, if I just be - lieve it, there's noth - ing
be
Dm7/G
C
to it. I be - lieve I can fly, I be - lieve I can

Am7
Dm7
touch the sky. I think a-bout it ev-'ry night and day, spread my wings and
Dm7/G
G♯dim7
Am7
fly a-way. I be-lieve I can soar, I see me run-ning through that
Dm7♭5/A♭
3fr
C/G
o-pen door. I be-lieve I can fly, I be-lieve I can
1
Dm7♭5/A♭
3fr
Am7
Fmaj7/G
fly, I be-lieve I can fly. See,

2
Dm7♭5/A♭
3fr
Am7
fly, oh, I be-lieve I can fly.
Dm7
C/E
Fmaj7/G
Hey, 'cause I be-lieve in me, oh. if I can
B♭m7
E♭m7♭5/A
D♭/A♭
4fr
see it, then I can do it, if I just be-lieve it, there's noth-ing
E♭m7/A♭
6fr
D♭
to it. I be-lieve I can fly, I be-lieve I can

Bbm7
Ebm7
6fr
touch the sky. I think a-bout it ev-ery night and day, spread my wings and
Ebm7/Ab
6fr
Adim7
Bbm7
fly a-way. I be-lieve I can soar, I see me run-ning through that
Ebm7b5/A
Db/Ab
4fr
o-pen door. I be-lieve I can fly, I be-lieve I can
Ebm7b5/A
Db/Ab
4fr
fly, I be-lieve I can fly, hey, if I just
3
3

Ebm7b5/A
Db/Ab
4fr
spread my wings. I can fly, I can
fly, I can fly, hey, if I just
spread my wings. I can fly.
Db
rit.

I DON'T WANT TO WAIT

Words and Music by
PAULA COLE

C6/9
du du du du du,
du du du du du du.
G(add2)
She had two ba - bies,
He showed up all wet
C6/9
one was six months, one was three,
in the war of for-ty - four.
on the rain - y front step
wear-ing shrap - nel in his skin.
G(add2)
Ev - 'ry tel - e - phone ring,
ev - 'ry heart - beat sting - ing when she
And the war he saw
lives in - side him still. It's so

Em7
D
Cmaj9
thought it was God call - ing her. Oh, would
hard to be gen - tle and warm. The years
Em
D6
C(add9)
her son grow to know his fa - ther?
pass by, and now he has grand - daugh - ters.
G(add2)
D(add4)/F#
Em11
7fr
Dsus
I don't want to wait for our lives to be o - ver. I want
C6
G(add9)/B
Dsus/A
Dsus
to know right now, what will it be?

G(add2)
D(add4)/F#
Em11
7fr
Dsus
I don't want to wait for our lives to be o - ver. Will it
C6
G(add9)/B
1
Dsus/A
G(add2)
be yes, or will it be sor - ry? Du du du du du,
C6/9
du du du du du, du du du du du du.
2
Dsus/A
G7(add4)
Oh, so you look at me from a - cross

Am9♭13
the room. You're wear-ing your an-guish a - gain. Be-lieve
B♭(add2)
Fsus
C(add9)
me, I know the feel - ing; it sucks you in-to the jaws of an - ger.
G7(add4)
Oh, so breathe a lit-tle more deep-ly, my love. All we
Am9♭13
B♭(add2)
have is this ver-y mo - ment, and I don't want to do what his fa-ther and his fa-ther and

Fsus
Gsus2
his fa-ther did. I want to be here now. So
Gsus2/F
Gsus2/E
Gsus2/D
Gsus2/C
o-pen up your morn-ing light and say a lit-tle prayer for I. You know that
Gsus2/F
Gsus2/E
Gsus2/D
Gsus2/C
if we are to stay a-live, then see the peace in ev-'ry eye.
G(add2)
D(add4)/F#
Em11
7fr
Dsus
I don't want to wait for our lives to be o-ver. I want

C6
G(add9)/B
Dsus/A
Dsus
G(add2)
D(add4)/F#
to know right now, what will it be?
I don't want to wait for our lives
Em11
7 fr
Dsus
C6
G(add9)/B
to be o - ver. Will it be yes, or will it be...
1
Dsus/A
Dsus
2
Dsus/A
G(add2)
sor - ry? Du du du du du,
C6/9
1
du du du du du,
du du du du du du.

2
Gsus2/F
Gsus2/E
So o - pen up your mor - ning light and
Gsus2/D
Gsus2/C
Gsus2/F
Gsus2/E
say a lit - tle prayer for I. You know that if we are to stay a - live, then
Gsus2/D
Gsus2/C
F(add2)
see the love in ev - 'ry eye.
Repeat and Fade
Reprise theme of "Me"

I FINALLY FOUND SOMEONE

Words and Music by BARBRA STREISAND, MARVIN HAMLISCH,
ROBERT LANGE and BRYAN ADAMS

Cm7
3fr
Cm7/F
It's fun-ny how from sim-ple things the best things be-gin.
G
Em7
Male:
This time it's dif - f'rent. It's all be-cause of you.
Cmaj7
Cm
3fr
It's bet-ter than it's ev - er been 'cause we can talk it through.
G(add9)
Em7
Female:
My fav - 'rite line was, "Can I call you some - time?"

Cmaj7
Cm
3 fr
It's all you had to say to take my breath a - way.
E
Both:
This is it. Oh, I fi - n'lly
mf
Amaj7
Am6
5 fr
E
found some - one, some - one to share my life. I fi - n'lly
Amaj7
Am6
5 fr
E
found the one to be with ev - 'ry night.
Female:
'Cause what -

G♯sus
G♯
4fr
C♯m
4fr
C
Male:
Both:
ev - er I do, ___ it's just got to be you. My
dim.
E/B
F♯m7/B
E
life has just be-gun. I fi - n'lly found some - one. ___
mp
C♯m7
4fr
Amaj7
E/F♯
F♯
B
G♯m7
4fr
Male:
Did I keep you wait - ing? I a - pol - o - gize. _
Female: I did - n't mind. ___ Ba - by, that's fine. ___
mf

Emaj7
Em6
I would wait for-ev - er just to know you were mine. You know,
just to know you were mine.
B
G♯m7
4 fr
I love your hair. I love what you wear.
Are you sure it looks right? Is-n't it too tight?
Emaj7
Em
You're ex-cep-tion-al. Both: I can't wait for the rest of my life.
F
This is it. Oh, I fi - n'lly
f

Bmaj7
B♭m6
6fr
F
found some - one, some - one to share my life. I fi - n'lly
B♭maj7
B♭m6
6fr
F
found the one to be with ev - 'ry night.
Female:
'Cause what -
Asus
A
Dm
ev - er I do,
Male:
it's just got to be you.
D♭
F/C
Both:
My life has just be - gun. I fi - n'lly

Gm7/C
Am7
Am7/D
D7
found some - one.
Female:
And what -
Gm7
3 fr
F/A
ev - er I do,
Male:
it's just got to be you.
Female:
My
dim.
Gm7/C
life has just be - gun.
Both:
I fi - n'lly
mp
F
B♭maj7
F
found some - one.
rit. e dim.
p

I WANNA GO BACK

Words and Music by MONTY BYROM,
IRA WALKER and DANIEL CHAUNCEY

Fsus
F
Gm
3fr
F
I heard a song, re - mind - ed me of long a - go.
The first slow dance, hop - in' that I'd get it right.
Ebmaj7
3fr
Fsus
F
Bb
Back then I thought that things
Back then I thought I'd nev -
Fsus
F
were nev - er gon - na change. It
- er, ev - er, stand a - lone. It
Bb
Fsus
used to be that I nev - er had to feel the pain.
used to be that a lone - ly heart was nev - er shown.

F
D/F♯
Gm
3fr
Gm/F
I know now that things will nev - er be the same.
E♭maj7
F/E♭
E♭maj7
F
B♭
E♭
I wan - na go back and do
F
F/A
B♭
E♭
it all o - ver, but I can't go back, I know. I wan - na go
F
B♭
E♭
F
F/A
B♭
E♭
back 'cause I'm feel - in' so much old - er, but I can't go back, I know.

1
B♭
E♭(add2)
6fr
2
F
B♭
E♭(add2)
6fr
F
F/A
B♭
E♭(add2)
6fr
You can't go back.
F
B♭
E♭(add2)
6fr
F
I can't go
F/A
B♭
E♭(add2)
6fr
Gm
3fr
back.
I know now that things

Gm/F
E♭maj7
F/E♭
E♭maj7
will nev-er be the same.
I wan-na go
F
B♭
E♭
F
F/A
B♭
E♭
back and do it all o-ver, but I can't go back, I know.
F
B♭
E♭
F
I wan-na go back 'cause I'm feel - in' so much old-er, but I
F/A
B♭
E♭
Repeat and Fade
Optional Ending
can't go back, I know. I wan-na go

I HOPE YOU DANCE

Words and Music by TIA SILLERS
and MARK D. SANDERS

Gm7
You get your fill to eat, but al - ways keep that
Nev - er set - tle for the path of least re -
hun - ger.
sis - tence.
E♭
3 fr
May you nev - er take one
Liv - in' might mean tak - in'
sin - gle breath for grant - ed.
chanc - es if they're worth tak - in'.
God for - bid
Lov - in' might
F
love ev - er leave you emp - ty hand - ed.
be a mis - take, but it's worth mak - in'.

Eb
F
I hope you still feel small when you stand be - side the
Don't let some hell - bent heart leave you
Bb
Eb
F
o - cean. When - ev - er one door clos - es, I
bit - ter. When you come close to sell - in' out,
Bb
hope one more o - pens. Prom - ise me
re - con - sid - er. Give the heav -
Cm7
Bb/D
that you'll give faith a fight - ing
- ens a - bove more than just a pass - ing

Eb
3fr
chance.
glance.
And when you get the choice to
sit it out or dance,
To Coda
Fsus
F
I hope you dance.
1
Gm
3fr
Eb
3fr
Bb
F/A
I hope you dance.
Gm
3fr
Eb
3fr

Fsus
F
2
Gm
3fr
Eb
3fr
Time is a
I hope you
Bb
F/A
wheel in con - stant mo - tion, al - ways roll -
I hope you
Gm
3fr
Eb
3fr
- ing us a - long.
dance.
Fsus
F
Gm
3fr
Eb
3fr
Tell me, who wants to
I hope you dance.

B♭
F/A
look back on their youth and won - der where
I hope you
Gm
E♭
Fsus
F
those years have gone?
dance.
D.S. al Coda
I hope you still
CODA
Fsus
N.C.
dance.
Gm
E♭
B♭
F/A
Dance,

Gm
Eb
3 fr
I hope you dance.
Fsus
F
Time is a
wheel in con - stant mo - tion, al - ways roll - ing us a - long.
I hope you dance.
Bb
F/A

Fsus
F
Gm
3fr
Eb
3fr
Tell me, who wants to
I hope you dance.
Bb
F/A
look back on their youth and won - der where
I hope you
Repeat and Fade
Gm
Eb
Fsus
F
those years have gone?
dance.
Optional Ending
Fsus
F
Bb
I hope you dance.
rit.

I WANT IT THAT WAY

Words and Music by MARTIN SANDBERG
and ANDREAS CARLSSON

2,3
E
A
D(add2)
E
F#m
that ___ way. ___
that ___ way. ___
Tell me why. ___ Ain't noth - in' but a heart - ache. ___ Tell me
D(add2)
E
F#m
D(add2)
why. ___ Ain't noth - in' but a mis - take. ___ Tell me why. ___ I nev - er wan - na
E
A
F#m
E
A
To Coda
D.S. al Coda
CODA
C#sus
C#
hear you say ___ I want ___ it that ___ way. ___ Am I ___
that way. ___
F#m
A/E
D
Bm
E
Now I can see ___ that we've fall - en a - part ___ from the way that it used ___ to ___ be, ___ yeah. ___ No

F♯m
A/E
D
Esus
E
mat-ter the dis - tance, I want you to know _ that deep down in - side _ of me ___ you are _
D(add2)
2fr
E
F♯m
D(add2)
2fr
E
F♯m
___ my fi - re, ___ the one ____ de - si - re. ___ You are, _
D(add2)
2fr
E
A
F♯m
Bm
___ you are, _ you are, ___ you are. _____ Don't wan - na hear _ you
E(add2)
F♯
G♯m
4fr
E(add2)
F♯
G♯m
4fr
Ain't noth - in' but a heart - ache. _ Ain't noth - in' but a mis - take. _
say...

E(add2)
F#
B
G#m
4fr
I nev - er wan-na hear you say I want it that way. Tell me
why. Ain't noth-in' but a heart - ache. Tell me why. Ain't noth-in' but a
mis - take. Tell me why. I nev-er wan-na hear you say I want it
1
2
that way. Tell me that way. 'Cause I want it that way.
rit.

I WILL REMEMBER YOU

Theme from THE BROTHERS McMULLEN

Words and Music by SARAH McLACHLAN,
SEAMUS EGAN and DAVE MERENDA

A
D
E7
A
Weep not for the mem - o - ries. Re -
A
D/F#
E7
mem - ber the good times that we had. We
I'm so tired, but I can't sleep.
so a - fraid to love you, more a - fraid to lose,
A
D
E7
F#m7
let them slip a - way from us when things got bad.
Stand - in' on the edge of some - thing much too deep. It's
cling - ing to a past that does - n't let me choose. Well
A
D
E7
Clear - ly I first saw you smil - in' in the sun. Wan - na feel
fun - ny how I feel so much but I can - not say a word. We are scream -
once there was a dark - ness, a deep and end - less night. You

A
D/F#
E7
___ your warmth up - on ___ me. I wan-na be the one. ___
ing in - side or we ___ can't be heard.
gave me ev - 'ry-thing you had, oh, you gave me light. ___
A
Dmaj7
A
I will re - mem - ber ___ you. ______
Dmaj7
Esus
E
A
D/F#
Will you re-mem - ber _ me? ___ Don't let your life ___
A/E
Bm7
2fr
A
D
pass ___ you by. ______ Weep not for ________ the

E7
To Coda
1
A
2
A
mem - o - ries.
A
Dmaj7
E/A
A
Dmaj7
1
E
F♯m7
2
E
A
D.S. al Coda
I'm
CODA
A
Dmaj7
I will re - mem - ber you.

A
Dmaj7
E7
Will you re-mem - ber me? Don't
A
D/F♯
A/E
Bm7
2 fr
let your life pass you by.
A
D
E7
F♯m7
Weep not for the mem - o - ries.
E/G♯
A
D
E7
A
Weep not for the mem - o - ries.
molto rit.

I WILL SURVIVE

Words and Music by DINO FEKARIS
and FREDERICK J. PERREN

Am
Dm
G
back from out - er space. I just walk in to find you here with that sad
me, some-bod - y new, I'm not that chained up lit - tle per - son still in
Cmaj7
Fmaj7
Bm7♭5
look up - on your face. I should have changed that stu - pid lock, I should have made you leave your key, if I'd -'ve
love with you. And so you felt like drop-pin' in and just ex - pect me to be free. Well now, I'm
E7sus
E7
Am
known for just one sec - ond you'd be back to both - er me. Go on, now
sav - in' all my lov - in' for some - one who's lov - in' me. Go on, now
go, walk out the
Dm
G
Cmaj7
door; just turn a - round, now, 'cause you're not wel-come an - y - more.

Fmaj7
Bm7♭5
E7sus
Weren't you the one who tried to hurt me with good-bye? Did you think I'd crum-ble, did you think I'd
E7
Am
Dm
lay down and die. Oh no, not I, I will sur-vive. Oh, as
G
Cmaj7
Fmaj7
long as I know how to love, I know I'll stay a-live. I've got all my life to live, I've got
Bm7♭5
E7sus
E7
2nd time D.S. and Fade
all my love to give and I'll sur-vive, I will sur-vive! It took
Now

I WISH IT WOULD RAIN

Words and Music by
PHIL COLLINS

Eb/G
Ab
Eb/G
All this time I stayed out of sight.
Ooh, I nev - er meant to cause you no pain, but it
Fm7
I start - ed won - der - ing why?
looks like I did it a - gain.
Chorus
Db
Now I, ooh, now I wish it would rain
Ebsus
Eb
Db
down, down on me.
Ooh, yes, I wish it would rain,

E♭sus
D♭
rain down on me now.
E♭sus
E♭
Ooh, yes, I wish it would rain down, down on me.
D♭
E♭sus
D♭/F
To Coda
Ooh, yes, I wish it would rain down on
1
E♭/G
2
E♭/G
A♭
me. me. Though your hurt
6fr
3fr
4fr

B♭/A♭
D♭/A♭
is gone, mine's hang - ing on
D♭/E♭
A♭
in - side, and I know, oh, it's eat -
B♭/A♭
ing me, it's eat - ing me through ev - 'ry night and day. I'm just
D♭/A♭
D♭/E♭
A♭
D.S. al Coda
wait - ing on your sign.
4fr

Additional Lyrics

3. 'Cause I know, I know I never meant to cause you no pain,
And I realize I let you down,
But I know in my heart of hearts,
I know I'm never gonna hold you again.
Chorus

I'D LOVE TO CHANGE THE WORLD

Words and Music by
ALVIN LEE

Em
G
Am
san - i - ty?
e - con - o - my.
C
B7
Em
G
Tax the rich, feed the poor,
Life is fun - ny, skies are sun - ny,
Am
C
B7
Em
'til there are no rich no more.
bees make hon - ey, who needs mon - ey, mo - nop - o - ly?
G
Am
C
B7
I'd

Em
G
Am
love to change the world,
but I don't
C
B7
Em
G
know what to do.
Am
C
B7
Em
So I'll leave it up to you.
G
Am
To Coda
C
B7

Em
G
Am
Guitar solo
C
B7
Play 4 times
Em
G
World _ pol - lu - tion,
there's no so-lu - tion,
Am
C
B7
in - sti - tu - tion,
e - lec - tro - cu - tion.
Em
G
Just black or white, _
rich or poor, _

Am
C
B7
Em
them and us,
stop the war.
G
Am
C
B7
Em
G
Am
C
B7
D.S. al Coda
I'd
CODA
C
B7
Em
rit.

I WOULDN'T WANT TO BE LIKE YOU

Words and Music by ALAN PARSONS
and ERIC WOOLFSON

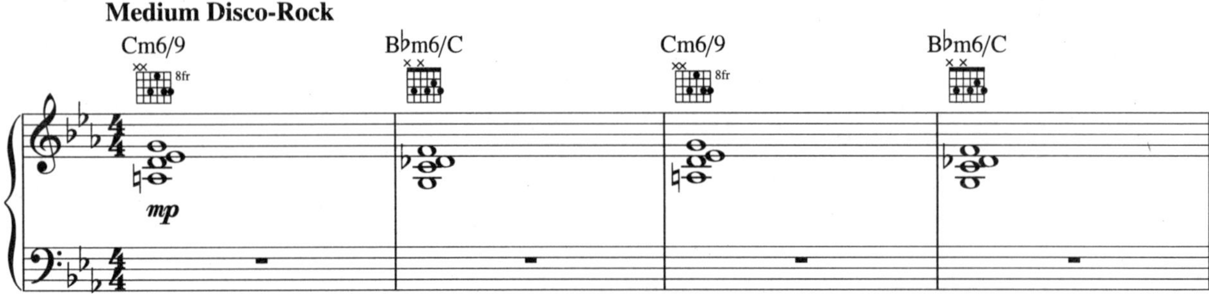

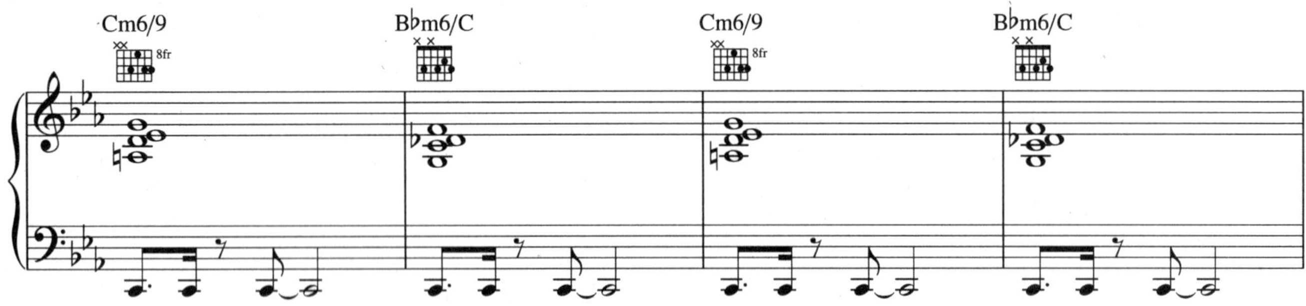

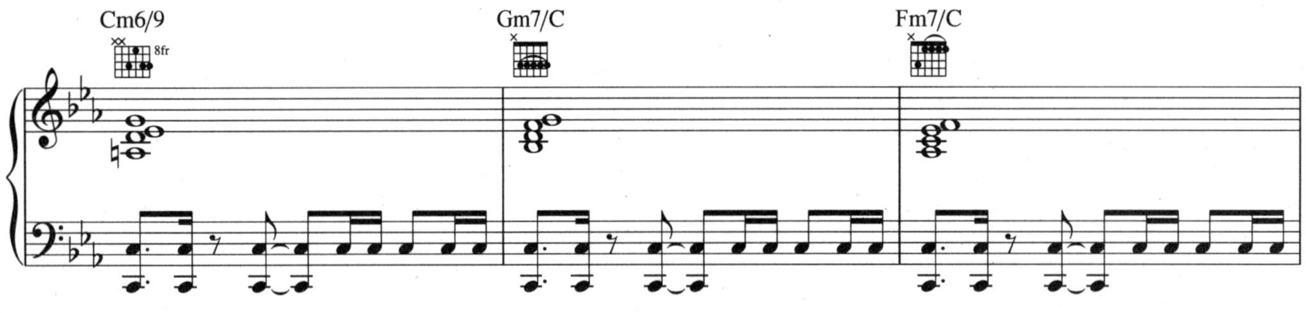

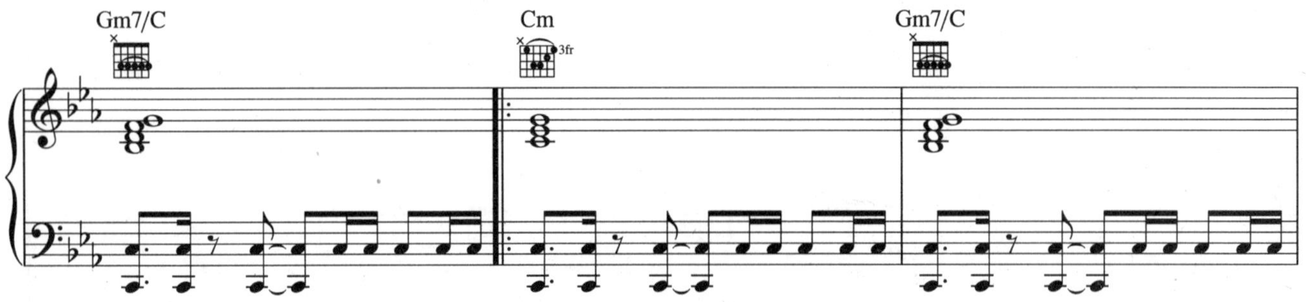

Fm7/C
Gm7/C
Cm7
3fr
If I had a
Fm7
mind to,
high class,
I would-n't wan - na
I would-n't need a
Cm7
3fr
be like you.
buck to pass.
And if I had
And if I was a

Fm7
time to,
fall guy,
I would-n't wan - na
I would-n't need no
Cm7
3fr
Gm7/C
Fm7/C
talk to you.
al - i - bi.
Oh, oh,
I don't care
what you do,
Gm7/C
Gm7
Fm7
Cm7
3fr
I would-n't wan-na
be like you,
yeah.
1
2
If I was

Fm7
Cm7
3fr
1
2
Gm7/C
Fm7/C
Gm7/C
Cm7
3fr
Fm7
Back on the bot - tom line,

Cm7
3fr
dig - gin' for a lous - y dime, yeah.
Fm7
If I hit a moth - er lode,
Cm7
3fr
I'd cov - er an - y - thing that showed. Oh,
Gm7/C
Fm7/C
I don't care what you do,

Gm7/C
Gm7
Fm7
Cm7
3fr
I would - n't wan - na be like you. Oh,
Gm7/C
Fm7/C
Gm7/C
Gm7
Fm7
I don't care what you do, I would - n't wan - na,
Cm7
Gm7/C
Fm7/C
1st time only:
I would - n't wan - na be like you. vocal ad lib to end
Gm7/C
Cm
B♭
Cm

IF

Words and Music by
DAVID GATES

A9
Bm7/A
can't I paint you? The words
I'd be with you to - mor -
Bm7♭5/A
A
will nev - er show the you
- row and to - day, be - side
Bm7♭5/D
E7
I've come to know. If a
you all the way. If the
A(add2)
Amaj9
face could launch a thou - sand ships, then
world should stop re - volv - ing, spin - ning

A9
Bm7/A
where am I to go?
There's no
slow - ly down to die,
I'd spend
Bm7♭5/A
A
one home but you;
you're all
the end with you;
and when
Bm7♭5/D
E7
that's left me to.
And when
the world was through,
then one
F♯m
F♯m/E♯
my love for life
by one the stars

F♯m/E
D6
is run - ning dry, you
would all go out. Then
C♯m7♭5
F♯m7
1
Bm7
come and pour your - self on
you and I would
E7
2
Bm7
D/E
me. If a sim - ply fly a -
rit.
A
Bm7/F♯
Bm7♭5/F
A
way.
a tempo
rit.

IF YOU LEAVE ME NOW

Words and Music by
PETER CETERA

Am7
D7
G
C
G
C
girl, I just want you to stay.
F9sus
B♭m/F
A love like ours is love
We've come too far to leave
that's hard to find.
it all be - hind.
F
Am7
How could we let
How could we end
it slip a-way?
it all this way?
F
G
1,3
C
Am7
E7
2,4
C
When to-mor -

Em7
Am7
Dm
Em
- row comes, then we'll both re - gret the things we said to - day.
Fm
To Coda
Cmaj7
Am7
Em7
Am7
D
G
C

Am7
D7
G
C
G
C
D.S. al Coda
(with repeats)
CODA
Cmaj7
If you leave me now, you'll
Am7
Em7
take a - way the big - gest part of me.
Ooh,
Am7
D7
G
no, ba - by, please don't go.

C
Am7
D7
G
C
G
C
G
C
G
C
Am7
D7
Ooh, girl, just
Ooh, ma - ma, I just
G
C
Am7
D7
got to have you by my side.
got to have your lov - in'.
G
C
G
C
G
C
G
C
Repeat and Fade
Ooh,

IF YOU LOVE SOMEBODY SET THEM FREE

Music and Lyrics by
STING

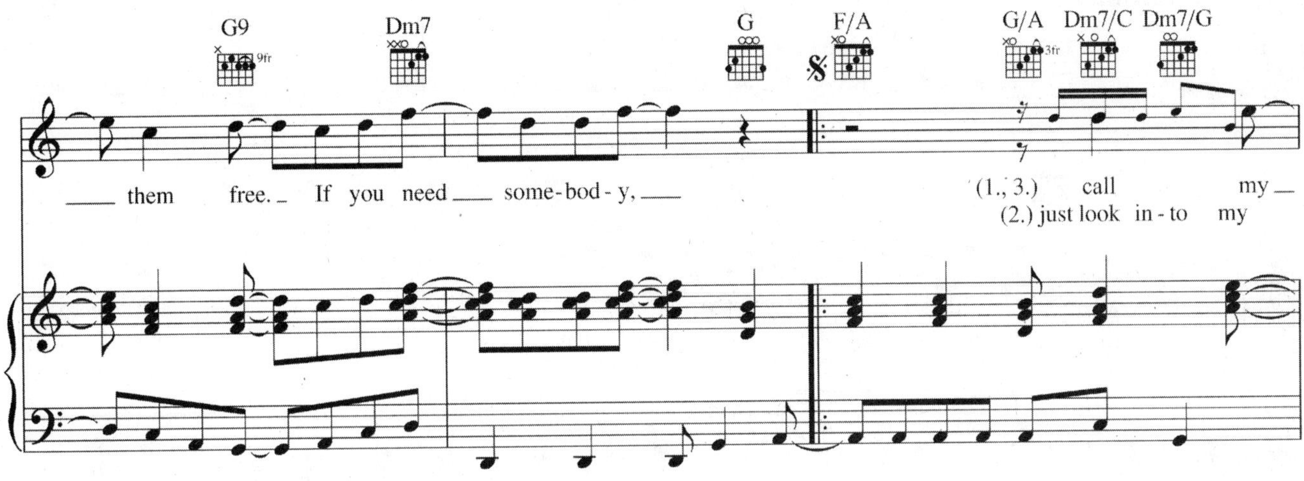

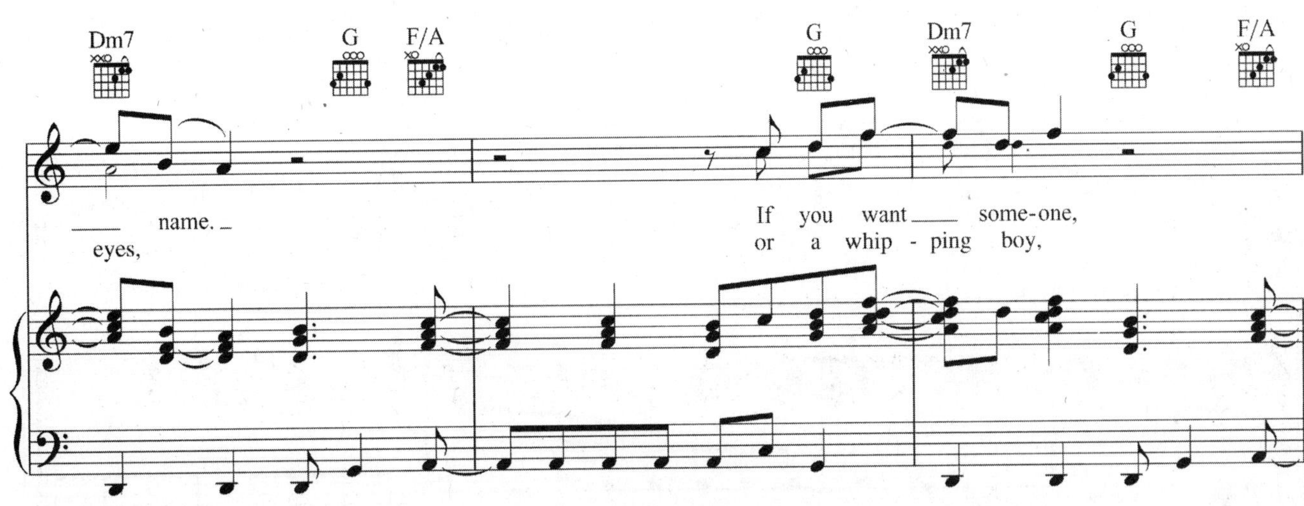

G
Dm7
G
F/A
G
you can do the same.
some-one to de-spise.
If you want to keep
Or a pris-'ner
Dm7
G
F/A
G
Dm7
G
F/A
some-thing pre-cious,
in the dark
got to lock it up and throw a-way the key.
tied up in chains, you just can't see.
G
Dm7
G
F/A
G
You want to hold on to your pos-ses-sion,
Or a beast in a gild-ed cage;
don't e-ven
that's all some peo-
Dm7
G
F/A
G
Bm7
think a-bout me.
ple ev-er want to be.
If you love some-bod-y

G
if you love some-one,
if you love
Bm7
some-bod - y,
G
if you love some-
Am7
Dm9
3fr
C/D
Am7
G
one set them free. (Free, free, set them free.) Set them
Dm9
3fr
C/D
Am7
G
Dm9
3fr
C/D
Am7
free. (Free, free, set them free.) Set them free. (Free, free, set

G
Dm9
3fr
C/D
Am7
1
G
To Coda
them free.) Set them free. (Free, free, set them free.) If it's a mir-ror
Dm7
G
2
G
Fsus
you want, them free.) You can't con -
F
C/E
C
trol an in - de - pen - dent heart.
(Can't love what you can't keep.)
Gm7 Gm7(add4)
F
C/E
Can't tear the one you love a - part.
(Can't love what you

C
Gm7
Gm7(add4)
F
For - ev - er con - di - tioned to be - lieve that we can't live, we can't
can't keep.)
C/E
C
Gm7
Gm7(add4)
live here and be hap - py with less.
With so man - y rich - es, so
F
C/E
C
man - y souls, with ev - 'ry - thing we see that we want to pos - sess. If you
Dm7
G
D.S. al Coda
need some - bod - y,
CODA
Dm9
3fr
C/D
Am7
Repeat and Fade
G
free. (Free, free, set them free.) Set them
Vocal ad lib.

IN MY LIFE

Words and Music by JOHN LENNON
and PAUL McCARTNEY

F#m
D
G
1. plac - es had their moments with lov - ers and friends I
2.,3. know I'll nev - er lose af - fec - tion for peo - ple and things that
A
F#m
still can re - call. Some are dead and some are
went be - fore, I know I'll of - ten stop and think a -
B7
Dm
To Coda
1A
2A
liv - ing, in my life I've loved them all.
bout them. In my life I love you more.
N.C.
8va
in 18th century style

1
2
D.S. al Coda
CODA
A
Though I
love you more.
E7
Dm
N.C.
In my life I love you
rit.
A
E7
A
more.
a tempo

INCENSE AND PEPPERMINTS

Words and Music by JOHN CARTER
and TIM GILBERT

Dm
B♭
Dm
C♯m
C
G
col - or of time. _
Who cares _ what games we choose, _
Dm
C♯m
C
G
To Coda
Dm
G
Lit - tle to win, _ but noth - in' to lose. _
In - cense and pep - per-mints,
Dm
B♭
Dm
G
Dm
B♭
mean-ing - less nouns, _
Turn on, tune in, turn your eyes _ a - round; _
C7
F
C7
F
Em
Em+7
Look at your - self, _
look at your - self, _
Yeah, yeah! _

Em7
Em6
C7
F
C7
F
Look at your - self,
look at your - self,
Em
Em#7
G
Yeah,
yeah,
yeah,
yeah!
Dm
G
Dm
B♭
Dm
G
To di - vide the cock - eyed
world in two,
Throw your pride to one side, it's the
Dm
B♭
Dm
G
Dm
B♭
least you can do;
Beat - niks in pol - i - tics,
noth - ing is new,
A

Dm G Dm B♭ Dm C♯m
yard - stick for lu - na - tics, one point of view. Who cares what
C G Dm C♯m C G
D.S. al Coda
games we choose, Lit - tle to win, but noth - in' to lose.
CODA
Dm C
mf
Dm C♯m C G Dm C♯m
in - cense, pep - per - mints, in - cense,

C
G
Dm
C#m
C
D
pep - per - mints.
D
C
Sha - la - la,
D
Sha - la - la,
Sha - la -
C
D
la,
Sha - la - la.

IT'S GONNA BE ME

Words and Music by MARTIN SANDBERG,
ANDREAS CARLSSON and RAMI YACOUB

Cm
Gm/B♭
Gm
A♭
Gm
I re-mem-ber you told me that it made you be-lieve__ in
Fm7
B♭
Cm
B♭
no man,__ no cry. May - be__ that's_ why ev - 'ry lit - tle
cresc.
f
Chorus:
A♭
Fm
B♭
E♭/G
Cm
thing I do nev-er seems e - nough for you. You don't wan-na
A♭
G/B
Cm
B♭
lose it__ a - gain, but I'm not__ like__ them. Ba - by, when you

1.
A♭
Fm
B♭
B♭6
Cm
B♭/D
fi - nal - ly get to love some - bod - y, guess
A♭
G7
N.C.
B♭5
what? It's gon - na be me.
2.
G/B
Cm
B♭/D
A♭
G7
N.C.
love some - bod - y, guess what? It's gon - na be me.
(It's gon-na be me.)
Oo, yeah, yeah.
dim.

Bridge:
A♭
B♭
Cm
B♭
A♭
There comes a day when I'll be the one, you'll see, (It's
mp
G7
N.C.
gon - na, gon - na, gon - na, gon - na.) it's gon-na be me.
A♭maj7
B♭
Gm
Cm
All that I do is not e-nough for you.
f
A♭
G/B
Cm
B♭
Don't wan - na lose it, but I'm not like that.

A♭maj9
B♭
Cm
B♭/D
When fi - nal - ly___ you get___ to love,___
Chorus:
A♭
B♭(9)
A♭
Fm
B♭
___ guess what? (Guess what?) Ev - 'ry lit - tle thing I do nev - er seems e -
E♭/G
Cm
A♭
G/B
nough for you. You don't wan - na lose it___ a - gain, but
Cm
B♭
A♭
Fm
B♭
I'm not___ like___ them. Ba - by, when you fi - nal - ly___ get to

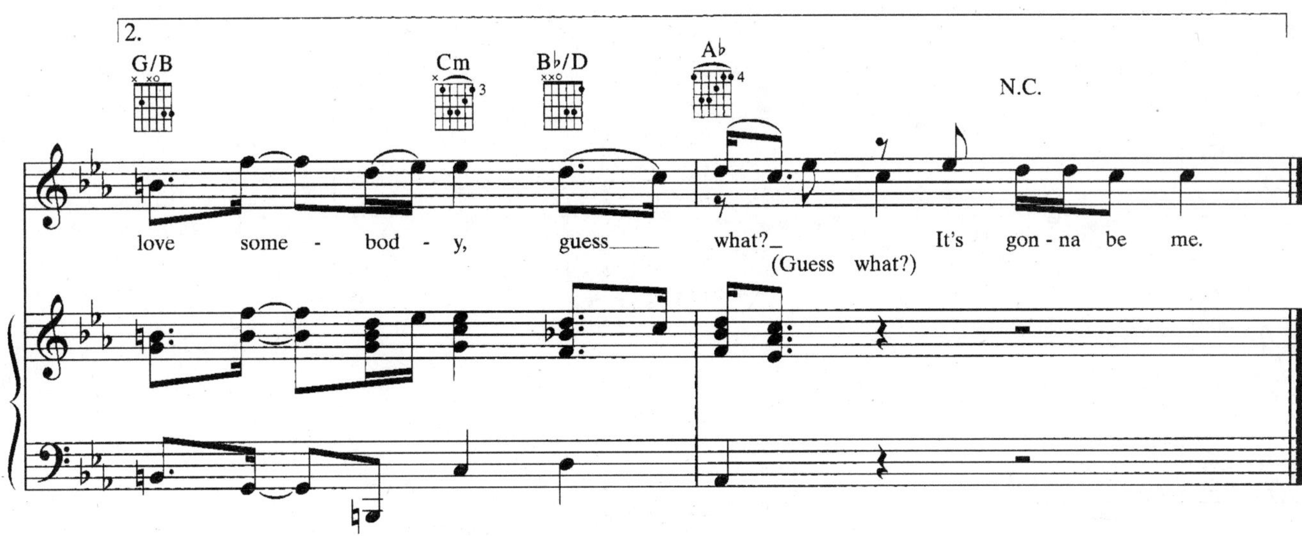

Verse 2:
You've got no choice, babe,
But to move on, you know
There ain't no time to waste,
'Cause you're just too blind to see.
But in the end you know it's gonna be me.
You can't deny,
So just tell me why…
(To Chorus:)

IT'S MY LIFE

Words and Music by MARK DAVID HOLLIS
and TIM FRESE-GREENE

* Recorded a half step lower.

B♭
F
Cm7
I'd pay to lose.
B♭
G♭
One half won't do.
Bm
Em/B
A
D
G
I've asked my - self how
I'd tell my - self what
Bm
Em/B
A
D
G
much do you com - mit
good do you do, con - vince

Bm7
Em
A
your - self?
my - self.
Oh, it's my life.
D
Bm7
Em
A
D
Bm7
Don't you for - get.
It's my life.
To Coda
Em
A
D
Bm7
Em
A
It never - er ends.
D
N.C.
F5
N.C.
(drums)

F
Cm7
B♭
Fun - ny how I blind my - self. I nev - er knew
if I was some - times played up - on,
a - fraid to lose.
G♭
D.S. al Coda

CODA
D
Cm
Cm
1,2
Gm/C
3
Gm/C
G♭
Bm
Em/B
A
D
G
I've asked
my - self, how much do you
Bm
Em
A

D
G
Bm7
com - mit ___ your - self? _
Oh, it's my life. _
Em
A
D
Bm7
Em
A
Don't _ you _ for - get. ___
D
Bm7
Em
A
D
Bm7
Caught _ in ___ the crowd. _
It ___ nev - er ends. _
Em
A
1,2
D
Bm7
3
D
It's my life. _ ___

JACK AND DIANE

Words and Music by
JOHN MELLENCAMP

D E A E
in the heart - land. Jack, he's gon - na be
D E
a foot - ball star.
A E D E A
Di - ane's deb - u - tante back seat of Jack - y's car.
E/A D/A E/A

A
E/A
D/A
A
A
E
Suck - in' on a chil - li dog out -
Jack, he sit back, col - lects his
mp
D
E
A
E
side the Tast - ee Freez;
thoughts for a mo - ment;
Di - ane sit - tin' on
Scratch - es his
D
E
A
Jack - y's lap. He's got his hands be - tween her knees.
head and does his best James Dean.

E D E

Jack, he says, "Hey, Di - ane, let's run off be - hind a shad - y tree;
"Well, then, there, Di - ane, we got - ta run off to the cit -

A E

dribble off those Bob - bie Brooks. Let me
- y." Di - ane says, "Ba - by, you ain't

D E A A E

do what I please." Say - in',
miss - in' a thing." But Jack, he says,

Oh yeah,

D E

life goes on,

A
E
D
E
long af - ter the thrill of liv - ing is gone.
Say - in',
A
E
Oh yeah,
D
E
A
E
life goes on,
long af - ter the
To Coda
D
E
A
1
thrill of liv - ing is gone. Now, walk on.

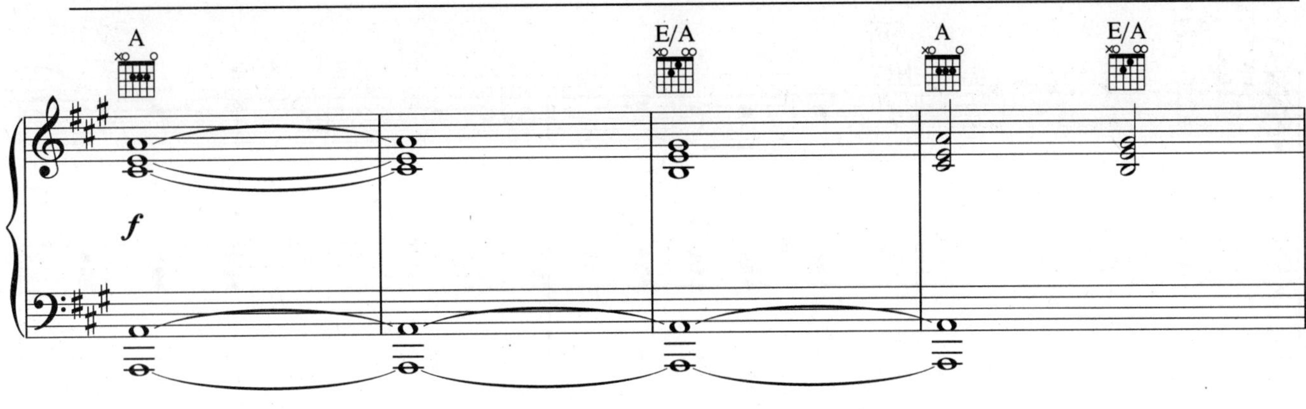
A
E/A
A
E/A
f

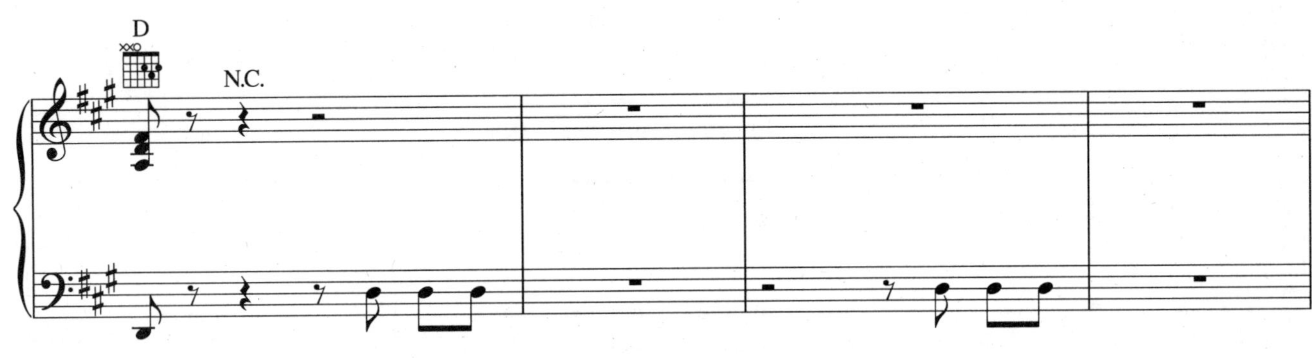
D
N.C.

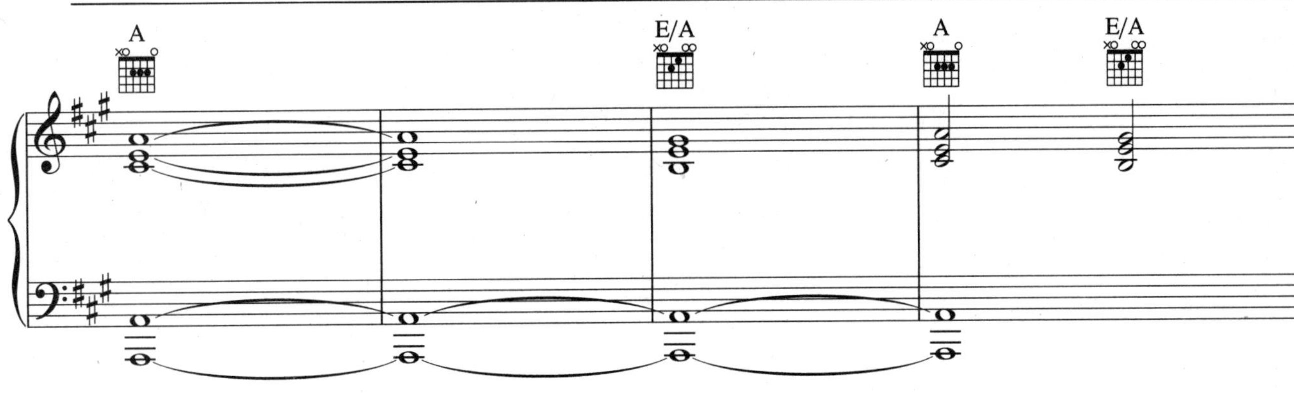
A
E/A
A
E/A

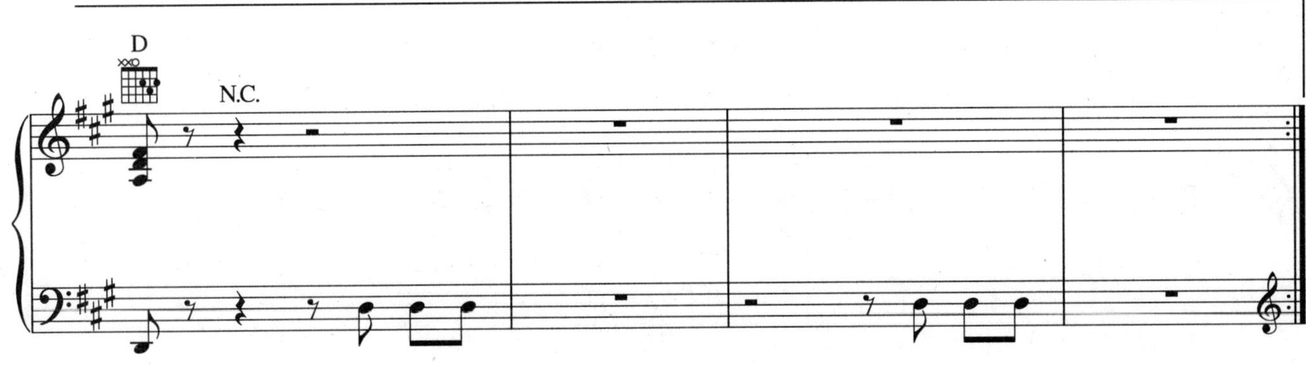
D
N.C.

2
N.C.
Oh, let it rock,
let it roll
let the Bi - ble Belt
come and
save my soul.
Hold - in' on to
six - teen
as long as you can;

change is com - in' 'round real soon, make us wom - en and men.
C
E/A
D/A
E/A
A
E/A
D/A
A
D.S. al Coda
CODA
A
E
A lit - tle

D
E
dit - ty a - bout Jack and Di - ane,
A
E
D
E
A
two A - mer - i - can kids do - in' the best that they can.
A
E/A
A
E/A
A
E/A
f
D
N.C.
Repeat and Fade

THE JOKER

Words and Music by STEVE MILLER,
EDDIE CURTIS and AHMET ERTEGUN

speak of the pom-pa-tus of love.
Peo-ple talk a-bout me, ba-by,
say I'm do-ing you wrong, do-ing you wrong.
Well, don't you wor-ry, ba-by, don't wor-ry 'cause I'm

right here, right here, right here, right here at home. 'Cause I'm a
F
B♭
F
B♭
pick - er. I'm a grin - ner. I'm a lov - er and I'm a sin - ner.
F
B♭
C
B♭
I play my mu - sic in the sun. I'm a
F
B♭
F
B♭
jok - er. I'm a smok - er. I'm a mid - night tok - er.

1
F
B♭
C
B♭
I sure don't want to hurt no one.
I'm a
2
F
B♭
Csus
3fr
I get my lov - ing on the run.
Oo, hoo.
Oo, hoo.
N.C.

You're the cut - est thing that I ev -
- er did see.
I real - ly love your peach - es, wan - na

shake your tree.
Lov - ey dov - ey, lov - ey dov - ey, lov - ey
To Coda
dov - ey all the time.
Oo, wee, ba - by, I'll sure show
F
B♭
you a good time.
'Cause I'm a pick - er. I'm a grin - ner. I'm a
F
B♭
F
B♭
lov - er, and I'm a sin - ner.
I play my mu - sic in the sun.

C
B♭
F
B♭
I'm a jok - er. I'm a smok - er. I'm a
F
B♭
1
F
B♭
mid - night tok - er.
I get my lov - ing on the run.
C
B♭
2
F
B♭
I'm a
I sure don't want't to hurt no one.
C
B♭
F
B♭
F
B♭

F
B♭
1 C
B♭
2 Csus
3fr
Oo, hoo.
Oo, hoo.
N.C.
Peo - ple keep talk - in' a - bout me, ba - by.
They say I'm do-ing you wrong.

Well, don't you wor-ry. Don't wor - ry. No, don't wor - ry, ma - ma,
D.S. al Coda
'cause I'm right here at home.
CODA
Come on babe, and I'll show you a good time.
Repeat and Fade
Optional Ending

JEALOUS GUY

Words and Music by
JOHN LENNON

I did-n't mean to hurt you
I'm sorry that I
G Dm C D7sus4 G Dm
made you cry Oh no I did-n't mean to hurt you
Bb G Em G6
1.2.3.
I'm just a jea-lous guy
4.
I'm just a jea-lous guy watch out
C G C G
I'm just a jea-lous guy look out babe I'm just a jea-lous guy
C G C G

JUST ONE LOOK

Words and Music by DORIS PAYNE
and GREGORY CARROLL

F
Oh, oh, I found out how good it fe - ee - eels to have your love. Oh, oh,
Oh, oh, just one look and I know o - ow I'll get you some - day. Oh, oh,
Dm
B♭
C
To Coda
F
Say you will, will be mi - i - ine
Dm

B♭
for - ev - er
and al -
C
ways.
Oh,
oh,
F
just one look
and I knew
Dm
ew - ew
that
B♭
you
C
were my on - ly
F
one.
Oh

B♭
I thought I was dream-in', but I was
F
G7
wrong. Oh yeah, yeah, Ah, but I'm gon-na keep on
C
C13
C7
D.S. al Coda
schem-in' til I can make you, make you my own.
CODA
F
B♭
C
Repeat ad lib. and Fade
just one look, that's all it took { yeah. wow. }

KEEP ON LOVING YOU

Words and Music by
KEVIN CRONIN

F G Am G
but you nev-er bled. In-stead you laid still in the grass all coiled up and hiss-
-in'.
F G/F
And though I know all a-
Instrumental
Am/F G/F F G/F Am/F G/F F
bout those men, still I don't re-mem-ber.
G/F Am/F G/F F G/F
'Cause it was us, ba-by, way be-fore them, and we're still to-geth-er.

Am/F
G/F
F
G
F
G
Instrumental ends
And I meant ev-'ry word I said. When I
Am
G
G/F
said that I love you I meant that I'll love you for-ev - er.
G/E
G/D
C
F
G
C
And I'm gon-na keep on lov - in' you, 'cause it's the on-
F
G
Am
- ly thing I wan-na do. I don't wan-na sleep. I

G
G/F
1
G/E
G/D
F
2
G/E
G/D
C
just wan-na keep on lov - in' you.
Ba - by, I'm gon - na keep
F
G
C
F
G
on lov - in' you,
'cause it's the on - ly thing I wan - na do.
Am
G
I don't wan - na sleep.
I just wan - na keep on lov -
G/F
G/E
G/D
Csus(add2)
C
- in' you.
dim.
mp

LANDSLIDE

Words and Music by
STEVIE NICKS

Eb
Bb/D
Cm7
Bb/D
land - slide brought me down.
Oh,
Eb
Bb/D
Cm
Bb/D
mir-ror in the sky, what is love?
Can the child
Eb
Bb/D
Cm7
Bb/D
with-in my heart rise a - bove?
Can I
Eb
Bb/D
Cm7
Bb/D
sail through the chang - ing o - cean tides?
Can I

E♭
B♭/D
Cm7
B♭/D
3fr
han - dle the sea - sons of my life?
E♭
B♭/D
Cm7
B♭/D
Mm mm, I don't know. Mm mm,
E♭
B♭/D
Cm7
F7/A
mm mm. Well, I've
B♭
F7/A
Gm
been a - fraid of chang - ing 'cause I

Eb
Bb/D
Cm7
F7/A
built my life around you. But time
Bb
F7/A
Gm7
makes you bolder. Children get older and I'm
Eb
Bb/D
Cm7
To Coda
Bb/D
getting older, too. So...
Ebsus2
Bb/D
F5/C
Bb/D

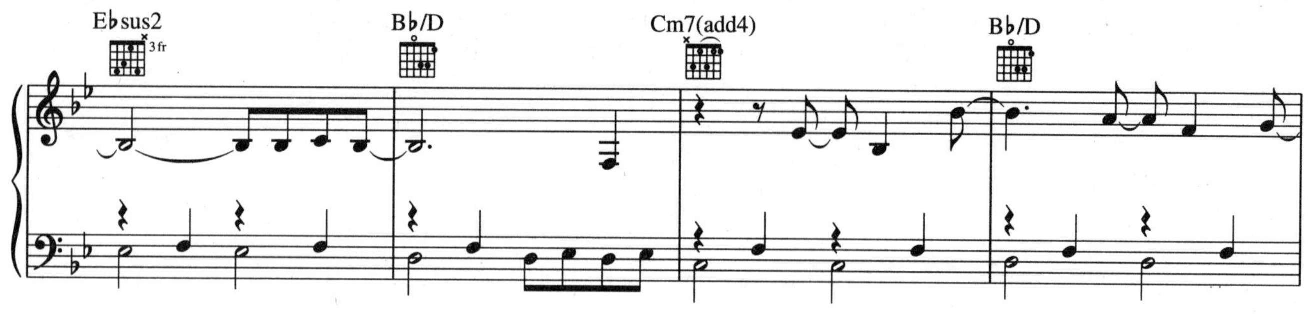
Ebsus2
3fr
Bb/D
Cm7(add4)
Bb/D

Eb(add2)
Bb/D
F5/C
3fr
Bb/D

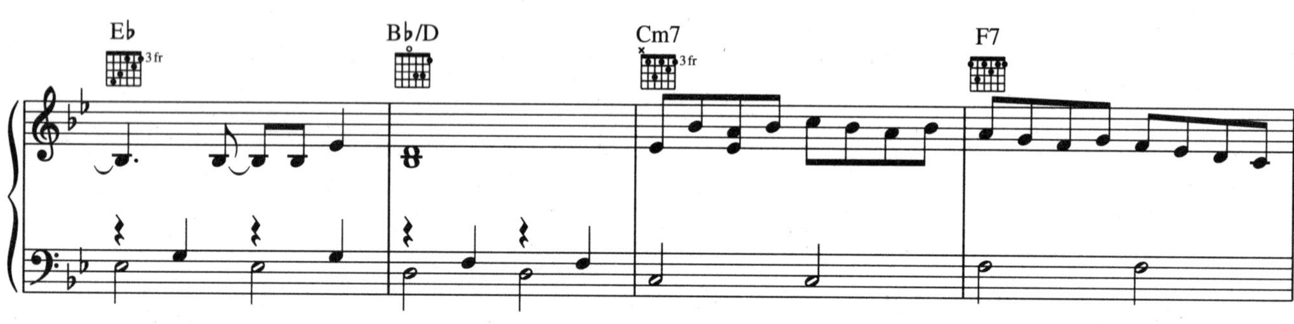
Eb
3fr
Bb/D
Cm7
3fr
F7

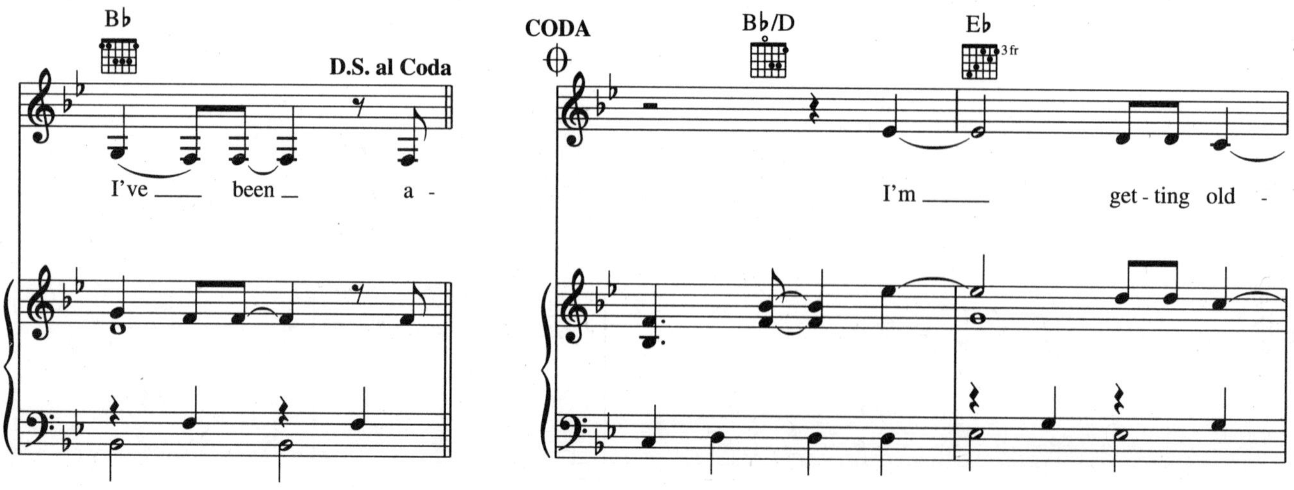
Bb
D.S. al Coda
I've ___ been ___ a -
CODA
Bb/D
Eb
3fr
I'm ______ get - ting old -

Bb/D
Cm7
Ebsus2
F5/C
Fsus/C
Eb
3fr
- er,
too.
So
take this love,
take it down.
Oh,
if you climb a moun -
- tain and you turn a - round,
if you see my re - flec -
- tion in the snow - cov - ered hills,
well, the land - slide will

Bb/D
Cm7
Bb/D
Eb
bring it down, down. And if you see my re-flec -
Bb/D
Cm7
Freely
Bb/D
- tion in the snow - cov - ered hills,
rall.
Tempo 1
Eb
Bb/D
Cm7
well, may-be the land - slide 'll bring it down. Well,
Bb/D
Eb
Bb/D
Cm
well, the land - slide 'll bring it down.
rall.

LIKE A ROLLING STONE

Words and Music by
BOB DYLAN

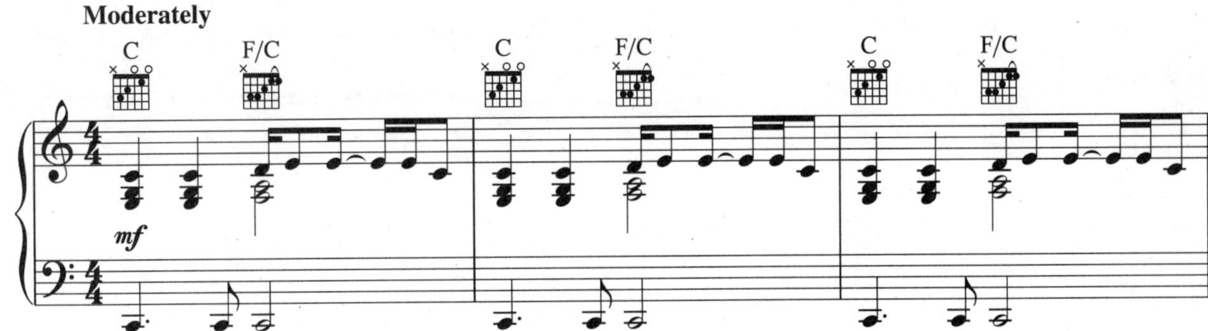

C
Dm
Em
F
Peo - ple call, say, "Be - ware, doll, you're bound to fall." You thought they were all
bod - y's ev - er taught you how to live out on the street and now you're gon - na have to get
Nev - er un - der - stood that it ain't no good you should - n't let oth - er peo - ple get your

G
F
3
a - kid - din' you.
used to it.
kicks for you.
You used to
You say you
You used to ride on a chrome horse with your

G
F
G
laugh a - bout ev - 'ry - bod - y that was hang - in' out.
nev - er com - pro - mise with the mys - ter - y tramp, but now you re - al - ize
dip - lo - mat who car - ried on his shoul - der a Sia - mese cat.

F
Em
Dm
C
F
Em
But now you don't talk so loud. Now you don't
he's not sell - ing an - y al - i - bis as you stare in - to the vac - uum
Ain't it hard when you dis - cov - er that he real - ly was - n't
Dm
C
Dm
F
seem so proud a - bout hav - in' to be scroung - ing for your next
of his eyes and say, "Do you want to make a
where it's at af - ter he took from you ev - 'ry - thing he could
G
Chorus
C
F
G
meal. How does it feel? How does it feel
deal?"
steal. How does it feel? How does it feel
C
F
G
C
F
to be with - out a home,
to be on your own,

G
C
F
1
like a com - plete un - known,
with no di - rec - tion home,
like a roll - ing stone?
Oh, you've
2, 3
a com - plete un - known,
Oh, you

Additional Lyrics

4. Princess on the steeple and all the pretty people
They're all drinkin', thinkin' that they got it made.
Exchanging all precious gifts,
But you better take your diamond ring,
You'd better pawn it, babe.
You used to be so amused
At Napoleon in rags and the language that he used.
Go to him now, he calls you, you can't refuse.
When you got nothin', you got nothin' to lose.
You're invisible now, you got no secrets to conceal.
Chorus

LIGHT MY FIRE

Words and Music by
THE DOORS

Am7
F#m7
If I was to say to you,
Try now we can on - ly lose,
and our
Am7
F#m7
girl, we could - n't get much higher.
love be - come a fu - neral pyre.
G
A
D
Come on, ba - by, light my fire.
G
A
D
B
G
D
Come on, ba - by, light my fire.
Try to set the night on

E
1, 2
3
fire.
The
You
cresc.
f
Am7
F#m7
Am7
know that it would be un - true,
you know that I would be a liar,
F#m7
Am7
F#m7
if I was to say to you,
Am7
F#m7
G
A
girl, we could-n't get much higher.
Come on, ba - by, light my fire.

D
G
A
D
Come on, ba - by, light my fire.
F
C
D
Play 3 times
F
C
Try to set the night on fire.
Try to set the night on
ff
D5
5 fr
G
D
fire.
F
B♭
E♭
3 fr
A♭
4 fr
A
3

LIVIN' LA VIDA LOCA

Words and Music by ROBI ROSA
and DESMOND CHILD

She's in - to new sen - sa - tions,
Wake up in New York Cit - y
new kicks in the can - dle - light.
in a funk - y cheap ho - tel.
She's got a
She took my heart and she
new ad - dic - tion for ev - 'ry day and night. She'll
took my mon - ey. She must - 've slipped me a sleep - in' pill. She
F♯m
G♯m
4fr
(1., 3.) make you take your clothes off and go danc - ing in the rain.
(2.) nev - er drinks the wa - ter and makes you or - der French cham - pagne.

A
She'll make you live her cra - zy life, but she'll take
Once you've had a taste of her you'll nev -
B
G♯
a - way your pain like a bul - let to your brain.
er be the same. Yeah, she'll make you go in - sane.
C♯m
Up - side in - side out, she's
B
C♯m
4 fr
liv - in' la vi - da lo - ca. She'll push and pull

B
C♯m
4fr
you down
liv - in' la vi - da lo - ca.
Her
B
lips are dev - il red and her skin's the col - or of mo -
C♯m
4fr
- cha.
She will wear you out
B
To Coda
C♯m
4fr
B
liv - in' la vi - da lo - ca.
You're liv - in' la vi - da lo -

C♯m
B
1
C♯m
4fr
- ca.
She's liv - in' la vi - da lo - ca.
2
C♯m
B/C♯
- ca.
C♯m
B/C♯

C♯m
D.S. al Coda
CODA
C♯m
She'll
- ca.
Up - side in -
lips are dev -
B
C♯m
- side out, she's liv - in' la vi - da lo - ca. She'll
- il red and her skin's the col - or of mo - cha.
B
push and pull you down liv - in' la vi - da lo -
She will wear you out liv - in' la vi - da lo -
1
C♯m
2
C♯m
B
- ca. Her - ca. You're liv - in' la vi - da lo -

C♯m
4fr
B
C♯m
4fr
- ca. She's liv - in' la vi - da lo - ca.
B
C♯m
4fr
Play 3 times
B
C♯m
4fr
Liv-in' la vi - da lo - ca. A -
B
C♯m
4fr
B
C♯m
4fr
got - ta, got - ta, got - ta la vi - da lo - ca. Got - ta, got - ta, got - ta la vi...

THE LOVECATS

Words and Music by
ROBERT SMITH

Am
G
F
G
move like ca - gey ti - gers, oh, we could-n't get clos-er than this. The
(Verses 2 & 3 see block lyrics)
Am
Am7
G
F
F6
G
way we walk, the way we talk, the way we stalk, the way we kiss. We
Am
G
F
F6
G
slip through the streets while ev-'ry-one sleeps get-ting big-ger and sleek-er and wid-er and bright - er. We
To Coda
Am
G
F
F6
G
bite and scatch and scream all night. Let's go and throw all the songs we know.

C
Cadd9
Dm
Dmadd9
In - to the sea. You and me, all these years and no - one heard. I'll
C
Cadd9
Dm
Dmadd9
show you in Spring it's a trea-cher-ous thing. We miss you hissed the
1.
Am
F
love - cats. We missed you hissed the
(Ba ba ba ba ba ba ba ba. Ba ba ba ba ba ba ba ba.)
Am
F
G
love - cats. 2. We're so
(ba ba ba ba ba ba ba ba. Ba ba ba ba ba ba ba ba.)

2.
Am
F
love - cats.
We
miss
you
hissed
the
Am
F
love - cats.
We
miss
you
hissed
the
Am
F
love - cats.
We
miss
you
hissed
the
(Ba ba ba ba ba ba ba ba. Ba ba ba ba ba ba ba ba.)
Am
F6
love cats.
Yes.
3. We're so

Coda
Em7
Hand in hand is the on - ly way to land and al -
Fmaj7
Em7
- ways the right way round.
Not bro - ken in piec - es like
F
hat - ed lit - tle mee - ces.
How could we miss some - one as dumb as
Am
F
this.
Missed you hissed the

Am
Fmaj7(♯11)
love - cats.
We miss
Am
F
(Ba ba ba ba ba ba ba ba, ba ba ba ba ba ba ba ba.)
Am
F
I love you let's go.
(Ba ba ba ba ba ba ba ba, ba ba ba ba ba ba ba ba.)
Am
F
Repeat ad lib.
Ooh. So - lid gone.

Verses 2:
We're so wonderfully, wonderfully, wonderfully
Wonderfully pretty
Oh you know that I'd do anything for you
We should have each other to tea huh?
2° (dinner)
We should have each other with cream
Then curl up in the fire and sleep for awhile
2° (get up for awhile)
It's the grooviest thing, it's a perfect dream.

Into the sea *etc.*

LIVIN' ON A PRAYER

Words and Music by JON BON JOVI,
RICHIE SAMBORA and DESMOND CHILD

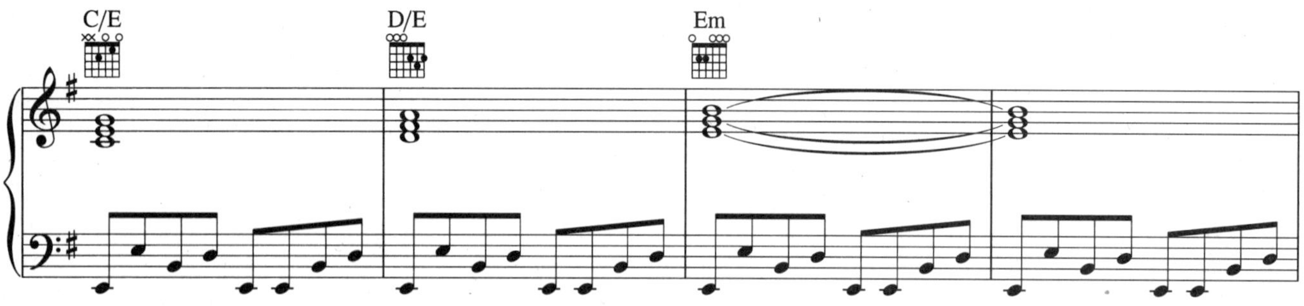

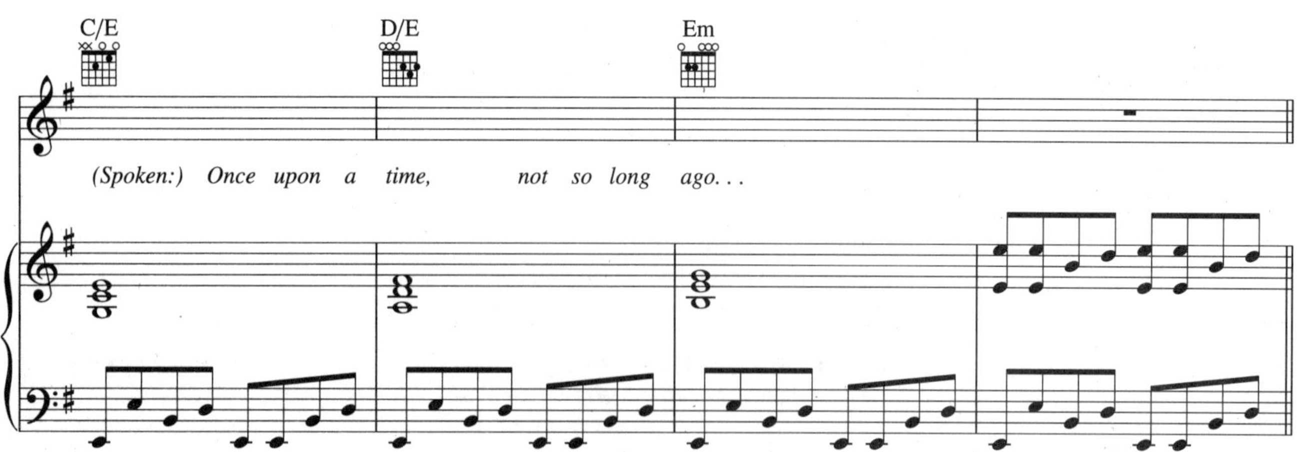

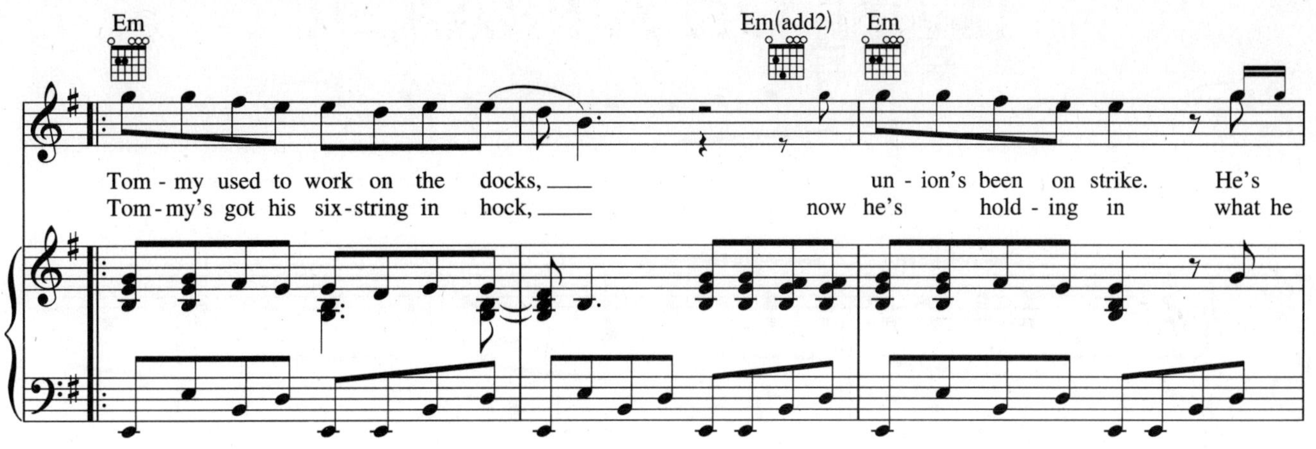
Em
Em(add2)
Em
Tom - my used to work on the docks, ___ un - ion's been on strike. He's
Tom - my's got his six-string in hock, ___ now he's hold - ing in what he

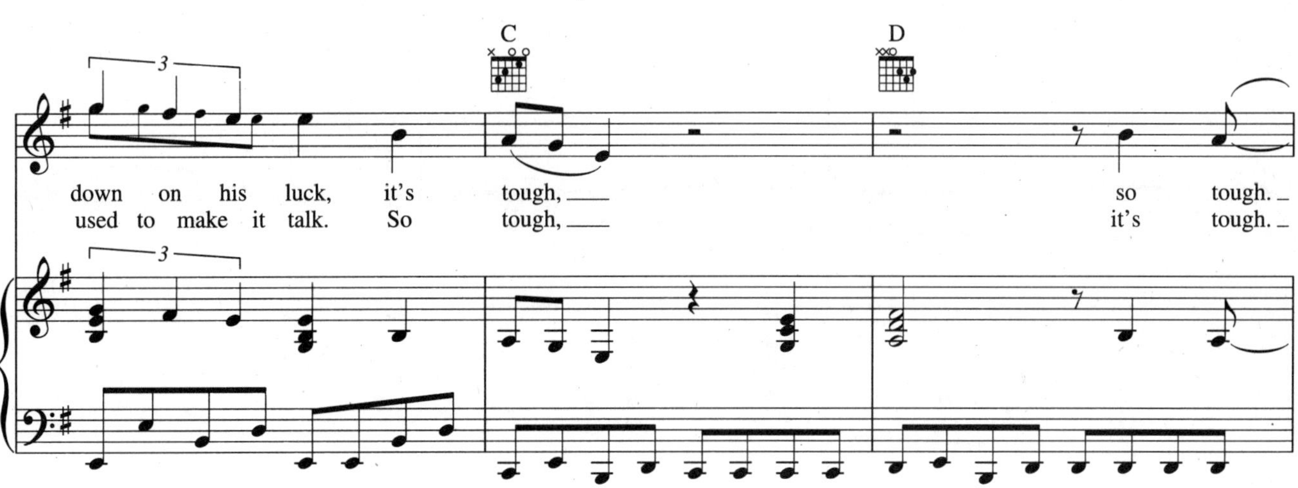
3
C
D
down on his luck, it's tough, ___ so tough. _
used to make it talk. So tough, ___ it's tough. _
3

Em
Gi - na works the di - ner all day ___
Gi - na dreams of run - ning a - way; ___

Em(add2)
Em
working for her man. she brings home her pay, for
when she cries in the night, Tom-my whis - pers: ba - by, it's
3
C
D
love, for love.
O. K. some - day.
C
D
Em
She says we've got to
We've got to
hold on to what we've got. It
f
C
D
Em
C
D
does - n't make a dif - f'rence if we make it or not. We've got each oth - er and

Em
C
D
that's a lot for love.
We'll give it a shot.
Em
C
D
G
D7sus
Whoa, we're half - way there.
Whoa, liv - in' on a prayer.
Em
C
D
Take my hand, we'll make it, I swear.
G
C
D7sus
1
Em
Whoa, liv - in' on a prayer.

2
C
Liv - in' on a prayer.
Em
C
D
Instrumental
G
C
D
Em
C
D
G
C
Em
Oh, we've got to

C
D
Em
D
C
hold on, ready - y or not, You live for the fight when it's
D
Gm
E♭
3fr
Fsus
F
all that you've got. Whoa, we're half - way there.
B♭
E♭
F7sus
Gm
E♭
Whoa, liv - in' on a prayer. Take my hand and we'll
F
B♭
E♭
F7sus
Repeat and Fade
Optional Ending
Gm
make it, I swear. Whoa, liv - in' on a prayer. Whoa.

LOLA

Words and Music by
RAY DAVIES

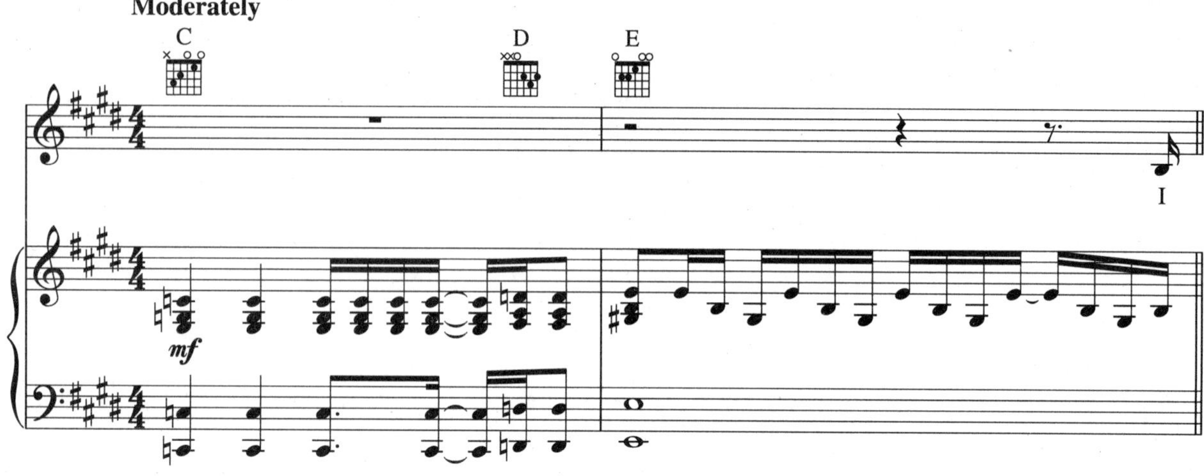

E
A
D
walked up to me and she asked me to dance. I asked her her name and in a dark brown voice she said,
I'm not dumb, but I can't un - der - stand why she walked like a wom - an and talked like a man. Oh my,
E
A
D
"Lo - la L - O - L - A Lo - la la la la la
Lo - la la la la la Lo - la la la la la
C
D
E
Lo - la."
Lo - la.
1
2
Well,
Well, we

B7
F♯7
drank cham-pagne and danced all night
un - der e - lec - tric can - dle - light. She
A
picked me up and sat me on her knee
and said, "Dear boy, won't you come home with me?" Well,
E
A
D
I'm not the world's most pas-sion-ate guy but when I looked in her eyes, well, I al-most fell for my
E
A
D
Lo - la la la la la Lo - la la la la la

C
D
E
Lo - la.
A
E
B
I pushed her a - way.
I
walked to the door.
I fell to the floor.
I got
E
G♯7
4fr
C♯m
4fr
B
down on my knees
then I looked at her, and she at me.
Well,

E
A
D
that's the way that I want it to stay, and I always want it to be that way for my
Lo - la la la la la Lo - la.
Girls will be boys, and boys will be girls, it's a mixed up, mud-dled up, shook up world ex-cept for
Lo - la la la la la Lo - la. Well,

B7
F#7
I left home just a week be-fore and I'd nev-er ev-er kissed a wo-man be-fore. But
A
Lo-la smiled and took me by the hand and said, "Dear boy, I'm gon-na make you a man." Well,
E
A
D
I'm not the world's most mas-cu-line man, But I know what I am, and I'm glad I'm a man and so is
Repeat and Fade
E
A
C
D
Lo-la la la la la Lo-la la la la la Lo-la.

LOVE THE ONE YOU'RE WITH

Words and Music by
STEPHEN STILLS

Fast Rock, in 2
F/G
F/C
C
it's al - right.
Go 'head and
love the one,
love the one,
love the one you're with.
Love the one,
love the one,
love the one you're with.

Dm/C
1 C
2 C
If you're down
F/C
C
Dm/C
and con - fused
- gry, don't be sad,
- ache right in - to joy.
C
F/C
C
and you don't re-mem - ber who you're talk - in'
and don't sit cry - in' o - ver good times you
She's a girl, and you're a
Dm/C
C
F/C
to; your con - cen - tra - tion
had. There is a girl
boy. Get it to - geth - er

C
Dm/C
C
slips a - way
right next to you
and make it to - night,
be - cause your ba -
and she's wait -
you ain't gon - na
F/C
C
- by, sweet - heart, sug - ar's so far a -
- ing for some - thing to
need an - y - more ad -
Dm/C
C
way.
do.
vice.
Well,
And
And
there's a rose
Am
G
F
in a fist - ed glove

Am
G
and the ea - gle flies with the dove.
F
Am
To Coda
And if you can't be
G
F
with the one you love, hon - ey, love the one you're with,
F/C
C
Dm/C
love the one you're with.

1
C
F/C
C
Love the one_ you're with,
love the one_ you're with.
Dm/C
C
2 C
Don't_ be an -
Bb/C F/C Bb/C F/C Bb/C F/C C
dit dit dit dit dit dit dit dit;
Bb/C F/C Bb/C F/C Bb/C
dit dit dit dit dit
F/C C
dit dit dit;
Bb/C F/C Bb/C F/C Bb/C F/C C
dit dit dit dit dit dit dit dit;

Am
dit dit dit dit dit dit;
G
F
1,2
3
F/C
C
Don't _ know why _ you don't. you don't. Don't _
Dm/C
C
F/C
_ know why _ you don't, you don't. Don't _ know why _ you

C
Dm/C
C
N.C.
D.S. al Coda
don't, you don't. Don't know why you don't. Turn your heart -
CODA
G
F
N.C.
with the one you love, love,
C
C7/E
love, love, love, love, love,
F
1,2, etc., (repeat ad lib.)
F/G
last time
F
F/G
C
love the one. Love love the one you're with.

LUCY IN THE SKY WITH DIAMONDS

Words and Music by JOHN LENNON
and PAUL McCARTNEY

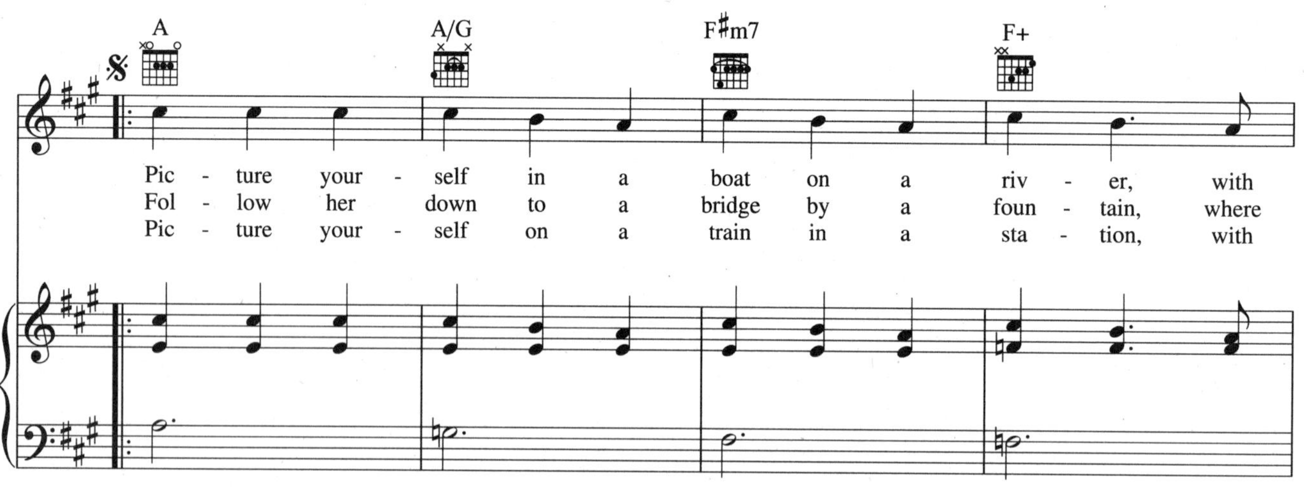

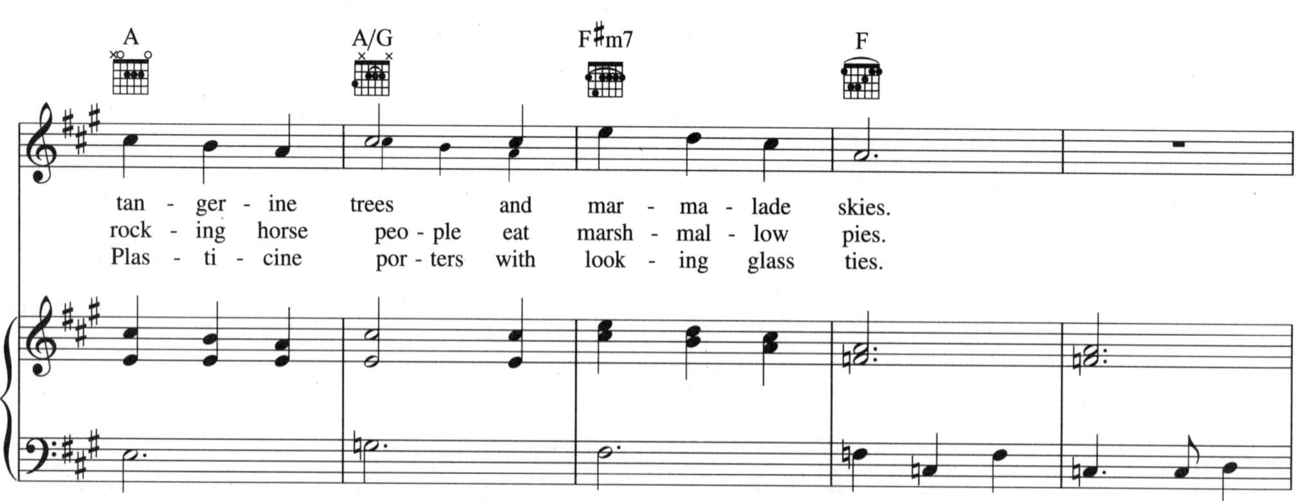

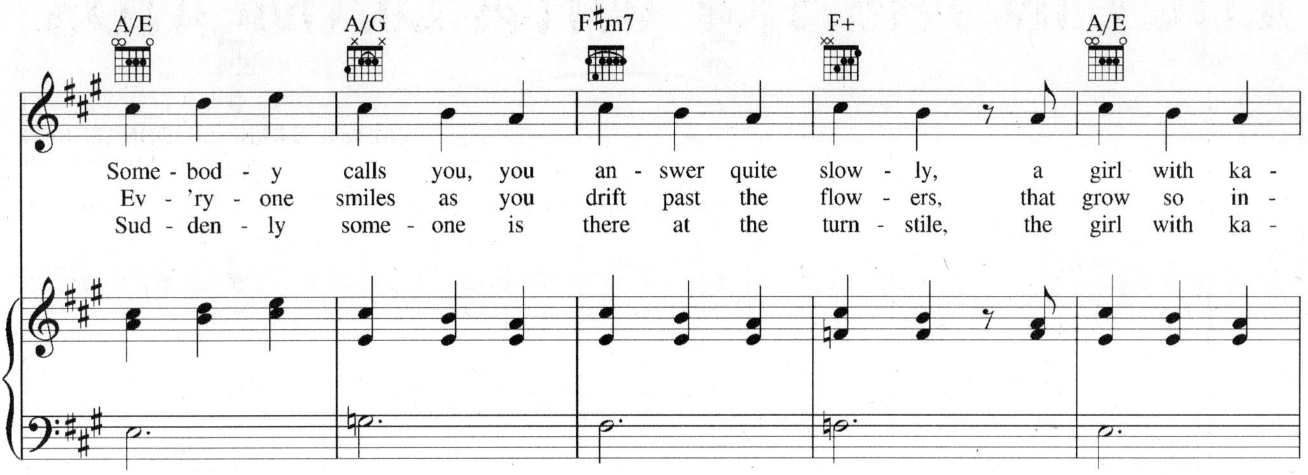
A/E
A/G
F♯m7
F+
A/E
Some - bod - y calls you, you an - swer quite slow - ly, a girl with ka -
Ev - 'ry - one smiles as you drift past the flow - ers, that grow so in -
Sud - den - ly some - one is there at the turn - stile, the girl with ka -

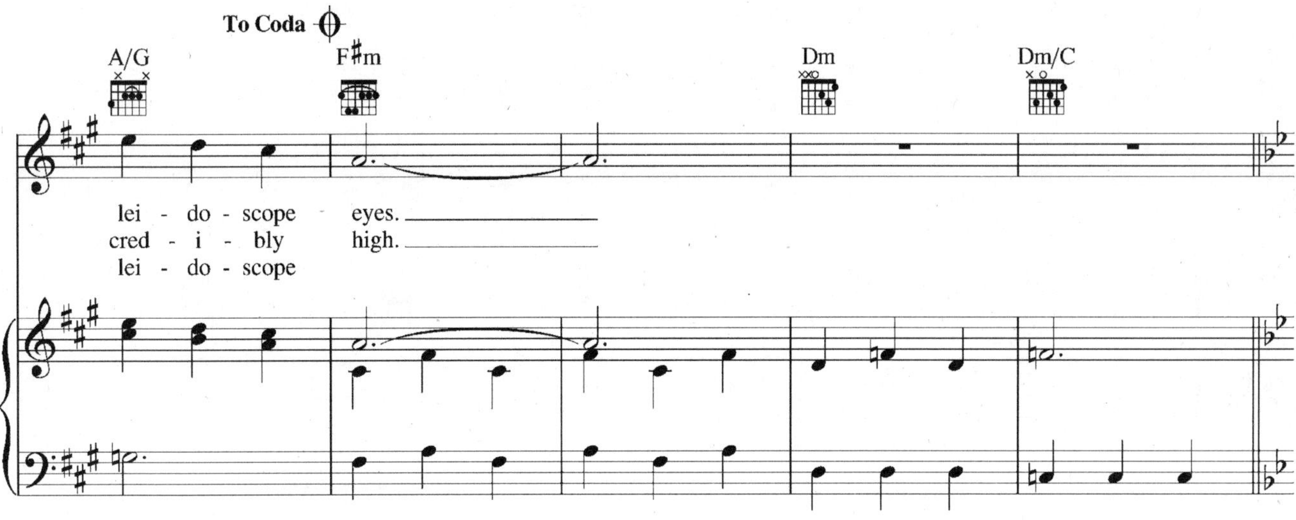
To Coda
A/G
F♯m
Dm
Dm/C
lei - do - scope eyes.
cred - i - bly high.
lei - do - scope

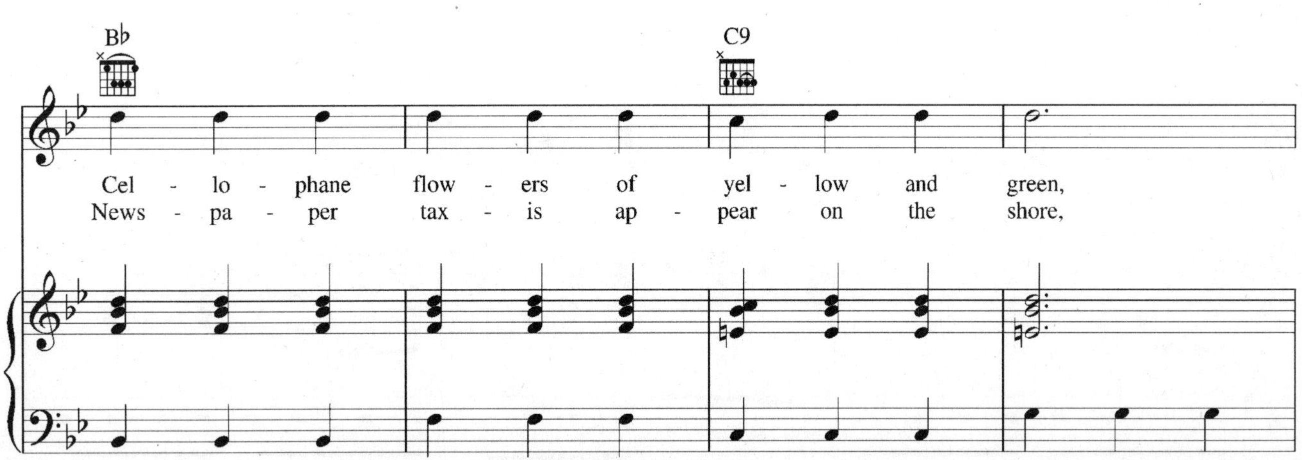
B♭
C9
Cel - lo - phane flow - ers of yel - low and green,
News - pa - per tax - is ap - pear on the shore,

F6 B♭ C7

tow - er - ing o - ver your head. Look for the
wait - ing to take you a - way. Climb in the

G D7 Em (𝅗𝅥. = 𝅗𝅥) D

girl with the sun in her eyes, and she's gone.
back with your head in the clouds, and you're gone.

G C D7 G C

Lu - cy in the sky with dia - monds, Lu - cy in the sky with

D7 G C D7

dia - monds, Lu - cy in the sky with dia - monds,

1
D
2
D
D.S. al Coda
CODA
F#m
Ah
Ah
eyes.
D
G
C
D7
Lu - cy in the sky with dia - monds,
G
C
D7
G
C
Lu - cy in the sky with dia - monds,
Lu - cy in the sky with
D7
D
A
Repeat and Fade
dia - monds,
Ah.

MAD WORLD

Words and Music by
ROLAND ORZABAL

E♭
B♭
Fm
go - ing no - where, go - ing no - where.
sit and lis - ten, sit and lis - ten.
Their tears are fill - ing
Went to school and I was
A♭
4fr
E♭
B♭
up their glass - es, no ex - pres - sion, no ex - pres - sion.
ve - ry ner - vous, no - one knew me, no - one knew me.
Fm
A♭
4fr
E♭
Hide my head, I wan - na drown my sor - row, no to - mor - row,
Hel - lo teach - er, tell me what's my les - son, look right through me,
B♭
Fm
B♭
no to - mor - row.
look right through me.
And I find it kin - da fun - ny, I find it kin - da

Fm
B♭
Fm
sad that dreams in which I'm dy - ing are the best I've ev - er had. I find it hard to
B♭
Fm
B♭
tell you, I find it hard to take when peo - ple run in cir - cles it's a ve - ry, ve - ry
Fm
B♭
Fm
B♭
mad world.
Mad world.
Fm
B♭
Fm
B♭
En - larg - en your world.
Mad world.

MANDOLIN RAIN

Words and Music by B.R. HORNSBY
and JOHN HORNSBY

G Am G/B D Am G/B

song came and went like the times that we spent_ hid - ing out__
cool eve - ning dance, lis - t'nin' to the blue grass band,_ takes the chill__
boat's steam - ing in. Oh, I watch the side wheel spin__ and I think_

C(add2) D Cmaj9/E G D

from_ the rain__ un - der the car - ni - val tent.__ I
from_ the air__ un - til they play the last song.__
a - bout_ her when__ I hear that whis - tle blow.__

G Am G/B D Am G/B

laughed and__ she'd smile._ It would last for__ a while._ You don't
I'll do__ my time,_ oh,__ keep - ing you off my mind, but there's
I can't change my mind._ Oh,__ I knew all the time__ that she'd

C(add2)
D
Cmaj9/E
G
D
know what you got till you lose it all a - gain.
mo - ments that I find I'm not feel - ing so strong.
go but that's a choice. I made long a - go.
Lis - ten to the
Am7
G
Em7
D
G
man - do - lin rain. Lis - ten to the mu - sic on the lake. Oh, lis - ten to my
Am7
G
D/E
Csus2
3fr
G
D
heart break ev - 'ry time she runs a - way. Oh, lis - ten to the
Am7
G
Em7
D
G
ban - jo wind, a sad song drift - ing low. Lis - ten to the

To Coda
1
2
Am7
G
G/F♯
Csus2
3fr
D
F
C/E
G(add2)/B
Cmaj7/E
C
Gsus2/B
D/F♯
tears roll down my face as she turns to go. A
turns to go. Run-ning down by the lake-shore, she did
love the sound of a sum-mer storm. It played on the lake like a man-do-lin. Now it's
wash-ing her a-way once a-gain. Whoa, a-gain.

Am7
G
Em7
D
G
Am7
G
Csus2
3fr
G
D
Am7
G
Em7
D
G
D.S. al Coda
Am7
G
C
G
D
The

CODA
Csus2
G
D
Am7
G
3fr
turns to go, as she turns to go.
Em7
D
G
Am7
G
Lis-ten to the, lis-ten to the man-do-lin rain.
Csus2
G
D
Am7
G
Du du whoa whoa whoa oh.
Em7
D
G
Am7
G

Csus2
G
D
Am7
G
D
Lis - ten to the tears roll down my face as she
C(add9)
G
D
Am7
G
D
turns to go. Lis - ten to the tears roll down my face as she
C(add2)
G
D
Csus2
turns to go.
Repeat and Fade
Optional Ending

MAN IN THE MIRROR

Words and Music by GLEN BALLARD
and SIEDAH GARRETT

D
C(add9)
my fav-orite win-ter coat, _
this wind is blow-in' my mind. _
I see the kids _
G
D/F♯
Em7
D
C(add9)
_ in the street _
with not e-nough to eat.
Who am I
to be blind?_ Pre-tend-ing not to
Am7(add4)
G/B
see their _ needs. _
A sum-mer's dis - re-gard,
a bro-ken bot-tle-top,
C(add9)
G/B
Am7(add4)
and a one _ man's soul. _
They fol - low each oth - er on the wind,

G/B
C(add9)
C/D
ya' know, 'cause they got ___ no - where _ to go, that's why I want you to know.
G
G(add9)/B
C
C/D
G
G(add9)/B
I'm start - ing with the man _ in the mir - ror, I'm ask - ing him to
C
C/D
G
G7/B
C
A/C#
change _ his ways. _ And no ___ mes - sage could have been an - y clear - er: If you
G7sus/D
C/D
wan - na make the world a bet - ter place, _ take a look at your - self and then make a change. ____

G
D/F#
Em7
D
C(add9)
Na na na, na na na, na na, na nah.
D
Em7
D/F#
G
D/F#
Em7
D
I've been a vic - tim of a self - ish kind of love.
C(add9)
G
D/F#
It's time that I re - al - ize, that there are some with no home, not a
Em7
D
C(add9)
nick - el to loan. Could it be real - ly me, pre - tend - ing that they're

Am7(add4)
G/B
not a - lone?
A wil-low deep-ly scarred,
some-bod-y's bro-ken heart,
C(add9)
G(add9)/B
Am7(add4)
and a washed out
dream.
They
fol-low the pat-tern of the wind,
G/B
C(add9)
C/D
ya' see,
'cause they got
no place
to be,
that's why I'm start-ing with me.
G
G(add9)/B
C
C/D
G
G(add9)/B
I'm
start-ing with the
man in
the mir-ror,
I'm
ask-ing him to

C
C/D
G
G7/B
change his ways. And no mes-sage could have
C
A/C♯
G7sus/D
been an-y clear-er: If you wan-na make the world a bet-ter place, take a
1
G/D
2
look at your-self and then make a change. look at your-self and then make that
A♭
4 fr
A♭(add9)/C
8 fr
D♭
D♭/E♭
change! I'm start-ing with the man in the mir-ror, (Oh,

Ab
Ab(add9)/C
Db
Db/Eb
yeah!) I'm ask - ing him to change his ways. (Bet - ter
Ab
Ab7/C
Db
Bb/D
change!) No mes - sage could have been an - y clear-er. If you
Ab7sus/Eb
wan-na make the world a bet-ter place, take a look at your-self and then make the change. You got-ta
'Cause when you close your heart then you close your
get it right, while you got the time. You can't close your, your

Ab
Ab(add9)/C
Db
Db/Eb
4fr
8fr
mind! With that man in the mir-ror, oh
mind! That man, that man, that man, that
Ab
Ab(add9)/C
Db
Db/Eb
yeah! I'm ask - ing him to change his ways. Bet-ter
man, that man, that man, that man. You
Ab
Ab7/C
Db
Bb/D
2fr
change! No mes - sage could have been an - y clear-er.
know, that man. If you
Ab7sus/Eb
wan-na make the world a bet - ter place, take a look at your-self and then make a

Ab
Eb/G
Fm7
Eb
Db(add9)
4 fr
3 fr
Hoo! Hoo! Hoo! Hoo! Hoo!
change. Na na na, na na na, na na, na nah.
Gon-na feel real good now! Yeah yeah! Yeah yeah! Yeah yeah!
Oh yeah! Na na na, na na na, na
Oh no, no no.
na, na nah.
I'm gon - na make a change, it's gon - na feel real

good! Come on! Just lift your - self, you know.
You've got to stop it. Your - self! (Yeah! Make that change!) I've got to make that
change, to - day! Hoo! (Man in the mir-ror) you got to,
D♭(add9)
Play 4 times ad lib.
4 fr
you got to not let your - self, broth-er. Hoo!
Spoken: Make that change.

MIDNIGHT BLUE

Words and Music by LOU GRAMM
and BRUCE TURGON

Fsus G G6 G C Csus C Csus
no, but I know my way.
F5 G Fsus G G6 G C Csus
I used to fol - low,
C Csus F5 G
yeah, that's true. But my fol - low - in' days are o - ver,
Fsus G G6 G C Csus
now I just got - ta fol - low through. And I re - mem - ber when my

C
Csus
3fr
F5
G
fa - ther said, he said "Son, life is sim - ple, it's ei - ther
Fsus
G
G6
G
C
G7/C
C
G7/C
C
F
cher - ry red or mid - night blue." Oh.
G
F
G
C
G7/C
C
G7/C
Mid - night blue,
C
F
G
F/A
F6/A
F/A
G/B
oh whoa.

C
Csus
3fr
You were the rest - less one
and you did not care that
F5
G
Fsus
G6
I was the trou-bled boy
look-in' for a dou-ble dare.
I won't a - pol - o - gize for the
things I've done and said,
but
when I win your heart
I'm gon-na paint it cher-ry red.

C Csus C Csus
I don't wan-na talk a-bout it. What you do to
F5 G Fsus G G6 G C Csus
me, I can't live with-out it. And you might think that it's
C Csus F5 G
much too soon for us to go this far,
Fsus G G6 G C G7/C C G7/C
in-to the mid-night blue.

C
F
G
F
Oh.
G
C
G7/C
C
G7/C
C
F
It's mid-night blue,
oh
G
F/A
F6/A
F/A
G/B
C
whoa.
If things could be dif-f'rent
F/C
that-'d be a shame, 'cause
I'm the one who can feel the sun
3
3

G/C
C
right in the pour - in' rain.
I won't say where and I
F/C
don't know when but
soon there gon - na come a day, ba - by,
G/C
C
G7/C
C
G7/C
C
I'll be back a - gain.
G7/C
C
G7/C
Yeah, I'll be back for you.

C
You see, I'm sav - in' up my love.
C
G7/C
C
G7/C
C
F
Mid - night blue,
oh.
(Vocal ad lib.)
G
C
G7/C
C
G7/C
C
F
Mid - night blue,
oh
whoa.
G
Repeat and Fade

MIDNIGHT TRAIN TO GEORGIA

Words and Music by
JIM WEATHERLY

F Am/E Gm/D B♭/C F Am/E
He said he's go - in' back to find ooh, what's left
Gm/D B♭/C F Am/E Gm/D Dm7/G
of his world, the world he left be - hind not so long
B♭/C F Am
a - go. He's leav - in'
B♭ B♭/C F Am B♭ B♭/C
on that mid-night train to Geor - gia, and he's

F
Am
Dm7
Dm7/G
B♭/C
go - in' back
to a sim - pler place and time.
F
Am
B♭
B♭/C
And I'll be with him
on that mid - night train to
Dm7
Dm7/G
B♭
Geor - gia.
I'd rath - er live in his world
3
3
B♭/C
F
Am/E
Gm/D
B♭/C
than live with - out him in mine.

F
Am/E
Gm/D
B♭/C
F
Am/E
He kept dream-in' that some-day he'd be a star,
Gm/D
B♭/C
F
Am/E
Gm/D
Dm7/G
but he sure found out the hard way that dreams don't
B♭/C
F
Am/E
al-ways come true. So he pawned all his
Gm/D
B♭/C
F
Am/E
Gm/D
B♭/C
hopes and he e-ven sold his old car; bought a

F
Am/E
Gm/D
Dm7/G
B♭/C
one - way tick-et to the life he once knew. Oh, yes he did!
F
Am
B♭
B♭/C
He said he would be leav - in' on that mid-night train to
F
Am
B♭
B♭/C
F
Am
Geor - gia, and he's go - in' back
Dm7
Dm7/G
B♭/C
to a sim - pler place and time.

F
Am
B♭
B♭/C
Dm7
And I'll be with him on that mid-night train to Geor-gia;
Dm7/G
B♭
B♭/C
I'd rath-er live in his world than live with-out him in
3
1
2
F
Am/E
Gm/D
B♭/C
Gm/D
B♭/C
mine. Ooh, he's Got-ta
Repeat and Fade
Optional Ending
F
Am/E
Gm/D
B♭/C
F
go, gon-na board, gon-na board, gon-na board the mid-night train. Got-ta go.

MINUTE BY MINUTE

Words and Music by MICHAEL McDONALD
and LESTER ABRAMS

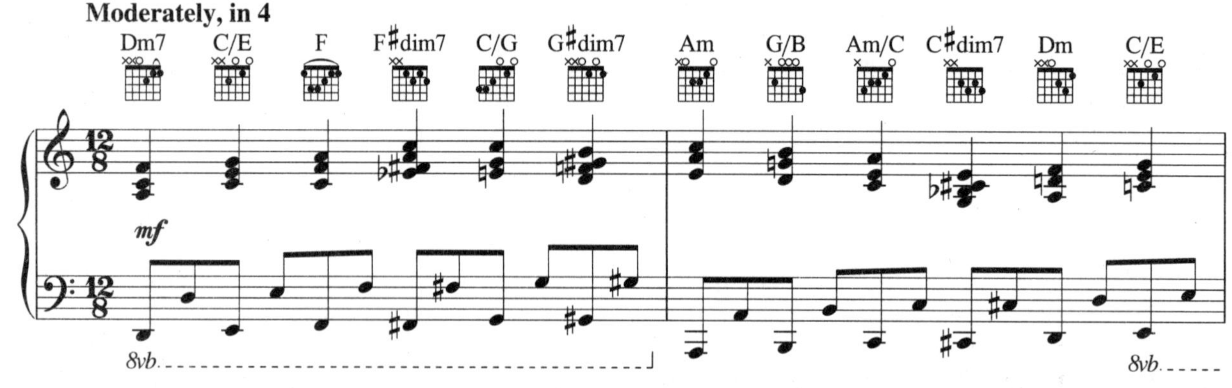

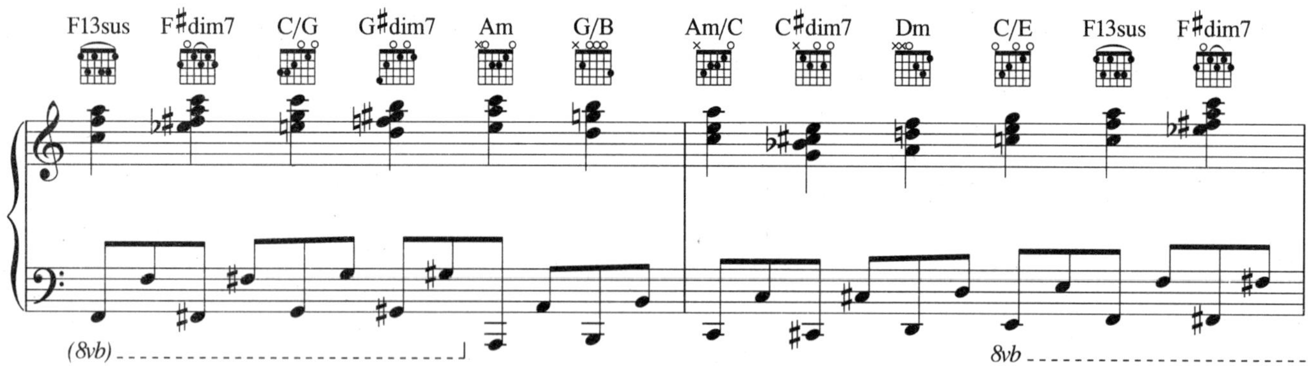

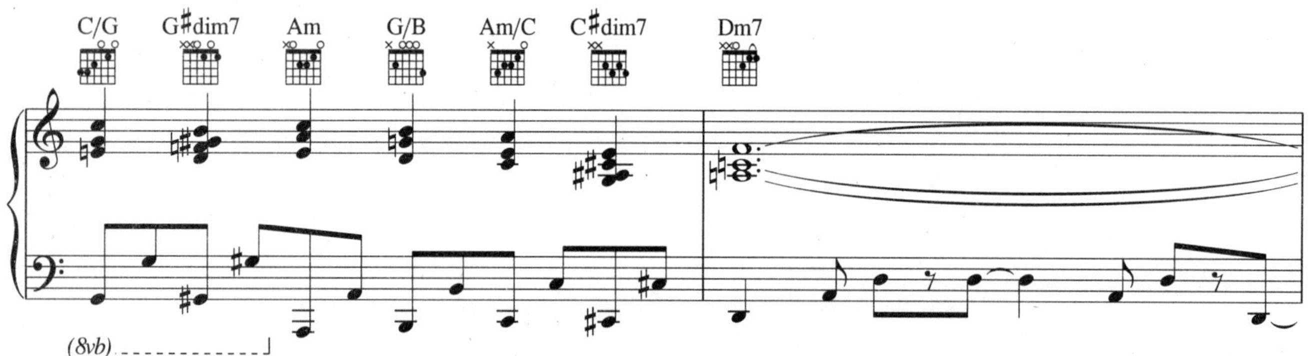

Cmaj7

F/G

Cmaj7
Hey, don't wor - ry; I've been lied to.
You would stay just to watch me, dar - ling,

I've been there man - y times be - fore. Girl, don't you
wilt a - way of lies from you. Can't stop the

F13sus
F13
wor - ry; I know where I stand. I don't need this
hab - it of liv - ing on the run. Take it all for
Am/G
Dm7/G
G♭7
love; I don't need your hand. I know I could
grant - ed, like you're the on - ly one. Liv - ing on my
F13sus
F13
turn, think - ing you'd be gone, that I must be pre -
own, some - how that sounds nice. You think I'm your
Am/G
Dm7/G
G♭7
pared an - y - time to car - ry on, but
fool; well, you may just be right, 'cause

Fmaj9
Dm7/G
(min-ute by min-ute by min-ute by min-ute) I keep hold-ing on.
Cmaj7
Bm11
B♭9
Am7
(I'll be hold - ing on, I'll be hold - ing
Fmaj9
Dm7/G
on.)
(Min-ute by min-ute by min-ute by min-ute) I keep hold-ing on.
Cmaj7
1
F/G

2
Bm11
B♭9
Am7
Dm7
C/E
F
F♯dim7
C/G
G♯dim7
I keep hold - ing on.
8vb
Am
G/B
Am/C
C♯dim7
Dm
C/E
F
F♯dim7
C/G
G♯dim7
Am
G/B
8vb
Am/C
C♯dim7
Dm7
N.C.
Em7
Call my name and
G/D
Cmaj9
Bm7
I'll be gone.
You reach out and I won't be there.

Em7/A
Am7
Em
Am7/D
Just my luck, you'll re - al - ize
you should spend your
G/A
Am7/D
3fr
F♯m7
Fmaj7
D/E
life with some - one.
You could spend your life with some - one.
Cmaj9
Am7/D
(Min-ute by min-ute by min-ute by min-ute) I'll be hold-ing on.
Repeat ad lib. and Fade
Gmaj7
F♯m11
F9
Em7
(Lead vocal ad lib.)

Optional Ending
Am7
G/B
C
C♯dim7
G/D
D♯dim7
Em
D/F♯
Em/G
G♯dim7
Am
G/B
C
C♯dim7
G/D
D♯dim7
Em
D/F♯
Em/G
G♯dim7
Am7
G/B
C
C♯dim7
G/D
D♯dim7
Em
D/F♯
Em/G
G♯dim7
Am7
Am7/D
G

MY LOVE

Words and Music by
PAUL and LINDA McCARTNEY

Gm7
3 fr.
B♭
To Coda
1.
F
wo - wo,
my love does it good.
2.
F
Gm7
3fr.
C7
F
Aaug
Wo - wo I love, oh wo my love, on - ly
mf
B♭
C7
F
Aaug
Gm7
3fr.
C7
my love holds the oth - er key to me. Oh wo my love, oh
F
Aaug
B♭
C7
F
Dm/B
my love, on - ly my love does it good to me. Wo - wo

F
Gm7
3 fr.
B♭
wo - wo, wo - wo wo - wo, my love does it good.
D.%. al Coda
Coda
C7
Wo - wo I love, oh wo
mf
Aaug
B♭6
my love, on - ly my love does it good to
Colla Voce
C13
2 fr.
me. Wo wo wo wo wo wo wo.
a tempo

A MOMENT LIKE THIS

Words and Music by JOHN REID
and JORGEN KJELL ELOFSSON

Original key: C♯ minor. This edition has been transposed up one half-step to be more playable.

E♭(add2)
B♭(add2)
6fr
3fr
tell me that you don't think I'm cra - zy when I
Gm7
C
Dsus
tell you love has come here and now. A mo - ment like this.
G
D/F♯
C
D
Some peo - ple wait a life - time for a mo - ment like this.
G
D/F♯
C
D
Some peo - ple search for - ev - er for that one spe - cial kiss.

Em
E♭+
G
G/B
C(add2)
Oh, I can't be - lieve it's hap - pen - ing to me. Some
Em7
Am7
D(add2)
peo - ple wait a life - time for a mo - ment like this.
G(add2)
Dm7
B♭
Gm7
C
Ev - 'ry - thing chang - es, but beau - ty re - mains
Dm7
B♭
Gm7
C
some - thing so ten - der I can't ex - plain.

Dm7
B♭
F/A
Gm7
Well, I may be dream - ing, but still lie a - wake.
E♭
3fr
B♭(add2)
3fr
Can't we make this dream last for - ev - er? And I'll
Gm7
C
Dsus
cher - ish all the love we share. A mo - ment like this.
G
D/F♯
C
D
Some peo - ple wait a life - time for a mo - ment like this.

G
D/F♯
C
D
Some peo - ple search for - ev - er for that one spe - cial kiss.
Em
E♭+
G
G/B
C(add2)
Oh, I can't be - lieve it's hap - pen - ing to me. Some
Em7
Am7
D
peo - ple wait a life - time for a mo - ment like this.
G(add2)
G/F
Em7
E♭maj7
3fr
Could this be the great - est love of

G
G/F
Em7
E♭maj7
3fr
all?
I wan-na know that you will catch me when I fall,
Em7
E♭+
G
G/B
C(add2)
3
so let me tell you this:
some
Em7
Am7
D(add2)
peo-ple wait a life-time for a mo-ment like this.
A
E/G♯
D
E
Some peo-ple wait a life-time for a mo-ment like this.

A
E/G♯
D
E
Some peo - ple search for - ev - er for that one spe - cial kiss.
F♯m
F+
A
A/C♯
D
Oh, I can't be - lieve it's hap - pen - ing to me. Some
F♯m7
Bm
F♯m/E
E
A/E
peo - ple wait a life - time for a mo - ment like this.
A
E/G♯
D(add2)
E
Esus
A
E/G♯
Choir: (Mo - ment like this.)
Lead vocal ad lib.

D
Esus
E
F♯m
F+
Lead vocal:
(Mo - ment like.) Oh, I can't be - lieve it's hap -
A
A/C♯
D
F♯m7
Bm7
- pen - ing to me. Some peo - ple wait a life - time for a
E
A5
5fr
E/G♯
mo - ment like this,
D(add2)
E
A(add2)
oh, like this.
rit.

MORE THAN WORDS

Words and Music by NUNO BETTENCOURT
and GARY CHERONE

* *Recorded a half step lower.*

Am7
C
D
Dsus
Em
want you not to say, but if you on - ly knew
have to do is close your eyes and just reach out your hands
G/B
Am7
D7
G
how eas - y it would be to show
and touch me. Hold me close don't ev -
Bm7/F#
Em
G/B
Am7
me how you feel. More than words is
- er let me go. More than words is
D7
G7
G7/B
C
Cm
3fr
all you have to do to make it real.
all I ev - er need - ed you to show.
Then you would -

G
Em
G/B
Em11
5fr
G/B
-n't have to say that you love me 'cause
Am7
D7
G
G/B
G
G/B
I'd al - read - y know. What would you do
D/F♯
Em
G/B
Bm7
C
if my heart was torn in two? More than words
Am
D7
G
to show you feel that your love for me is real.

G/B
G
G/B
D/F#
Em
What would you say if I took
G/B
Bm7
C
Am7
those words a - way? Then you could - n't make things new
To Coda
D7
G
G/B
C
just by say - in' "I love you."
Am7
C
D5
5fr
D7
G
La di da da di da di dai dai da. More than words.

G/B
C(add2)
Am7
La di da da di da.
D7
D.S. al Coda
CODA
D7
G
G/B
C
in' "I love you."
Am7
C
D5
5fr
D7
G
La di da da di da di dai dai da.
More than words.
C(add2)
Am7
1, 2
C
La di da da di da di dai dai da.

D5
D7
G
3
C
D5
D
More than words.
More than words,
La da dat da da da.
G
D/F♯
Fmaj13
ooh,
rit.
E(add4)
Am7
D
ooh.
(Guitar cadenza, freely)
More than
Slowly
G
Csus2
G/B
Gm/B♭
Am7
G
words.

MY FAVOURITE GAME

Words by NINA PERSSON
Music by PETER SVENSSON

Cm
fr3
B♭
F
You rip me up, you spread me all a-round in the dust of the
A♭
fr4
B♭
Cm
fr3
B♭
F
deed of time.
A♭
fr4
B♭
Cm
fr3
B♭
And this is not a case of lust, you see,
F
A♭
fr4
B♭
Cm
fr3
it's not a mat-ter of you ver-sus me, it's fine the way you want me

B♭
F
A♭
B♭
on your own, but in the end it's al-ways me a-lone. And I'm
Cm
Fm/C
B♭/C
Gm7
Cm
los-ing my fav-'rite game, you're los-ing your
Fm/C
B♭/C
Gm7
To Coda
Cm
mind a-gain. I'm los-ing my ba-
Fm/A♭
F
B♭sus2
G7
by, los-ing my fav-'rite game.

D.%. al Coda
Cm
B♭
F
A♭
B♭
Coda
Cm
Fm/A♭
B♭
Gm7/C
los - ing my fav - 'rite game, you're
Cm
Fm/A♭
B♭
Gm7
Cm
los - ing your mind a - gain, I'm los - ing my ba -
Fm/A♭
F
B♭sus2
G7
- by, los - ing my fav - 'rite game.

Cm
B♭
F
A♭
B♭
I'm
Cmadd9
D♭maj9
Cmadd9
D♭maj9
Cmadd9
los - ing my fav - 'rite game, you're los - ing your
D♭maj9
Cmadd9
D♭maj9
Cmadd9
mind a - gain, I've tried but you're
D♭maj9
Cmadd9
D♭maj9
Cm
still the same, I'm los - ing my ba -

Verse 2:
I only know what I've been working for
Another you so I could love you more
I really thought that I could take you there
But my experiment is not getting us anywhere

I had a vision I could turn you right
A stupid mission and a lethal fight
I should have seen it when my hope was new
My heart is black and my body is blue.

And I'm losing *etc.*

NIGHT MOVES

Words and Music by
BOB SEGER

C
F
G
and points all her own, sit-tin' way up high,
F
C
F
way up firm and high.
G
F
Out past the corn - fields, where the woods got heav - y,
C
F
G
out in the back seat of my Six - ty Chev - y, work-in' on mys-t'ries with - out

F
C
D
an - y clues,
work - in' on our
Em
D
C
D
Em
D
night moves,
try'n' to make some front page, drive - in news.
C
D
Em
D
C
Work - in' on our night moves
G
F
C
in the sum - mer - time.
Mm,

F
G
F
in the sweet _ sum - mer - time. _______
C
F
G
We were-n't in love. Oh,
F
C
F
no, far from it. We were-n't search - in for some pie - in - the - sky sum - mit.
G
F
C
We were just _ young and _ rest - less and bored, _ liv-ing by the sword. _

F
G
F
And we'd steal a - way ev-'ry chance we could,
C
F
to the back room, to the al - ley, or the trust - y woods.
G
F
I used her, she used me, but nei-ther one cared.
C
D
Em
D
We were get-tin' our share, work - in' on our night moves,

C
D
Em
D
C
D
try'n' to lose the awk-ward, teen-age blues, work-in' on our
Em
D
C
G
night moves. It was sum-mer-time.
F
C
F
Mm,
G
F
C
sweet sum-mer-time, sum-mer-time.

D
Em
D
G
G7
3fr
Cmaj7
G
And oh,
the won - der.
Cmaj7
We felt the light - ning.
Yeah,
F
D
and we wait - ed on the thun - der,
wait - ed on the thun - der.

G
Freely
G
Cmaj7
I a-woke last night to the sound of thun-der.
How far off, I
G
Cmaj7
sat and won-dered.
Start ed hum-ming a song from nine-teen six-ty-two.
Em
C
Em
Ain't it fun-ny how the night moves?
When you just don't seem to have as much to lose.

C Em C Cmaj7 G

Strange how the night moves, __ with au - tumn clos - ing in. __

Tempo I

G F C F G

G F C 1-7 F

Night moves. Night moves.

Lead vocal ad lib.

8 Em Bm

Vocal ad lib. continues

Am7 C G

NOTHING'S GONNA STOP US NOW

Words and Music by DIANE WARREN
and ALBERT HAMMOND

Dm7
Bb
C
__ so much to give you this love__ in my heart that I'm feel - ing for you._
__ you through the bad times, what-ev - er it takes is what I'm__ gon-na do.__
F
Dm7
Let them say we're cra - zy, I don't care a-bout that.
Let them say we're cra - zy, what _ do _ they know.
Bb
C
Put your hand in my hand, ba - by, don't ev - er look back.
Put your arms a - round me, ba - by, don't ev - er let go.
F
Dm7
Let the world a - round us just fall a - part.

B♭
E♭
3 fr
C
Ba - by we can make it if we're heart to heart.
And we can build
F
Dm7
B♭
this dream to - geth - er, stand - ing strong for - ev - er, noth - ing's gon - na stop us now.
mf
C
F
Dm7
And if this world runs out of lov - ers we'll still have each oth - er, noth -
B♭
1 C
2 C
To Coda
- ing's gon - na stop us, noth - ing's gon - na stop us. I'm - ing's gon - na stop us.

F
C/F
F
B♭
Oh, all that I need _ is you, ____
Gm7
3fr
C
F
F/C
F
you're all I ev - er need. ____ All that I want _ to do _
B♭
Gm7
3fr
C7
____ is hold you for - ev - er, for - ev - er and ev - er. ____
C
D.S. al Coda
__ And we can build _
CODA
C
- ing's gon - na stop _ us.
And we can build _

F
Dm7
this dream to - geth - er, stand - ing strong for - ev - er, noth -
B♭
C
- ing's gon - na stop us now. And if this world
F
Dm7
runs out of lov - ers, we'll still have each oth - er, noth -
B♭
C
Repeat ad lib. and Fade
- ing's gon - na stop us, noth - ing's gon - na stop us.
And we can build.

OH SHERRIE

Words and Music by STEVE PERRY, RANDY GOODRUM,
BILL CUOMO and CRAIG KRAMPF

B♭/D
C/D
Dm
gone
af - ter all your words of steel.
B♭
F/C
C
Oh, I must-'ve been a dream - er
(Must-'ve been a dream - er,
no,
And I must-'ve been some - one else.
Some - one else.)
And we should-'ve been o - ver.
(O - ver by now.)

F
C/F
F
Ab/F
3fr
Eb/F
Oh Sher - rie, our love holds on,
(Hold - in' on.)
Gm/F
F
C/F
F
holds on. Oh Sher - rie, our love
(Hold - in' on.)
Ab/F
3fr
Eb/F
Gm/C
3fr
F
holds on, holds on. But I wan - na let
Dm
Bb/D
C/D
Dm
go. You'll go on hurt - in' me.

Bb/D
C/D
You'd be bet-ter off a - lone_ if I'm not who_ you
Dm
Dm/C
Bb
thought_ I'd be.
But you know that there's a
F/C
C
Bb
fe - ver,
(Know that there's a fe - ver, no,
oh, that you'll nev - er find
F/C
C
Bb
F/C
no - where else.
no - where else.)
(No - where else.
Can't you feel it burn - ing on and on?
On and on.)

F
C/F
F
Ab/F
3fr
Eb/F
Oh, Sher - rie, our love holds on,
(Hold - in' on.)
Gm/F
F
C/F
F
holds on. Oh Sher - rie, our love
(Hold - in' on.)
Ab/F
3fr
Eb/F
Gm/F
F
F
holds on, holds on.
C/F
F
Bbsus2
Gm7
3fr
Csus4
Oh, Sher - rie.

F
C/F
F
Ab/F
3fr
Eb/F
Gm/F
F
Ab/F
3fr
Eb/F
Gm/F
F
Dm
Bb/D
C/D
But I should-'ve been gone
long a - go,
Dm
far a - way.
And you should-'ve been gone.

B♭/D
C/D
Dm
F
Now I know just why you stay.
Oh Sher - rie,
(Hold - in' on.)
C/F
F
A♭/F
E♭/F
Gm/F
F
our love holds on, holds on.
F
C/F
F
A♭/F
E♭/F
Oh Sher - rie, our love holds on,
(Hold - in' on.)
1
Gm/F
F
holds on.
2
Gm/F
F
holds on.

C/F
F
A♭/F
3fr
E♭/F
Gm/F
F
Hold on.
Oh Sher-rie.
A♭/F
3fr
E♭/F
Gm/F
F
F
C/F
F
B♭/F
B♭/A
Gm7
3fr
C
F
C/F
F
A♭/F
3fr
E♭/F
Gm/F
F
rit.

ONE MORE NIGHT

Words and Music by
PHIL COLLINS

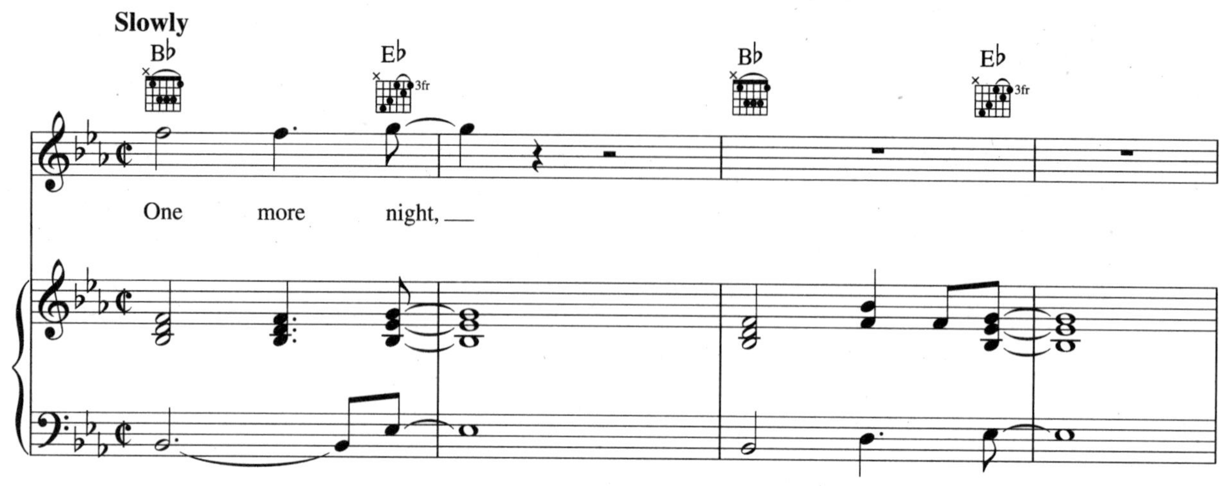

Eb
Ab
Eb(add9)/G
let you know, let you know how I feel,
wast - ing time, just star - ing at the phone,
feel the same, and I know it's on - ly right.
Fm
Ab
Eb(add9)/G
and if I stum - ble, if I fall,
and I was won - d'ring should I call
But if you'll change your mind,
Fm
Eb
Ab
just help me back, so I can
you? Then I thought may - be you're
you know that I'll be here, and may - be we

E♭(add9)/G
Fm
B♭
E♭
3fr
make you see.
not a - lone.
both can learn.
Please, give me one more night,
Please, give me one more night,
Give me just one more night,
give me one more night,
give me just one more night,
give me just one more night,
one more night
one more night
one more night
'cause I can't wait for - ev - er.
'cause I can't wait for - ev - er.
'cause I can't wait for - ev - er.
Give me just
Please, give me
Give me just

E♭
3fr
B♭
E♭
3fr
one more night, oh, just one more night,
one more night, oh, just one more night,
one more night, give me just one more night,

B♭
E♭
3fr
oh, one more night 'cause I can't
oh, one more night 'cause I can't
oh, one more night 'cause I can't

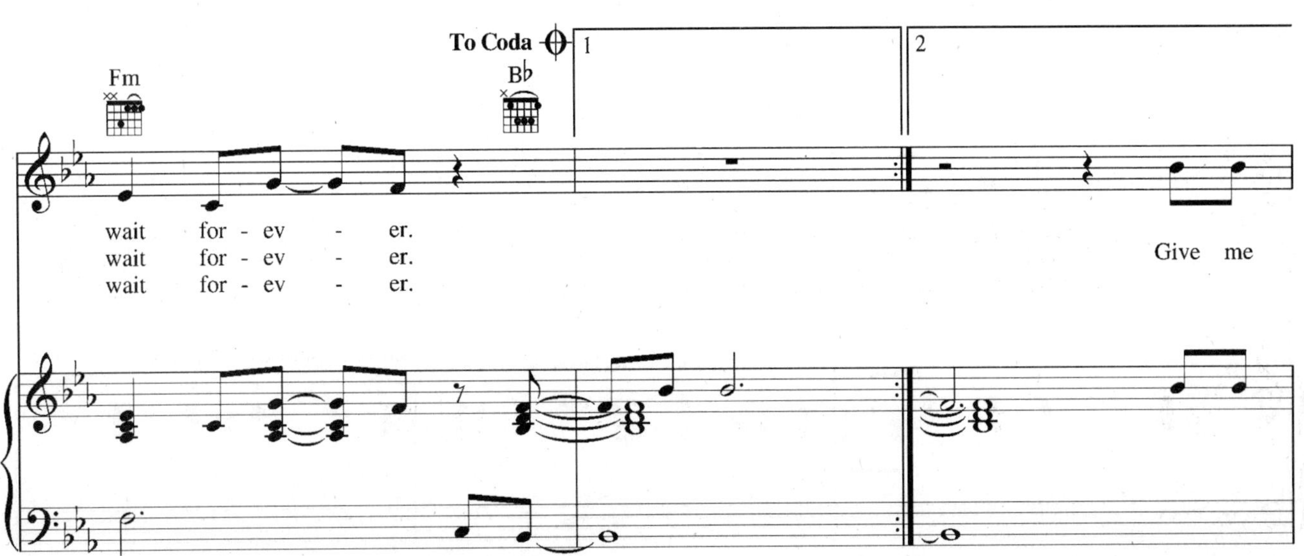
To Coda
1
2
Fm
B♭
wait for - ev - er.
wait for - ev - er.
wait for - ev - er.
Give me

E♭
3fr
B♭
E♭
3fr
one more night, give me just one more night,
B♭
E♭
3fr
just one more night 'cause I
Fm
B♭
Cm7
3fr
E♭/D♭
can't wait for-ev - er.
Like a riv -
Cm7
3fr
D♭/E♭
- er to the sea,
I will al - ways be with

Cm7
E♭/D♭
Cm7
D♭/E♭
3fr
you, and if you sail a - way, I will fol -
B♭/D
E♭
- low you. Give me one more night,
B♭
E♭
B♭
E♭
give me just one more night, oh, one more night
Fm
B♭
D.S. al Coda
'cause I can't wait for - ev - er.

CODA
E♭
3fr
Ooh
ooh
ooh.
B♭
E♭
3fr
Ooh
ooh
ooh.
B♭
E♭
3fr
Ooh
ooh
ooh.
Fm
B♭
Repeat and Fade
Ooh
ooh
ooh.
Optional Ending
Fm
B♭
Ooh
ooh
ooh.

OOPS!...I DID IT AGAIN

Words and Music by MARTIN SANDBERG
and RAMI YACOUB

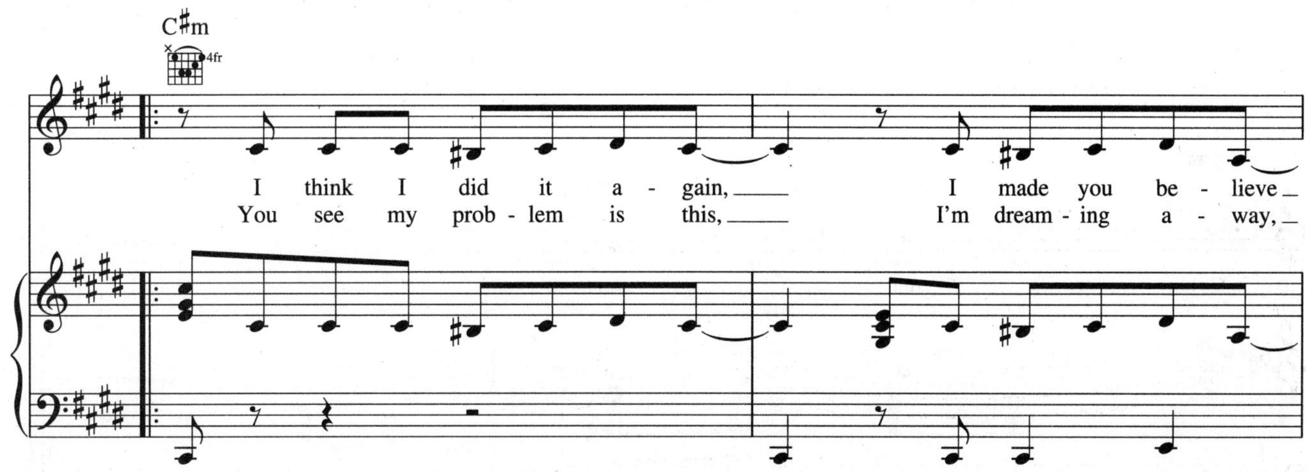

A
G#sus
G#
4fr
we're more than just friends. Oh, ba - by,
wish - ing that he - roes, they tru - ly ex - ist.
C#m
G#/B#
6fr
it might seem like a crush, but it does - n't mean
I cry watch - ing the days, can't you see I'm a fool
that I'm se - ri - ous. 'Cause to
in so man - y ways? But to
F#m7
lose all my sens - es, that is

A
B5
N.C.
just so typ - i - cal-ly me.
Oh, ba - by, ba - by.
C♯m
G♯
C♯m
B
4fr
Oops!... I did it a - gain,
I played with your heart,
E
B
E
B
G♯/B♯
6fr
got lost in the game.
Oh, ba - by, ba - by.
C♯m
G♯
C♯m
B
4fr
Oops!... You think I'm in love,
that I'm sent from a - bove.

E
1
G♯
4fr
I'm not that in - no - cent.
2
G♯
4fr
C♯m
4fr
not that in - no - cent.
Yeah,
yeah, yeah, yeah, yeah, yeah.
Yeah,
Amaj7
yeah, yeah, yeah, yeah, yeah.
(Spoken:) "All Aboard!" "Britney,
rit.
a tempo

B
Amaj7
before you go, there's something I want you to have."
"Oh, it's beautiful! But wait a minute,
Bsus
G♯
4fr
Amaj7
isn't this...?"
"Yeah, yes, it is."
"But I thought the old lady dropped it into the ocean at the end."
B
G♯+
4fr
G♯
4fr
C♯m
4fr
"Well, baby, I went down and got it for you."
"Oh, you shouldn't have."
C♯m
4fr
G♯
4fr
N.C.
C♯m
4fr
B
Oops!... I
did it a - gain to your heart,

E
B
E
B
G♯/B♯
6fr
got lost in this game, oh, ba - by.
C♯m
4fr
G♯
4fr
C♯m
4fr
B
Oops!... You think that I'm sent from a - bove
E
Amaj7
B
I'm not that in - no - cent.
C♯m
4fr
G♯
4fr
C♯m
4fr
B
Oops!... I did it a - gain, I played with your heart,

E/G#
B
E
B
G#/B#
6fr
got lost in the game.
Oh, ba - by, ba - by.

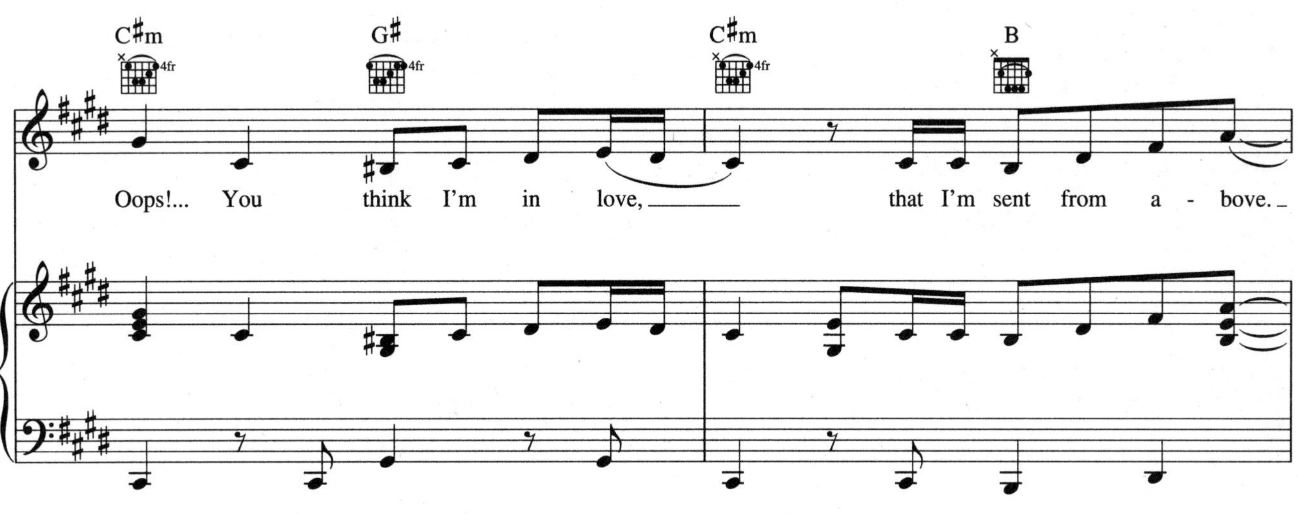
C#m
4fr
G#
4fr
C#m
4fr
B
Oops!... You think I'm in love,
that I'm sent from a - bove.

E
1
G#sus
4fr
G#
4fr
2
G#
4fr
N.C.
I'm not that in - no - cent.
not that in - no - cent.

OPERATOR
(That's Not The Way It Feels)

Words and Music by
JIM CROCE

D/F#
Em
match - book is old and fad - ed.
that you just gave me.
want - ed to talk to.
D
G
She's liv - ing in L. A.
There's some - thing in my eyes;
Thank you for your time
Bm
C
Bm7
2 fr
Am7
G
C
Bm
Am
G
with my best old ex - friend, Ray,
you know it hap - pens ev - 'ry time
'cause you've been so much more than kind,
Am7
D/F#
a guy she said she knew well and some - times hat -
I think a - bout the love that I thought would save me.
and you can keep the dime.

Em
D
G
C/G
- ed.
Is - n't that the way
they say it goes?
But let's for - get all that, and
G
C
D
give me the num - ber, if you can find it, so I can call just to
Am
Em
Bm
Bm/D
Am7
D7
tell them I'm fine and to show
I've o - ver - come the blow,

C G Am7
I've learned to take it well. I on - ly wish my words could just con-vince my - self
C D C
that it just was-n't real, but that's not the way it feels.
G Bm Am
1, 2
C Bm Am G D7/F♯
3
C Bm Am G D7/F♯ G

OTHER SIDE OF THE WORLD

Words and Music by KT TUNSTALL
and TERENFE HOLMSTROM

G
D
Dsus2
Dsus4
Dsus2
the wa - ter.
A
Em7
A
2. All the mus-cles tight - en in her face, bu-ries her soul
(3.) on comes the pa-nic light, hold-ing on with fin-gers and feel-ings a - like.
Em7
A
in one em - brace. They're one and the same,
But the time has come to move
G
1° only
D
just like wa - ter.
a - long.
And the fire fades a-way

Bm7
G
Bm/F♯
and most of ev - 'ry day
is full of tired ex - cu - ses,
Em
A
D
Bm7
but it's too hard to say.
I wish it were sim - ple
but we give up ea - si - ly.
G
Bm/F♯
Em
A
Bm
Bm/A
You're close e - nough to see that
you're
the oth - er
1.
G
A
D
Dsus2
Dsus4
Dsus2
side of the world to me.
3. And

2.
G
A
Em7
Gmaj7
side of the world. Can you help me? Can you let me go?
D
Dsus2
Dsus4
Dsus2
Em7
And can you still love
Bm
A
A/G
F#m
A/E
me when you can't see me a - ny - more?
D
Bm7
G
Bm/F#
And the fire fades a - way, most of ev - 'ry day is full of tired ex - cu -

Em A D Bm7
ses, but it's too hard to say. I wish it were sim - ple but we give up ea - si - ly.
G Bm/F# Em A Bm Bm/A
You're close e - nough to see that you're the oth - er
G A Bm Bm/A G A
side of the world, oh, the oth - er side of the world.
Bm Bm/A G A D
You're the oth - er side of the world to me.

PEOPLE AIN'T NO GOOD

Words and Music by
NICK CAVE

G
G/A
G7/B
C
just ain't no good.
We were mar - ried un - der cher - ry trees;
on the sheets;
G/B
F
C
G
un - der blos - soms we made our vows.
wok - en by the morn - ing bird.
F
C
G/B
F/A
All the blos - soms come sail - ing down
through the
We'd buy the Sun - day news - pa - pers
and nev - er
1.
G
G/A
G/B
streets and through the play - grounds.
The sun would stream
read a sin - gle word.

2.
G/B
C
G/B
F/A
F/G
C
People, they ain't no good. People, they ain't
G/B
F/A
F/G
C
G/B
To Coda
F/A
no good. People, they ain't no good.
G
C
G/B
Seasons came and seasons went.
fist.
F
C
G
The winter stripped the blossoms bare.
The windows rattling in the gales,

F
C
G/B
A dif - f'rent tree now lines the streets,
to which she drew the cur - tains
F/A
G
G/A
shak - ing its fists in the air.
made out of her wed - ding veils.
1.
2.
D.S. al Coda
The win - ter slammed us like a
Peo - ple, they
Coda
F/A
good at all.
To our

C
F
C
love send a doz - en white lil - ies.
love send back all the let - ters.
To our love send a
To our love, a val - en -
F
C
cof - fin of wood.
tine of blood.
To our love let all the pink - eyed
To our love let all the jilt - ed
F
Dm
1.
G
pi - geons coo
lov - ers cry
that peo - ple, they just ain't no good.
2.
G
To our good.
It ain't that in their

C
G/B
F
hearts they're bad.
hearts they're bad.
They can com - fort you; some
They'd stick by you
C
G
F
e - ven try.
if they could.
They nurse you when you're
Ah, but that's just
C
G/B
F/A
ill of health.
bull, ba - by.
They bur - y you when you
Peo - ple just ain't no
G
G/A
1.
G/B
go and die.
good.
It ain't that in their

2.
G7/B
C
G/B
F/A
Peo - ple, they ain't no good.
F/G
C
G/B
F/A
F/G
Peo - ple, they ain't no good. Peo - ple, they
C
G/B
1.
F/A
G
ain't no good at all.
2.
F/A
G
Peo - ple, they good at all.
rit.

PLEASE FORGIVE ME

Words and Music by
DAVID GRAY

Cadd9
Em7
Am7add11
Feels like light - ning run - ning through my veins
G6
F
C
ev - 'ry - time I look at you,
Gsus4
F
ev - 'ry - time I look at
1-3.
Cadd9
Em7
Am7add11
G6
you.

Verse 2:
Help me out here, all my words are falling short
And there's so much I want to say
Want to tell you just how good it feels
When you look at me that way
Ah, when you look at me that way.

Verse 3:
Throw a stone and watch the ripples flow
Moving out across the bay
Like a stone, I fall into your eyes
Deep into that mystery
Ah, deep into some mystery.

Verse 4:
I got half a mind to scream out loud
I got half a mind to die
So I won't ever have to lose you, girl
Won't ever have to say goodbye
I won't ever have to lie
Won't ever have to say goodbye.

REAL LOVE

Words and Music by MARK C. ROONEY,
MARK MORALES and KIRK ROBINSON

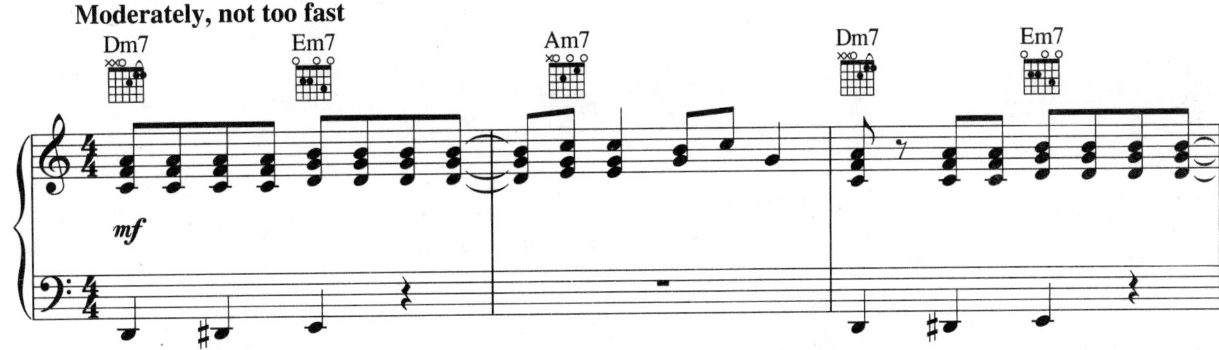

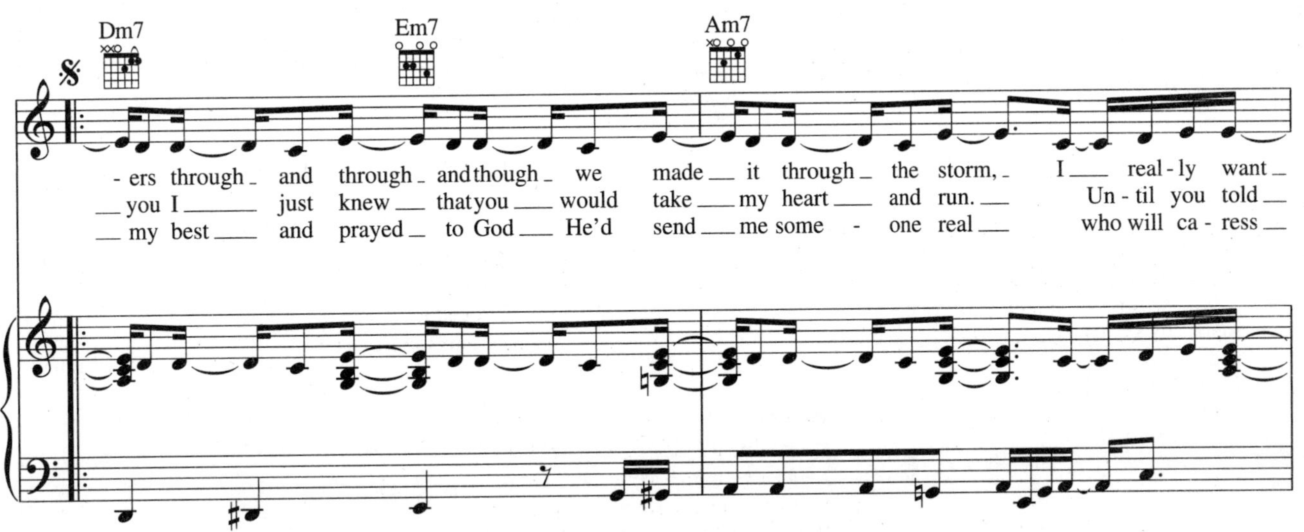

Dm7
Em7
Am7
you to re - al - ize I real - ly want to put you on. I've been search -
me how you fell for me, you said I'm not the one. So, I slow -
me in, to guide me towards a love my heart can feel. Now, I know
Dm7
Em7
Am7
- in' for some - one to sat - is - fy my ev - 'ry need. Won't you be
- ly came to see all of the things that you were made of and now I hold
I can be faith - ful. I can be your all and all. I'll give you good lov -
Dm7
Em7
Am7
my in - spir - a - tion, be the real love that I need? Yeah.
my dreams and in - spir - a - tion, lead me to want some real,
- in' through the sum - mer - time, win - ter, spring and fall.
Dm7
Em7
Am7
Dm7
Em7
Real love,
real love,
Real love,
I'm search - ing for a real love, some -

Am7
Dm7
Em7
Am7
To Coda
- one to set my heart free. Real love, I'm searching for a
1 Dm7
Em7
Am7
2 Dm7
Em7
real love. Ooh, when I met real love. real love. I've
Am7
Dm7
got to have a real love, love so true
B7♯9
E7♯9
6fr
Am7
and oh, ba - by, I thought

Dm7
that love was you. I thought you were the an - swer to the ques-
B7#9
E7#9
6fr
Dm7
- tion in my mind, but it seems that I was wrong, if I stand strong,
E7#9
6fr
Dm7
Em7
Am7
may - be I'll find our real love.
(Vocal 1st time only)
Dm7
Em7
1
Am7
2
Am7
D.S. al Coda
So, I've tried

CODA
Dm7
Em7
Am7
Dm7
Em7
real love.
Real love,
Am7
Dm7
Em7
Am7
I'm search-ing for a real love,
some - one to set my heart free.
Dm7
Em7
Am7
Dm7
Em7
Real love,
I'm search-ing for a real love.
Am7
Play 4 times
N.C.
Real love.

RIKKI DON'T LOSE THAT NUMBER

Words and Music by WALTER BECKER
and DONALD FAGEN

D
A
E
I guess you kind of scared your self, you turn and run.
We could stay in - side and play games I don't know.
F#m7
A
But if you have a change of heart,
And you could have a change of heart.
N.C.
E7
Rik - ki, don't lose that num - ber; you don't wan - na
G
A
call no - bod - y else.
Send it off in a

G
D
let - ter to your - self.
Cmaj7
Em
Rik - ki, don't lose that num - ber; it's the on - ly one you own.
Cmaj7
D A
You might use it if you feel bet - ter
N.C.
To Coda
when you get home.

Amaj7
G♯m7
You tell your-self you're not my kind,
Amaj7
C♯m7
F♯m7
but you don't e-ven know your mind.
And you could have a
A
change of heart.
D.S. al Coda
CODA
E7
Rik-ki, don't lose that num-
E9
ber,
(Rik-ki, don't lose that num-ber)
Rik-ki, don't lose that num-ber.

ROLL WITH IT

Words and Music by WILL JENNINGS,
STEVE WINWOOD, EDDIE HOLLAND,
LAMONT DOZIER and BRIAN HOLLAND

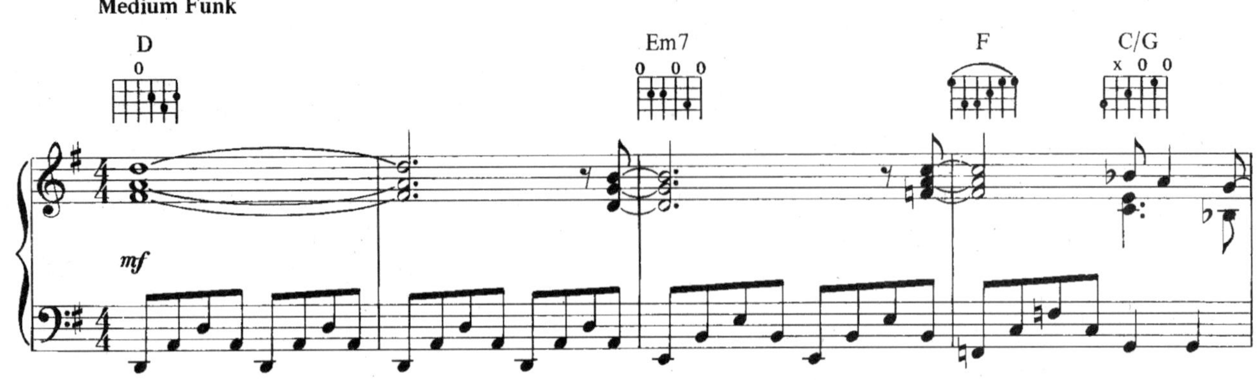

stop and lose your touch, oh no, ba - by. Hard time knock-
swear by stars a - bove, sweet as hon - ey. Peo - ple think
hear the mus - ic play, you'll dance, ba - by. You'll leave

C7
ing at your door, I'll tell them you ain't there no more.
you're down and out, You show them what it's all a - bout.
bad times be - hind, noth - ing but good times on your mind.

G7
Get on through it, roll with it, ba - by.
You can make it, roll with it, ba - by.
You can do it, roll with it, ba - by.

D
Em7
Luck-'ll come and then slip a-way, You've got a move, bring it
When this world turns it's back on you, hang in and do that
Then you'll see life will be so nice, it's just a step up to
F
C/G
G7
C/G
G7
back to stay.
sweet thing you do. You just roll with it, ba-by; come on and just
par-a-dise.
C/G
G7
C/G
roll with it, ba-by, you and me. Roll with it, ba-by;
G7
To Coda
1.
No Chord
hang on and just roll with it, ba-by, hey. The way

2.
N.C.
Em7
Bb
Dm7
Ab
4fr.
F
D.S. al Coda
Now there
Coda
N.C.
Repeat and fade (ad-lib vocal)
G7
x000

SAILING

Words and Music by
CHRISTOPHER CROSS

E/D
A/D
E/D
A/D
- vas can do mir - a - cles, just you wait and see.
Be - lieve me.
E/A
A
E/A
A
A/C#
D(add2)
It's not far to nev - er - nev -
far back to san -
- er land, no rea - son to pre - tend, and if the wind
- i - ty, at least it's not for me, and if the wind

F#m9
is right you can find the joy of in - no-cence a - gain.
is right you can sail a - way and find se - ren - i - ty.
E/D
A/D
Oh, the can - vas can do mir - a - cles,
E/D
A/D
E/A
A
just you wait and see. Be - lieve me.
E/A
A

E/A
A
E/A
A
Sail - ing takes me a - way to where
D(add2)
I've al - ways heard it could be.
Bm9
Just a dream and the wind to car -
F♯m9
C♯m7
D(add2)
- ry me, and soon I will be free.

To Coda
E/A
A
E/A
A
Fan - ta - sy, it gets the best of me
F♯m9
when I'm sail - ing.
E/D
A/D
All caught up in the rev -

E/D
A/D
- er - ie,
ev - 'ry word _ is a sym - pho - ny.
Won't you be - lieve _
E/A
A
E/A
A
me? _
E/A
A
Sail - ing
takes me a - way _
E/A
A
D(add2)
_ to where _ I've al - ways heard it _ could be. _

Just a dream
and the wind to car - ry me, and soon I will be free.
Bm9
F#m9
C#m7
D(add2)
A
D.S. al Coda
Well, it's not
CODA
Play 3 times
8vb.

SECRET AGENT MAN

from the Television Series

Words and Music by P.F. SLOAN
and STEVE BARRI

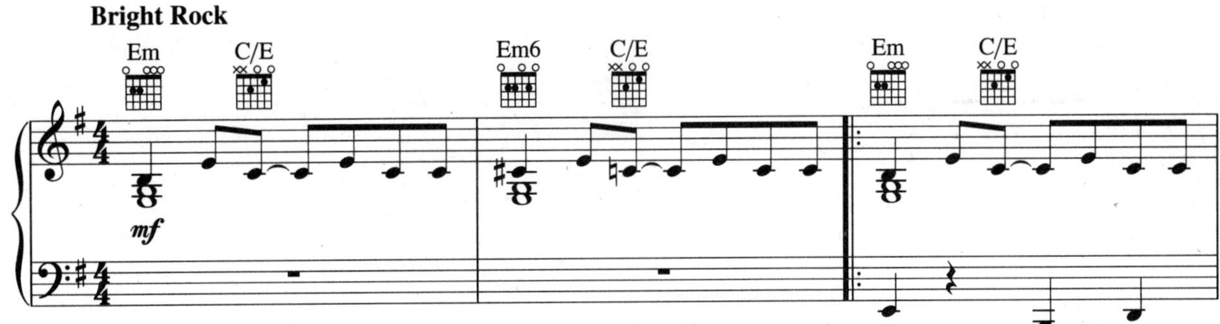

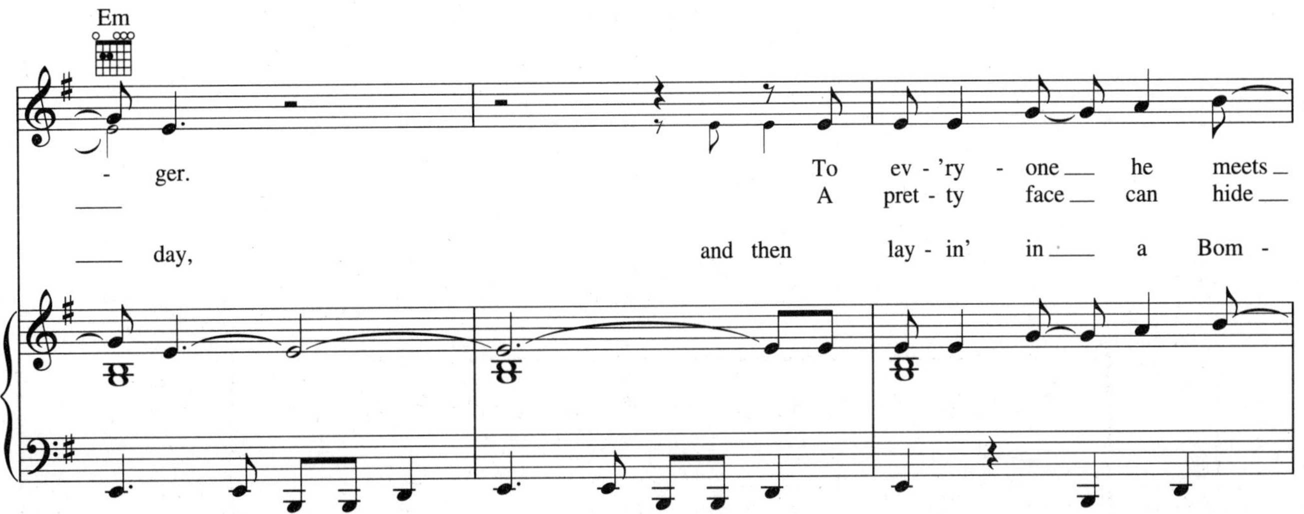

B7
he stays a stran - ger.
an e - vil mind.
bay al - ley next day.
Oh, with
Be
Oh, no, you
Em
Am
ev - 'ry move he makes an - oth - er chance he takes.
care - ful what you say. You'll give your - self a - way.
let the wrong word slip while kiss - ing per - sua - sive lips.
Em
Am
Em
Odds are he won't live to see to - mor - row.
Odds are you won't live to see to - mor - row.
End instrumental
The odds are you won't live to see to - mor - row.
Bm
Em
Se - cret a - gent man, se - cret

Bm
Em
C7
a - gent man.
They've - giv - en you a num -
B7
Em C/E
- ber and tak - en 'way your name.
Em6 C/E
Em C/E
1
Em6 C/E
Be -
2, 3
Em6 C/E
4
Em6 C/E
Em6 C/E
Em6 C/E
Em

SEVEN BRIDGES ROAD

Words and Music by
STEPHEN T. YOUNG

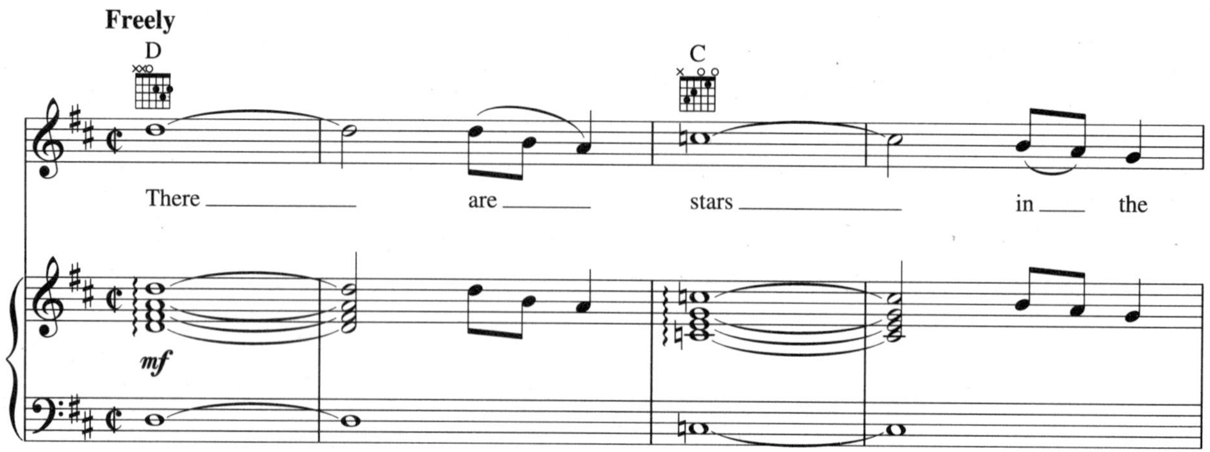

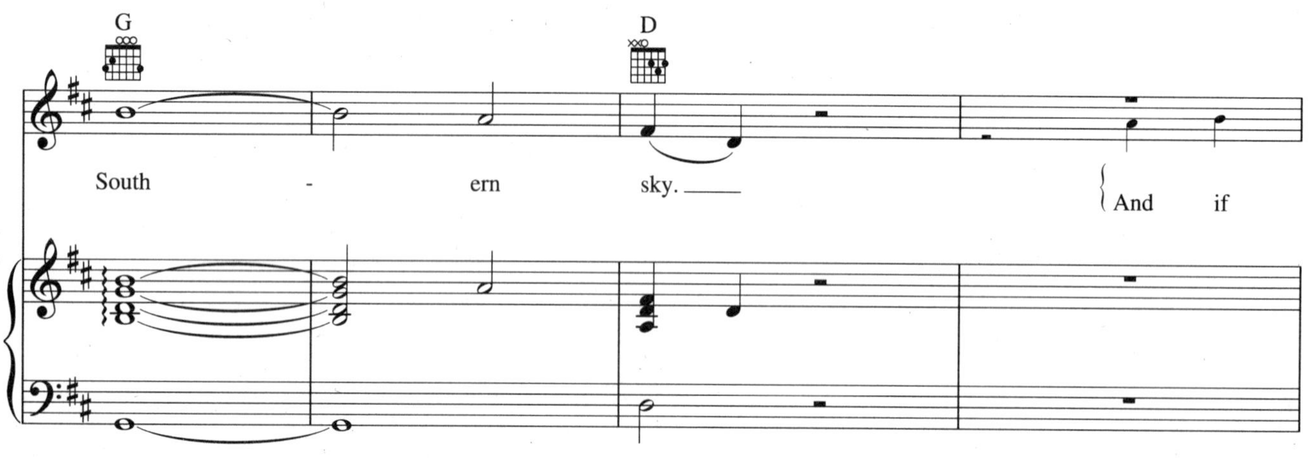

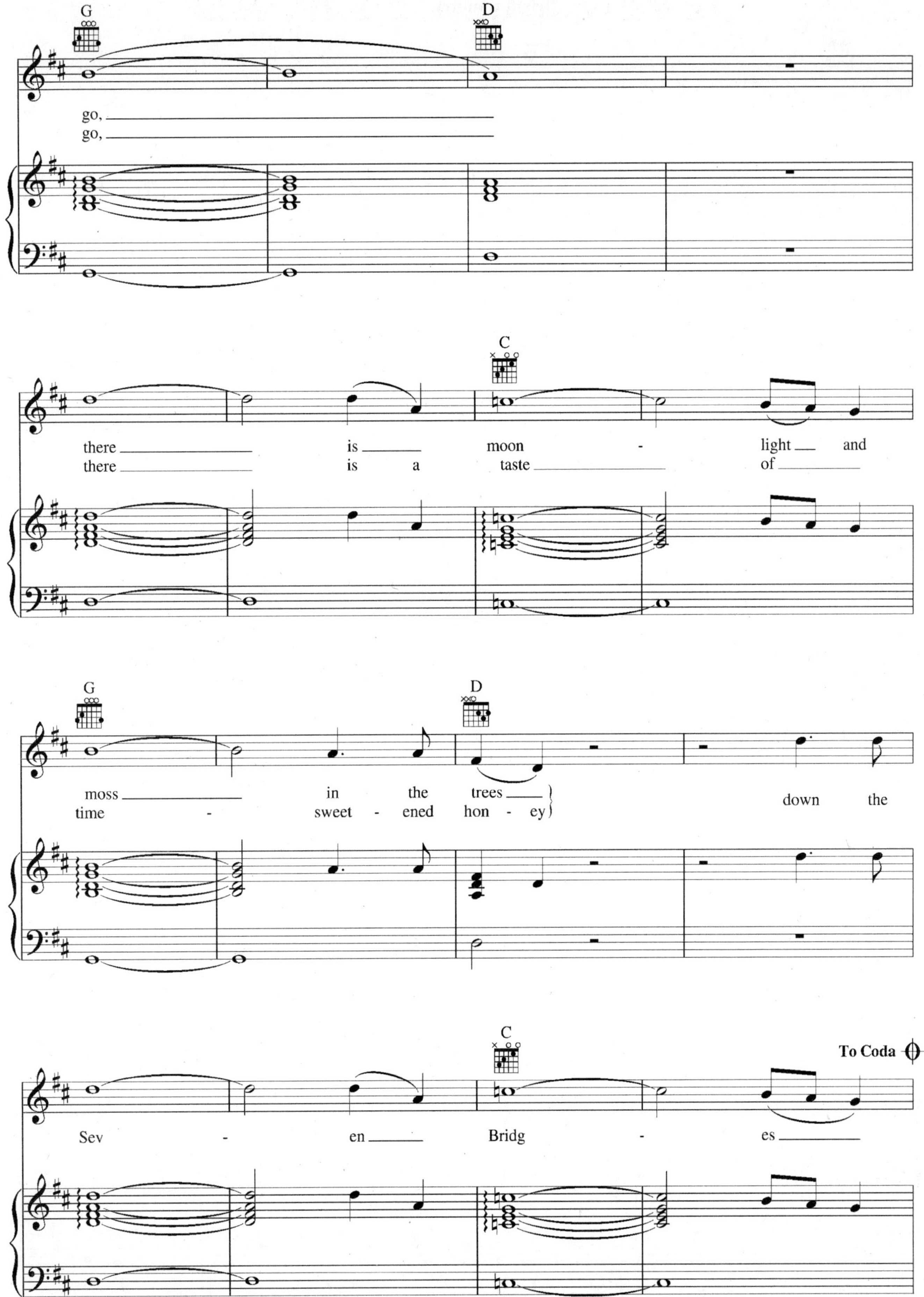
G
D
go, ___
go, ___
C
there ___ is ___ moon - light ___ and
there ___ is a taste ___ of ___
G
D
moss ___ in the trees ___
time - sweet - ened hon - ey
down the
C
To Coda
Sev - en ___ Bridg - es ___

Bright Country
G
D
Road.
Now, I have
I have
C
G
loved you
loved you
D
like a ba - by, like
in a tame way and I

C
G
some
lone -
some
child.
have
loved
you
wild.
D
1
2
And
Some - times
C
there's
a
part
D

of me
has to
C
turn
from
here
and
D
go,
C
run - ning
like
a child
from

D
these
warm
stars
down the
C
Sev
-
en
Bridg
-
es
G
D
D.C. al Coda
Road.
CODA
G
D
Road.

SHE WORKS HARD FOR THE MONEY

Words and Music by DONNA SUMMER
and MICHAEL OMARTIAN

G
F
G
F
G
F
G
Dm7
for it, hon - ey.
She works hard
for the mon - ey, so you
Em7
Am
G
Am
G
Am
G
Am
bet - ter treat her right.
She works hard
G
Am
G
Am
G
Am
G
F
G
F
for the mon - ey.
So hard
for it, hon - ey.
G
F
G
Dm7
Em7
She works hard
for the mon - ey so you
bet - ter treat her right.

Am G Am G Am G Am G/A Am
O - net - ta there in the cor -
Twen-ty - eight years have come
G/A Fmaj7 G/F Fmaj7 G/F
- ner stands and she won - ders where she is. And it's strange
and gone and she's seen a lot of tears. Of the ones
D7sus D7 E7sus E7 Am G Am G
to her some peo - ple seem to have ev - 'ry - thing.
who came in, they real - ly seem to need her there.
Am G Am G/A Am G/A
Nine a. m. on the ho - ur hand and she's wait -
It's a sac - ri - fice work - ing day to day for lit - tle
3fr

Am/G
G
Am/G
G
1
Fmaj7
G/F
Am/E
- ing for the bell.
mon - ey just tips for pay.
And she's look - ing real pret - ty just
But it's worth
E
Am
G
Am
G
Am
G
Am
wait - ing for her cli - en - tele.
She works hard
2
Fmaj7
G/F
Am/E
E
Am
G
Am
G
it all just to hear them say that they care.
Am
G
Am
G
Am
G
Am
G
Am
She works hard for the mon - ey.
So hard

G F G F G F G Dm7
for it, hon - ey. She works hard for the mon - ey so you
Em7 Am G Am G Am G Am
bet - ter treat her right.
F G7/F
She al - read - y knows she's seen her bad
Am G Am G Am G Am
times.

F
G7/F
She al - read - y knows these are the
Am
G
Am
G
Am
G
Am
good times.
Dm7
Em7
She'll nev - er sell out. She nev - er will,
Fmaj7
F/G
D.S. and Fade
not for a dol - lar bill. She works hard

SHE'S A BEAUTY

Words and Music by STEVEN LUKATHER, DAVID FOSTER,
JOHN WAYBILL and BILL SPOONER

Bm
G
Asus4
A
Bm
You can look in - side a - noth - er world ___ and you get to
You can step out - side your lit - tle world. ___ You can
Em7
A
Bm
G
Asus4
Bm
talk to a pret - ty girl. ___ She's ev - 'ry - thing you dream a - bout. ___
C
G
Em7
___ But, don't fall ___ in love ___
C(add2)
C/D
G
Em7
C(add2)
F
She's a beau - ty. She's one in ___ a mil - lion girls. ___ She's a beau -

G
Em7
C(add2)
C/D
G
Em7
ty. Why would I lie?
Why would I lie?
1
C
F
C/E
D
A5
5fr
G
D/F♯
A5
5fr
G
D/F♯
2
C
But, don't fall in
G
Em7
C(add2)
C/D
love 'Cause if you do you'll find out she don't love you. She's

G
Em7
C(add2)
F
G
Em7
one in a mil - lion girls.
One in a mil - lion girls.
Why would I
C(add2)
C/D
G
Em7
C
F
C/E
D
lie?
Why would I lie?
A
G
D/F♯
A
G
D/F♯
Bm
G
A

Bm
Em7
A
Bm
G
Asus4
Bm
C
Bsus
C♯m7
B7sus
A
A
F♯m7
But, don't fall _ in love ___
Dsus2
D/E
A
F♯m7
D
G
She's a beau - ty. She's one in ___ a mil - lion girls. ___ One in a mil - lion

A
F#m7
Dsus2
D/E
girls. Why would I lie?
Why would I lie? But, don't fall in love
'Cause if you do you'll find out she don't love you. She's
one in a mil - lion girls.
One in a mil - lion girls.
D
G
lie?
Why would I lie? But, don't fall in
Repeat and Fade

SHOULD'VE NEVER LET YOU GO

Words and Music by NEIL SEDAKA
and PHIL CODY

F/Eb
Dm7
hard to find the words to say.
life too hard to bear.
walls are tumb - ling down.
G7-9
Cm7
Dm7
Wan - na run a - way and hide
I don't care who's right or wrong.
You're the kind I can't for - get.
Ebm7
Ab7
Bbmaj7
I just got to let you know.
On - ly know I love you so.
Let the tears be - gin to flow.

Gm
C/E
To Coda
feel so tang - led up in - side,
Why did I have to write this song?
I have on - ly one re - gret.
Ebm6
1. Bb
Ebmaj7
I should - 've nev - er let you go.
Bbmaj7
2. Bb
2. An- y- one can make mis- you go.
8va
Eb
F/Eb
Why, in all the wide

E♭
F/E♭
wide world, have I run in - to you
here? Wish I could dis - ap - pear. I'll nev - er un - der -
Dm7
Cm7
stand why I ev - en give
(I'll nev - er un - der - stand)
a damn.
E♭maj7
A♭7sus
A♭
B♭
Gm7
Cm11
E♭m6/F
rit.
8va

B♭maj9
D.S. 𝄋 al Coda
Coda
E♭m6
3. When you walk in - to a
a tempo
I should-'ve nev-er let you
rit.
B♭m
E♭9sus
E♭maj7
A♭maj7
go.
Should-'ve nev-er let you go.
Should-'ve nev-er let
a tempo
D♭maj7
Am7-5
D9sus
Should - 've nev - er let you go.
you go.
Should - 've nev - er let you
molto rit.
Bmaj7
go.
8va
a tempo
rit.

SILLY LOVE SONGS

Words and Music by
PAUL and LINDA McCARTNEY

Em7
Fmaj7
And what's wrong with that?
I'd like to know,
G
'Cause here I go again.
C
Em7
Fmaj7
I love you.
C
Em7
Fmaj7
I love you.
C
Em7
Fmaj7
I love you.

C
Em7
Fmaj7
I love you.
C
Em7
Fmaj7
I can't ex - plain, the feel - ing's plain to me; say,
C
Em7
Fmaj7
can't you see? Ah, she gave me more, she gave it all to me; now
Em7
Fmaj7
can't you see, What's wrong with that I need to know
G
'Cause here I go a - gain.

C
Em7
Fmaj7
I
love
you.
C
Em7
Fmaj7
I
love
you.
Em7
Am
Dm7
Love does-n't come in a min - ute,
Some-times it does-n't come at all.
C
Em7
Am
Dm7
C
Dm7
I on-ly know that when I'm in it,
It is-n't sil-ly,
C/A
Dm7
Dm7/G
no, it is-n't sil-ly,
Love is-n't sil-ly at all.

C
Em7
Fmaj7
G
How can I tell you a - bout my loved one?
I love you.
I love you. I
love you.
I can't ex -
I
plain, the feel - ing's plain to me, say, can't you see? Ah, he gave me
love you. I

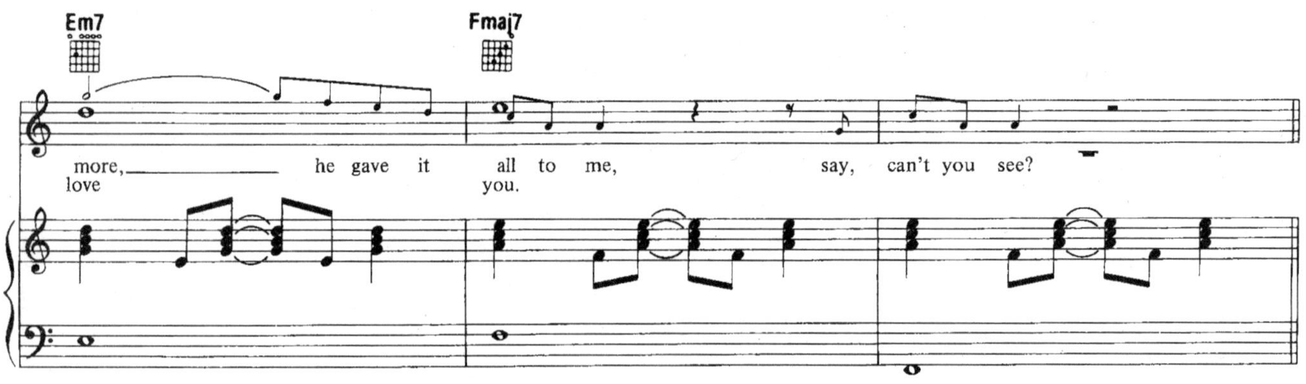
Em7
Fmaj7
more, he gave it all to me, say, can't you see?
love you.

C
Em7
Fmaj7
I can't ex - plain, the feel-ing's plain to me, say, can't you see?
How can I tell you a - bout my loved one?
I love you.

C
Em7
Fmaj7
Ah, he gave me more, he gave it all to me, say, can't you see?
How can I tell you a - bout my loved one?
I love you.

C
Em7
Fmaj7
You'd think that peo - ple would have had e - nough of Sil - ly Love Songs.
C
Em7
But I look a - round me and I see it is-n't
Fmaj9
C
Em7
so. Oh, no.
Some peo-ple wan-na fill the world with Sil-ly
Fmaj7
Em7
Love Songs,
And what's wrong with that?

SING FOR ABSOLUTION

Words and Music by MATTHEW BELLAMY,
CHRIS WOLSTENHOLME and DOMINIC HOWARD

E
4fr
A7
5fr
on - ly dream of you my beau - ti - ful.
truth burns deep in - side and will ne-ver die.
Dm
5fr
B♭
6fr
Dm
5fr
B♭
6fr
Tip - toe to your_ room, a star - light in the_ gloom, I
Lips are turn - ing_ blue, a kiss_ that can't re - new, I
E
4fr
A7
5fr
on - ly dream of you, and you_ ne - ver_ knew._
on - ly dream of you my_ beau - ti - ful._
C
Gm
Sing for ab - so - lu - tion, I will_

C
Gm
be sing - ing
and fall - ing from your grace.
1.
Gm(add9)
Dm
B♭
Dm
B♭
Ooh.
E
A7
2.There's

2.
Gm(add9)
3fr
Dm
5fr
Oh.
B♭
E
A7
5fr
C
Gm
Sing for ab - so - lu -

C
-tion, I will be sing-ing and fall - ing from your
Gm
Gm(add9)
3fr
grace.
Yeah.
Dm
5fr
B♭
I won't re-main un - rec - ti-fied,
E
4fr
and our souls

Asus4
won't
be
ex
-
humed.
A
Dm
5fr
B♭
6fr
Dm
5fr
B♭
6fr
Dm
5fr
B♭
6fr
Dm
5fr
B♭
6fr
Dm
5fr
F
rall.

SMOOTH OPERATOR

Words and Music by HELEN ADU
and RAY ST. JOHN

G
Dm7
Dia-mond nights and ru - by lights
high in the sky,
heav-en
G
Dm7
G
help him
when he falls.
Dm7
Am7
Gm7
Am7
Dm7
Am7
Gm7
Am7
Dia mond life,
lov - er boy,
he
Dm7
Am7
Gm7
Am7
Dm7
Am7
Gm7
Am7
move in space with
min - i - mum waste
and max - i - mum joy.

Dm7
Am7
Gm7
Am7
Dm7
Am7
Cit - y lights and busi - ness nights,
Face to face each clas - sic case,
Gm7
Am7
Dm7
Am7
Gm7
Am7
when you re - quire street - car de - sire for
we shad - ow box and dou - ble cross yet
Dm7
Am7
Gm7
Am7
Gm7
high - er heights. No place for be -
need the chase. A li - cence to
Am7
Dm7
gin - ners or sen - si - tive hearts,
love, in - sur - ance to hold,

Gm7
Am7
Dm7
when sen - ti - ment is left to chance,
melt all your mem-'ries and change in - to gold,
Gm7
Am7
no place to be end - ing but some where to
his eyes are like an - gels but his heart is
Dm7
start.
cold.
Dm7
Am7
No need to ask he's a smooth op - er - a - tor,
Smooth op - er - a - tor,
Gm7
Am7
Dm7
Am7
Gm7
Am7
Dm7
Am7
smooth op - er - a - tor,
smooth op - er - a - tor,

Gm7
Am7
Dm7
smooth op - er - a - tor.
Coast to coast, L. A. to Chi - ca - go, west - ern male.
A - cross the north and south to Key Lar - go,
1
love for sale.
2
love for sale.
D.S. and Fade

SOMEWHERE OUT THERE

from AN AMERICAN TAIL

Words and Music by JAMES HORNER,
BARRY MANN and CYNTHIA WEIL

Dm7 C/E F Gsus G C(add9) Cmaj7/E
lov - ing me to - night. Some - where out
C/F F/G C(add9) C/E F
there, some - one's say - ing a prayer that
Dm7 G/F Em7 Am Dm7 C/E F/G
we'll find one an - oth - er in that big some - where out
C F G/F F G/F
there. And e - ven though I know how ver - y far a - part we are it

Fmaj7
G/F
F
G/F
helps to think we might be wish - in' on the same bright star. And
A♭
B♭/A♭
A♭
B♭/A♭
4fr
when the night wind starts to sing a lone - some lull - a - by it
A♭
B♭/A♭
G
helps to think we're sleep - ing un - der - neath the same big sky.
C
Cmaj7/E
Fmaj9
F/G
C
C/E
To Coda
Some - where out there if love can see us

F
Dm7
G/F
Em7
Am7
F
through, then we'll be to - geth - er some - where out there, out
G
C
D/C
C
D/C
C/B♭
B♭maj7
where dreams come true.
Am/B♭
D/E
A
C♯m7
4fr
A/D
D/E
A
A/C♯
D
D+
D6
A/C♯

Bm7
Dmaj7
C#m
F#m7
Bm7
C#m
D/E
A
D.S. al Coda
And
CODA
C
C/E
F
love can see us through,
(love can see us
Dm
G/F
Em7
Am
F
G
then we'll be to - geth - er some - where out there, out where dreams come
through)
C
Cmaj7/E
C/F
G7sus
C(add9)
true.
rit.

SOMEBODY TOLD ME

Words and Music by BRANDON FLOWERS,
DAVE KEUNING, MARK STOERMER
and RONNIE VANNUCCI

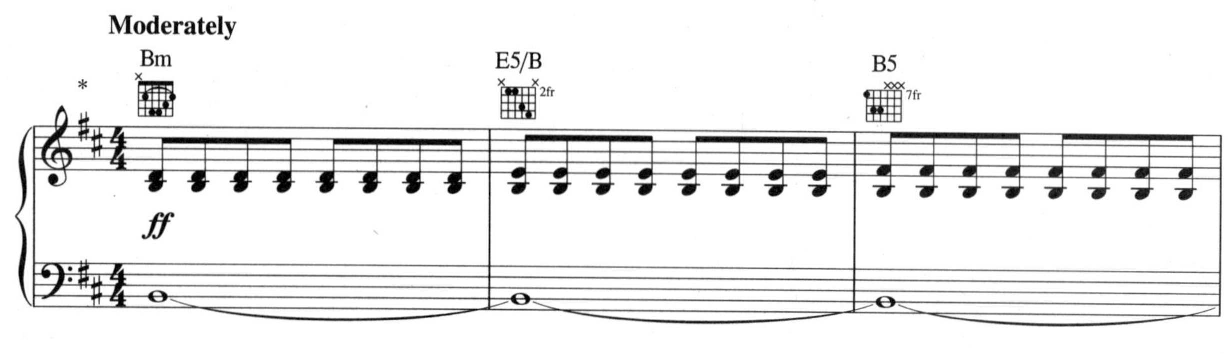

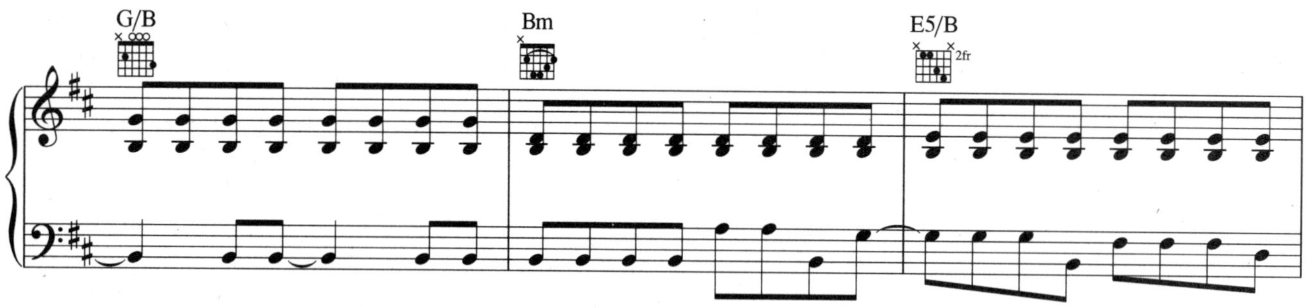

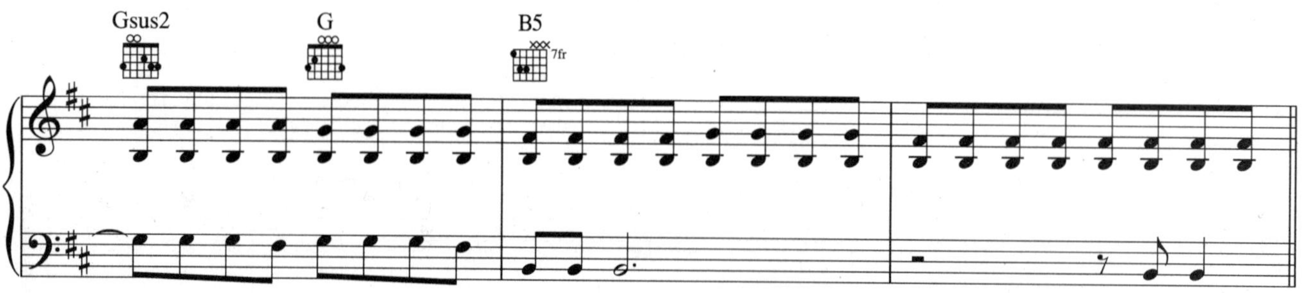

* *Recorded a half step lower.*

Break - in' my back just to know your name. Sev - en - teen tracks and I've
Em
had it with this game. I'm
B5
7fr
break - in' my back just to know your name. But heav - en ain't close in a
Read - y, let's roll on - to
place like this. An - y - thing goes, but don't blink you might miss.
some - thing new. Tak - in' its toll, then I'm leav - ing with - out you.

Em
B5
7fr
'Cause heav - en ain't close in a
place like this. I said a heav - en ain't close in a place like this.
G5
3fr
Asus
Bm
Bring it back down. Bring it back down to - night, hoo,
hoo.
G5
3fr
Nev - er thought I'd let a ru - mor ru - in my

Asus
N.C.
B5
7fr
moon - light.
Well, some-bod - y told me you had a boy-
G5
3fr
A5
5fr
F♯5
friend who looks like a girl - friend that I had in Feb - ru - ar - y of last
B5
7fr
G5
3fr
1
A5
5fr
year. It's not con - fi - den - tial. I've got po - ten - tial.
N.C.
2
A5
5fr
F♯5
tial a rush - ing, a rush - ing a - round.

N.C.
Pace your - self for me. I said
may - be, ba - by, please.
But I just don't know now.
May - be, ba - by, when all I wan - na do is try.

A5
5fr
B5
7fr
Well, some-bod - y told me you had a boy-
G5
3fr
A5
5fr
F♯5
- friend who looks like a girl - friend that I had in Feb - ru - ar - y of last
B5
7fr
G5
3fr
A5
5fr
year. It's not con- fi- den - tial. I've got po- ten - tial a rush - ing, a rush-
1, 2
F♯5
3
F♯5
Bm
ing a - round. Now some - bod - y told ing a - round.

SON OF A PREACHER MAN

Words and Music by JOHN HURLEY
and RONNIE WILKINS

we'd go walk - in'. And then he'd look in - to my eyes,
thing is al - right, and "Can I sneak a - way a - gain to - night?"
C
Lord knows, to my sur - prise: The on - ly one who could ev - er reach me
F
C
was the son - of - a - preach - er man. The on - ly boy who could ev - er teach me
F
C
G7
was the son - of - a - preach - er man, yes he was, he was.

F
1
C
Ooh.
2
B♭
How well I re - mem - ber
F
the look that was in his eyes.
Steal - in' kiss - es from me on the sly,
G7
tak - in' time to make time,
tell - in' me that he's all mine.

C7
Learn - in' from each oth - er knowin' and look - in' to see how much we've grown. And the
F
Bb
F
on - ly one who could ev - er reach me was the son - of - a - preach - er man. The
Bb
F
on - ly one who could ev - er teach me was the son - of - a - preach - er man; yes, he was.
Repeat and Fade
Optional Ending
C7
Bb
F
Yeah!
The

THE SPACE BETWEEN

Words and Music by DAVID J. MATTHEWS
and GLEN BALLARD

A
A/G♯
The space be - tween the tears we cry
Dmaj9/F♯
E/G♯
is the laugh - ter keeps us com - ing back for more.
A
A/G♯
The space be - tween the wick - ed lies
Dmaj9/F♯
N.C.
Dsus2
we tell and hope to keep us safe from the pain.

E
Dsus2
But will I hold you a - gain?
E
Dsus2
These fick - le, fud - dled words con - fuse me,
E
Dsus2
like, will it rain to - day?
E
Dsus2
We waste the hours with talk - ing, talk - ing,

E
these twist - ed games we're play - ing.
A
A/G#
We're strange al - lies with war - ring hearts.
Dmaj9/F#
E/G#
What a wild - eyed beast you be.
A
A/G#
The space be - tween the wick - ed lies

Dmaj9/F#
N.C.
Dsus2
we tell and hope to keep us safe from the pain.
E
Dsus2
But will I hold you a - gain?
E
will I hold...
B5
B5/A
E/G#
Em/G
B5/F#
3
Look at us spin-ning out in the mad - ness of a roll - er coast - er.

B5
B5/A
E/G♯
Em/G
B5/F♯
You know you went off like the dev - il in a church in the mid - dle of a crowd - ed room.
B5
B5/A
E/G♯
Em/G
F5
All I can do, my love, is hope we don't take this ship down.
A
A/G♯
The space be - tween where you smile and
Dmaj9/F♯
E/G♯
hide is where you'll find me if I get to go.

A
A/G♯
1. The space be - tween the bul - lets in our fire -
2.-5. See additional lyrics
Play 5 times
Dmaj9/F♯
E/G♯
fight is where I'll be hid - ing, wait - ing for you.
A
A/G♯
Dmaj9/F♯
The space be - tween what's wrong and right is where you'll find
E
A
me hid - ing, wait - ing for you. The space be - tween

Additional Lyrics

2. The rain that falls splashed in your heart,
Ran like sadness down the window into your room.

3. The space between our wicked lies is where
We hope to keep safe from pain.

4. Take my hand 'cause
We're walking out of here.

5. Oh, right out of here.
Love is all we need, dear.

SPINNING WHEEL

Words and Music by
DAVID CLAYTON THOMAS

E7 A7 D7 G E7 A7
You got no mon - ey, you got no home, spin - ning wheel
D7 G E7 A7 D7 G
all a - lone, talk - in' 'bout your trou - bles and you, you nev - er learn,
D7 N.C. D7#9
ride a paint - ed po - ny, let the spin - ning wheel turn.
C B♭
Did you find your di - rect - ing sign on the

A♭
4fr
G
C
straight and nar - row high - way.
Would you mind a re -
B♭
A♭
4fr
G
flect - ing sign?
Just let it shine
with - in your mind, and
A♭
4fr
B♭
C
show you the col - ors that are real.
D9
4fr

E7
A7
D7
G
Some - one is wait - ing just for you, spin - ning wheel
spin - ning true. Drop all your trou - bles by the riv - er - side,
catch a paint - ed po - ny on the spin - ning wheel ride.
N.C.
D7#9
Repeat and Fade

STAGES

Words and Music by BILLY F GIBBONS,
DUSTY HILL and FRANK BEARD

Em7
D/E
Em7
D/E
ain't got a sin - gle thing to do.
- n't e - ven get you on the phone.
- n't have it an - y oth - er way.

G
D/G
Hap - pened be - fore I knew what was go - ing on.
Were you just con - fused and did - n't know
Tell me it's for real and let me know

G
D/G
Em7
D/E
I fell out and knew
if you should stay or if
why does lov - in' have

Em7
D/E
that I was gone.
you had to go?
to come and go.
Csus
C
Csus
Stag - es keep on chang - ing. Stag - es re -
G5
- ar - rang - ing love.
To Coda
Bm7
Guitar solo ad lib.

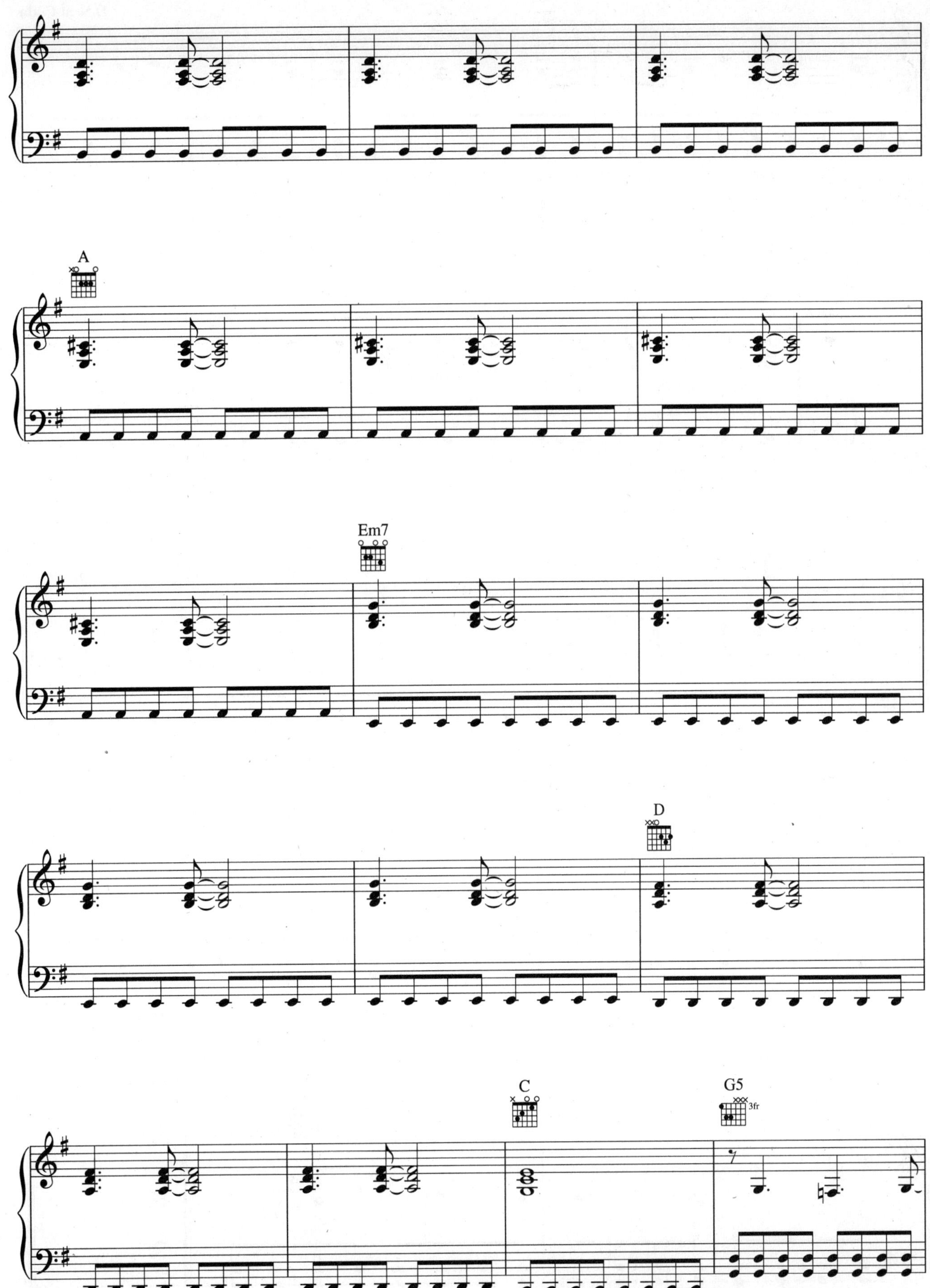
A
Em7
D
C
G5
3fr

D.S. al Coda
CODA
Csus
C
Csus
Guitar solo ad lib.
C
Csus
C
Csus
G5
Repeat and Fade
Optional Ending

(Just Like)
STARTING OVER

Words and Music by
JOHN LENNON

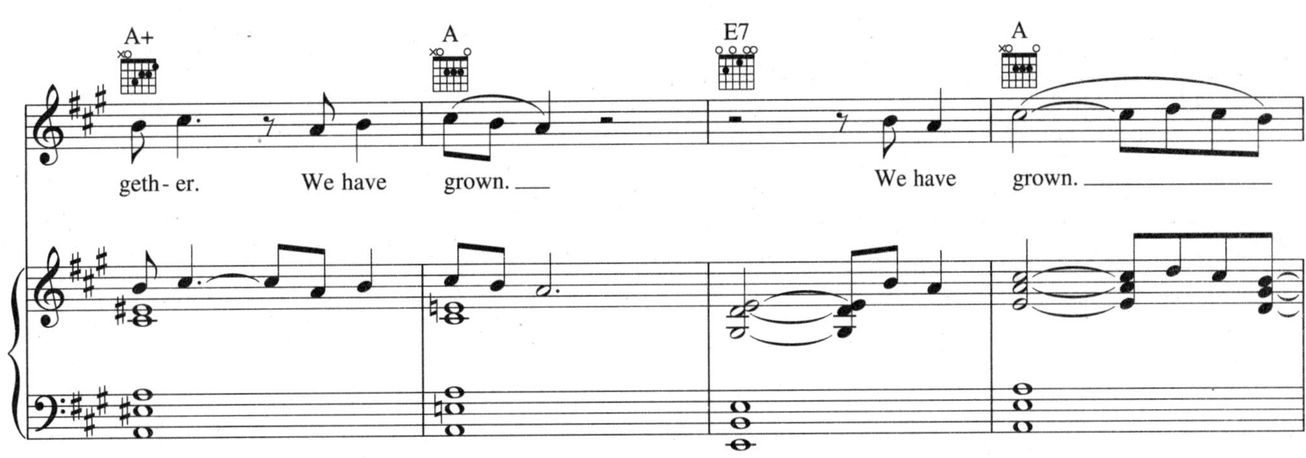

A7
D/A
Dm/A
A
let's take a chance and fly a - way some - where a - lone. It's
Moderately, with a strong beat
A
A+
been too long since we took the time. No ones's to blame. I know time flies so
day we used to make it, love. Why can't we be mak - in' love nice and
Bm
E
quick - ly!
eas - y?
Bm
E
But when I see you, dar - lin',
It's time to spread our wings and

C♯m
F♯
it's like we both are fall - ing in
fly. Don't let an - oth - er day go
Bm
E
love a - gain.
by, my love.
It - 'll be just like start - ing
A
A+
o - ver, start-ing
A
To Coda
1
A+
o - ver.
Ev - 'ry

2
G
N.C.
Why don't we take off a-
Am
D7
lone, _
take a trip some-where far,
G
Em
far a - way. _
We'll be to - geth - er all a -
Am
D7
lone a - gain,
like we used to _ in the

D.S. al Coda
G
E
D/F♯
E/G♯
ear - ly days.
Well, well, dar - lin'. It's
CODA
A+
A
Our life
to - geth - er
is so
F♯m/A
pre - cious
to - geth - er.

A
We have grown.
E
A
We have grown.
E
Al - though our
A
A+
love
is still spe - cial,

F♯m/A
A7
let's take a chance and fly a - way
D
some - where.
Dm
A
A+
Repeat and Fade
Optional Ending
A

STAY
(I Missed You)

Words and Music by
LISA LOEB

Dm7
C
Dm7
C
And I thought what I felt was sim - ple.
And I thought that I don't be - long. _
Dm7
C
Dm7
C
And now_ that I am_ leav - in'_
now I know that I did some-thing wrong. 'Cause I
Fsus2
Fm
Dm7
C
missed you,
yeah, ______ yeah,
I missed you.
Dm7
C
Am7
And you say _
I on-ly hear what I want to. I

Dm7
C/E
F
C
don't lis-ten hard, I don't pay at-ten-tion to the dis-tance that you're run-ning, or to an-y-one, an-y-where. I
Dm7
C/E
Fsus2
don't un-der - stand if you real-ly care. I'm on-ly hear-ing neg-a-tives, no, no, no.
Dm7
C
So I turned the ra-di-o on. I turned the ra-di-o up,
Dm7
C
Dm7
C
and this wom-an was sing-in' my song. Lov-ers in love and the oth-ers run a-way. The

Dm7
C
Dm7
C
lov - er is cry - in' 'cause the oth - er won't stay. _ Some of us hov - er when we weep for the oth - er who was
Dm7
C
Dm7
C
dy - in' since the day they were born, well, this is not _ that. I think I am throw - in', but I'm
Dm7
C
Dm7
thrown. And I thought I'd live for - ev - er, but now I'm not so sure. You try to
Fsus2
Dm7
C/E
tell me that I'm clev - er, but that won't take me an - y - how, or an - y - where with you. _

Fsus2
Dm7
C
Dm7
C
And you said that I was na - ive and I thought that I was strong.
Dm7
C
Dm7
C
I thought, "Hey, I can leave, I can leave, oh." But now I know that I was wrong 'cause I
Fsus2
Fm
Dm7
C
missed you, yeah, missed you.
Dm7
C
Dm7
You said you caught me 'cause you want me and one day you'll let me go. You try to

Fsus2
Dm7
C/E
give a-way a keep-er, or keep me 'cause you know you're just too scared _ to lose. _
Fsus2
C(add9)
Am7
And you say, ___ "Stay." _
Dm7
C/E
Fsus2
C
You say _
Am7
Dm7
C/E
Fsus2
I on-ly hear what I want to. ___

STEPPIN' OUT

Words and Music by
JOE JACKSON

*Recorded a half step higher.

A♭/F
B♭/F
E♭/F
D♭/F
E♭/F
A♭/F
E♭/F
F(add9)
E♭
Now, the
We are
D♭
E♭
F
mist a - cross the win - dow hides the lines;
young, but get - ting old be - fore our time.
E♭
D♭
E♭
but noth - ing hides the col - our of the lights
We'll leave the T. - V. and the ra - di - o

Cm7
Db
Eb
that shine.
E - lec - tric - i -
be - hind.
Don't you won - der
Cm7
Db
Db/Eb
ty so fine;
look and dry your eyes.
what we'll find,
step - pin' out to - night?
Fmaj9
Ebmaj7/F
Dm7/F
Ab/F
Bb/F
Eb/F
Bb/F

D♭/F
E♭/F
A♭/F
E♭/F
F(add9)
We,
You
E♭
D♭
E♭
3fr
so tired of all the dark - ness in our lives,
can dress in pink and blue just like a child,
F
E♭
D♭
with no more an - gry words
and in a yel - low tax -
E♭
Cm7
D♭
to say, can come a - live;
i, turn to me and smile.

E♭
Cm7
D♭
3fr
get in - to a car and drive
We'll be there in just a while,
D♭/E♭
Fmaj9
to the oth - er side.
if you fol - low me.
Me, babe, step - pin'
E♭maj7/F
Dm7/F
A♭/F
B♭/F
E♭/F
out, in - to the
B♭/F
D♭/F
E♭/F
A♭/F
E♭/F
night, in - to the light.

Fmaj9
E♭maj7/F
Dm7/F
You, babe, step - pin' out,
A♭/F
B♭/F
E♭/F
B♭/F
in - to the night,
D♭/F
E♭/F
A♭/F
1
E♭/F
2
E♭/F
in - to the light.
light.
Fmaj9/C
E♭maj7
3fr
Dm7

A♭
4fr
B♭
E♭/B♭
6fr
B♭
D♭
E♭
3fr
A♭/E♭
1 E♭
3fr
2 E♭
3fr
Fmaj9
E♭maj7/F
Dm7/F
Me, babe, stepin' out,
A♭/F
B♭/F
E♭/F
B♭/F
in - to the night,

D♭/F
E♭/F
A♭/F
E♭/F
Fmaj9
in - to the light.
You, babe,
E♭maj7/F
Dm7/F
step - pin' out,
A♭/F
B♭/F
E♭/F
B♭/F
D♭/F
E♭/F
A♭/F
in - to the night,
in - to the
Repeat and Fade
E♭/F
light.
Optional Ending
E♭/F
F(add9)
light.

STILL CRAZY AFTER ALL THESE YEARS

Words and Music by
PAUL SIMON

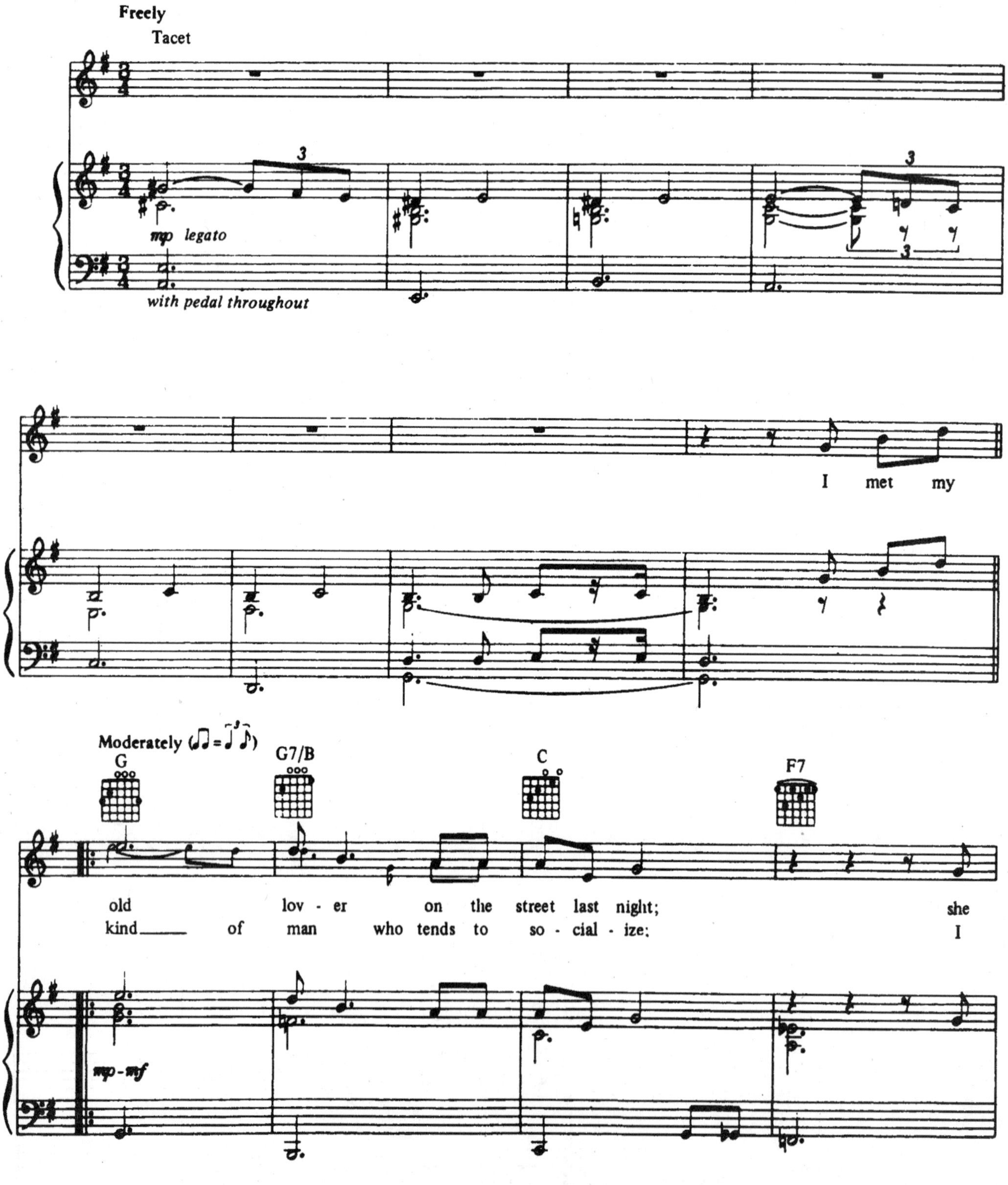

I met my

Moderately (♩♩ = ♩♪)

G G7/B C F7

old lov - er on the street last night; she
kind___ of man who tends to so - cial - ize; I

mp-mf

G
F♯°7
Bsus4
B7
Em7
E♭m7
seemed so glad to see me, I just smiled. And we
seem to lean on old fa - mil - iar ways. And I
3
3
Dm7
G7
C
C♯°7
talked a - bout some old times and we drank ___ our - selves some beers. ___
ain't no fool for love songs that whis - per in my ___ ears. ___
Still
G
D7
Em
C♯°7
3
3
cra - zy ___ af - ter all these ___ years; oh, still
3
3
3
G/D
D7
1. Cm
3fr
3
cra - zy ___ af - ter all these ___ years.
3
mf

D7
G
C
G
2. G9
3fr
I'm not the years.
gradual cresc.
Amaj7
Four in the morn - ing;
f
E
Em
G♯m7
4fr
C♯sus4
4fr
C♯
4fr
crapped out, yawn - ing; long - ing my life a -
F♯maj7
Em7
B
C
way. I'll nev - er wor - ry;

B
C
G
G7
C
why should I?
It's all gon - na
decresc.
B
C
B
C
fade.
mp
B
Am7
G
G
G7/B
Now I sit by my win - dow and I
C
F7
G
F#°7
watch the cars;
I fear I'll do some dam - age one fine

Bsus4 B7 E D/E A A7/C♯
day. But I would not be con - vict - ed by a
cresc.
mf
D D♯°7 A E E♯°7
ju - ry of my peers. Still cra - zy af - ter all these
F♯m D♯°7 A
years; oh, still cra - zy, still
f
D A/E E7 A D A
cra - zy. still cra - zy af - ter all these years.
rit.
mp

STUCK IN THE MIDDLE WITH YOU

Words and Music by GERRY RAFFERTY
and JOE EGAN

feel - in' that some - thing ain't right.
I'm so scared
- d'ring what it is I should do.
It's so hard
it makes no sense at all.
Is it cool
G7
in case I fall off my chair
and I'm won -
to keep this smile from my face.
Los - ing con -
to go to sleep on the floor?
You don't think
D
- d'ring how I'll get down the stairs.
- trol I'm all o - ver the place.
that I can take an - y - more.
(1.-3.) Clowns
(4.) Instrumental
A
C
G
D
to the left of me, jok - ers to the right. Here I am, stuck in the mid-dle with you.

1, 3
2, 4
G7
Yes, I'm
Instrumental ends
Well, you start-ed out with lov-in' and you
D
found that you're a self-made man.
And you
G7
fan-cy I'll come crawl-in', slap you on the back and say
D
please,
Am/D
To Coda
D.S. al Coda
please.

CODA
D
And I don't know why I came here to - night.
I got the feel- in' that some - thing ain't right.
I'm so scared
G7
in case I fall off my chair
D
and I'm won - d'ring how I'll get down the stairs.

A
C
G
Clowns to the left of me, jok - ers to the right. Here I am,
D
stuck in the mid - dle with you. Yes, I'm stuck in the mid - dle with you.
Stuck in the mid - dle with you. Here I am,
stuck in the mid - dle with you.

STRAWBERRY FIELDS FOREVER

Words and Music by JOHN LENNON
and PAUL McCARTNEY

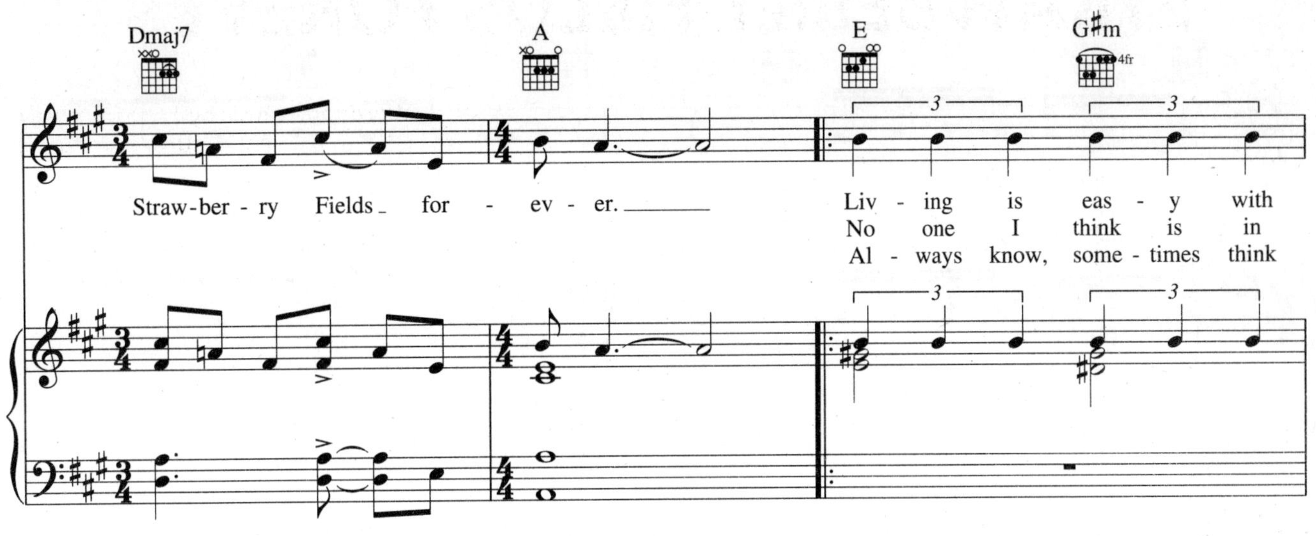
Dmaj7
A
E
G#m
4fr
Straw-ber - ry Fields for - ev - er.
Liv - ing is eas - y with
No one I think is in
Al - ways know, some - times think

E7
Bm7
C#7
F#m
F#m7
eyes closed,
my tree,
it's me.
mis - un - der - stand - ing all you
I mean, it must be high or
but you know, I know when it's a

Dmaj7
D
E7
see.
low.
dream.
It's get - ting hard to be some -
That is, you can't, you know, tune
I think a "No," I mean a

A
F#m
D
E
one, but it all works out; it does - n't mat - ter much to
in, but it's all right. That is, I think it's not too
"Yes," but it's all wrong. That is, I think I dis - a -
D
A
me.
bad. Let me take you down, 'cause I'm go - ing to
gree.
Em7
C#dim
4fr
Straw - ber - ry Fields. Noth - ing is
D
E
F#
real, and noth - ing to get hung a - bout.

1, 2
Dmaj7
A
Straw-ber - ry Fields_ for - ev - er.

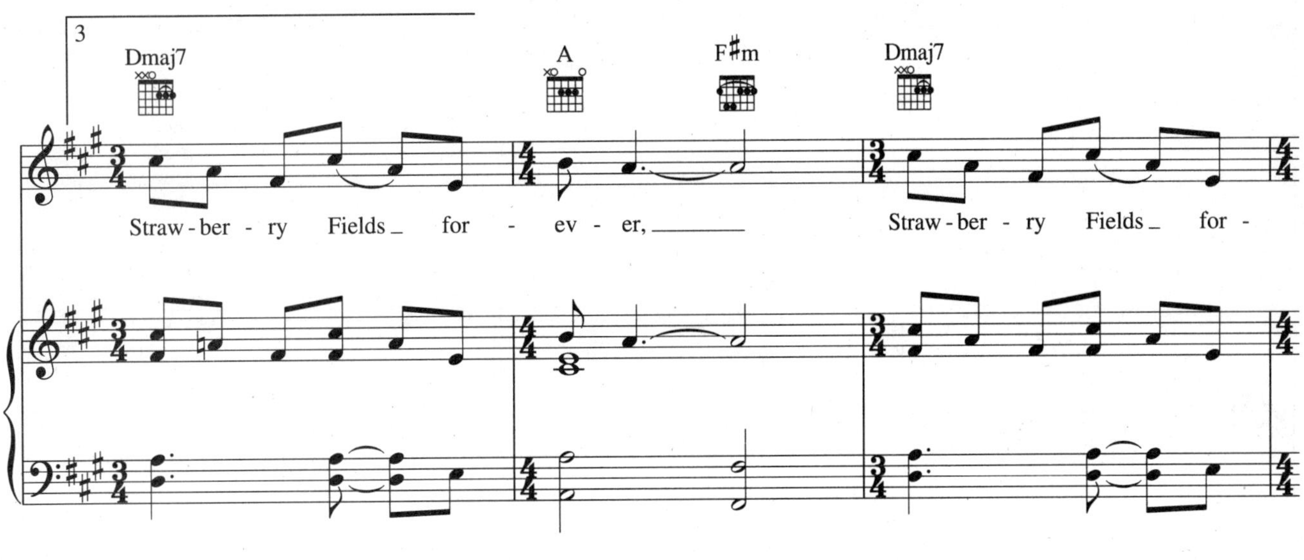
3
Dmaj7
A
F♯m
Dmaj7
Straw-ber - ry Fields_ for - ev - er,
Straw-ber - ry Fields_ for -

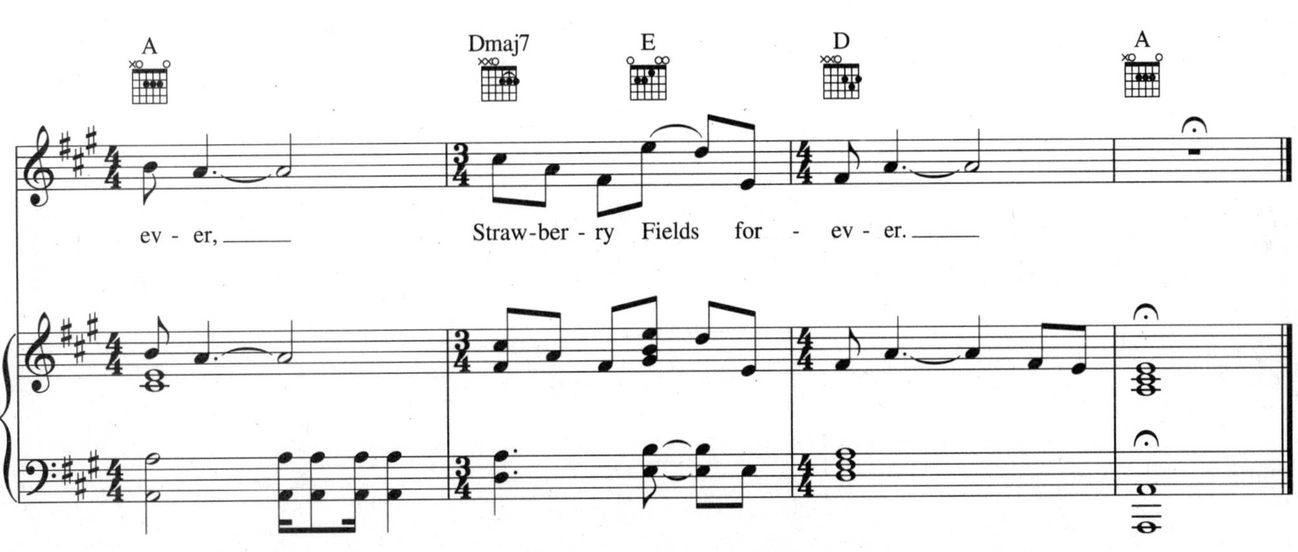
A
Dmaj7
E
D
A
ev - er,
Straw-ber - ry Fields for - ev - er.

STRONG ENOUGH

Words and Music by KEVIN GILBERT,
DAVID BAERWALD, SHERYL CROW,
BRIAN McLEOD, BILL BOTTRELL
and DAVID RICKETTS

A
D
G
Bm
I'd be the last to help you un - der - stand.
You can't change the way I am.
It's try and love me if you can.
When I'm bro - ken down and can - not stand.
A
D
G
Bm
Are you strong e - nough to be my man?
Are you strong e - nough to be my man?
Are you man e - nough to be my man?
Will you be strong e - nough to be my man?
1. 3.
A
D
G
Bm
A
My man.
My man.

D
G
Bm
A
2. 4.
Chorus:
A
E
D/F♯
G
Lie to me,
A
Bm
C
G
I prom - ise I'll be - lieve.
A
E
D/F♯
G
Lie to me,

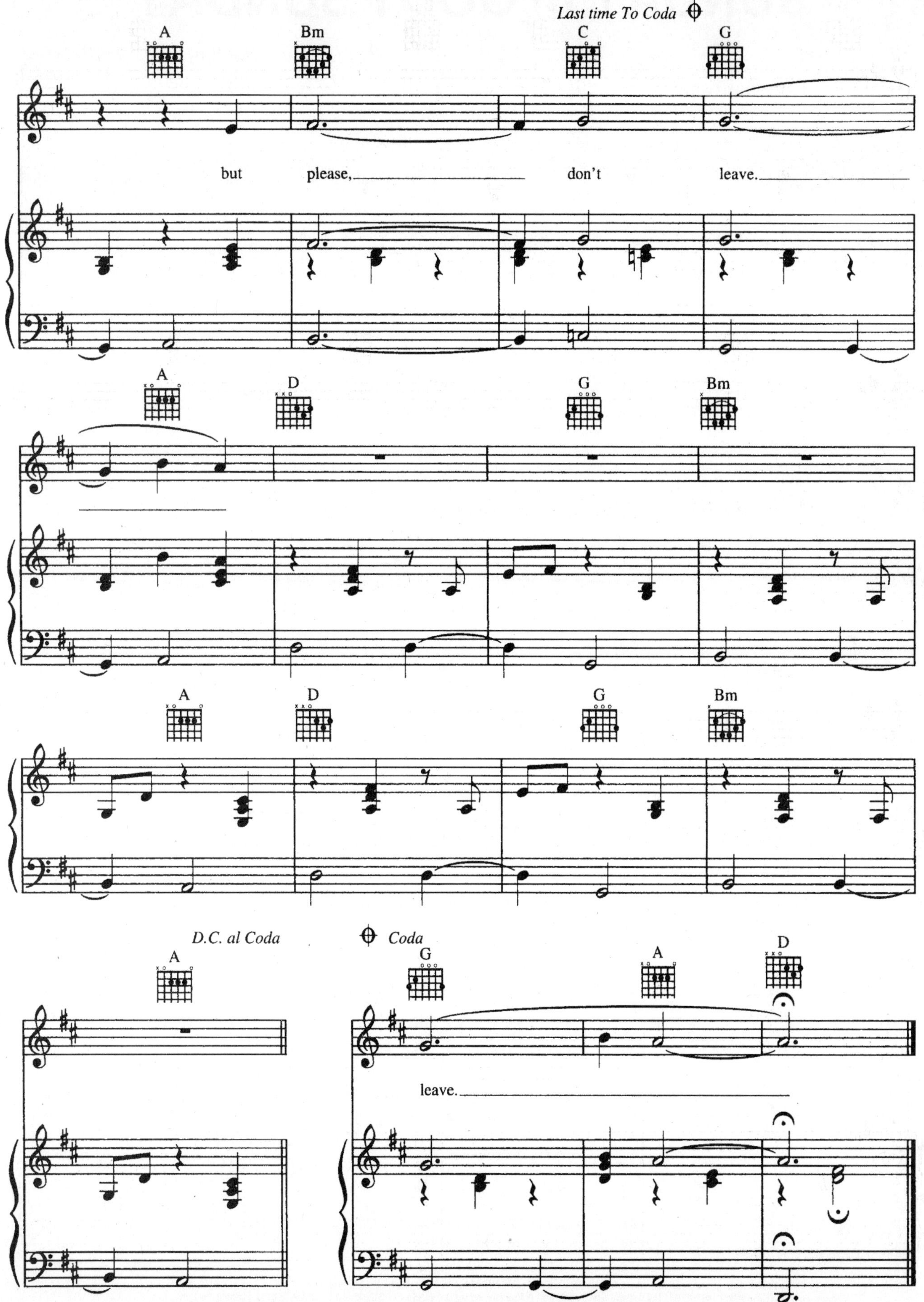
Last time To Coda
A
Bm
C
G
but please, don't leave.
A
D
G
Bm
A
D
G
Bm
D.C. al Coda
Coda
A
G
A
D
leave.

SUNDAY BLOODY SUNDAY

Words by BONO and THE EDGE
Music by U2

* Recorded a half step lower.

Em
Bm
D
long?
'Cause to - night
G
Bm
D
G
we can be as one to - night.
Bm
D
G
Bro - ken bot - tles un - der chil - dren's feet,
And the bat - tle's just be - gun.
Bm
D
G
bod - ies strewn a - cross the dead - end street.
There's man - y lost, but tell me who has won.

Bm D G Bm D
But I won't heed the bat - tle call; it puts my back up, puts my
The trench is dug with-in our hearts, and moth-ers, chil-dren, broth-ers,
G Bm D
back up a-gainst the wall.
sis-ters torn a-part.
(Sun - day Blood - y Sun -
G Bm D G
- day.) (Sun-day Blood-y Sun - day.)
1
F6 C/E D F6 Em
Sun - day Blood-y Sun - day.
(Sun-day Blood-y Sun - day.)

D
Bm
D
G
Bm
D
G
2
D
How long,
Em
D
Em
how long must we sing this song?
How long,
how long?
Bm
D
G
'Cause to - night
we can be as one. To -

Bm
D
G
night,
to - night. (Sun - day Blood - y Sun -
day.)
(Sun - day Blood - y Sun - day.)
Play 4 times
Instrumental solo ad lib.
Wipe the tears from your eyes.
Wipe your tears

Bm
D
G
Bm
D
a - way.
Wipe your tears a - way.
G
Bm
D
Wipe your tears a - way.
(Sun - day Blood - y Sun -
G
Bm
D
G
Oh, wipe your blood - shot eyes.
- day.)
(Sun - day Blood-y Sun - day.)
F6
C/E
D
F6
Em
Sun - day Blood-y Sun - day.
(Sun - day Blood-y Sun - day.)

1
2
D
D
Bm
D
G
Bm
D
G
And it's true, we are _ im-mune _
Bm
D
G
when fact is fic - tion and T - V re - al - i - ty. ___
Bm
D
G
Bm
D
And to - day _ the mil - lions cry.
We eat and drink while to -

G
Bm
D
morrow they die.
The real battle is begun
to claim the vic - t'ry Je - sus won for
you. (Sun - day Blood - y Sun - day.)
(Sun - day Blood - y Sun - day.)
Bm7

SWEET DREAMS
(Are Made Of This)

Words and Music by DAVID A. STEWART
and ANNIE LENNOX

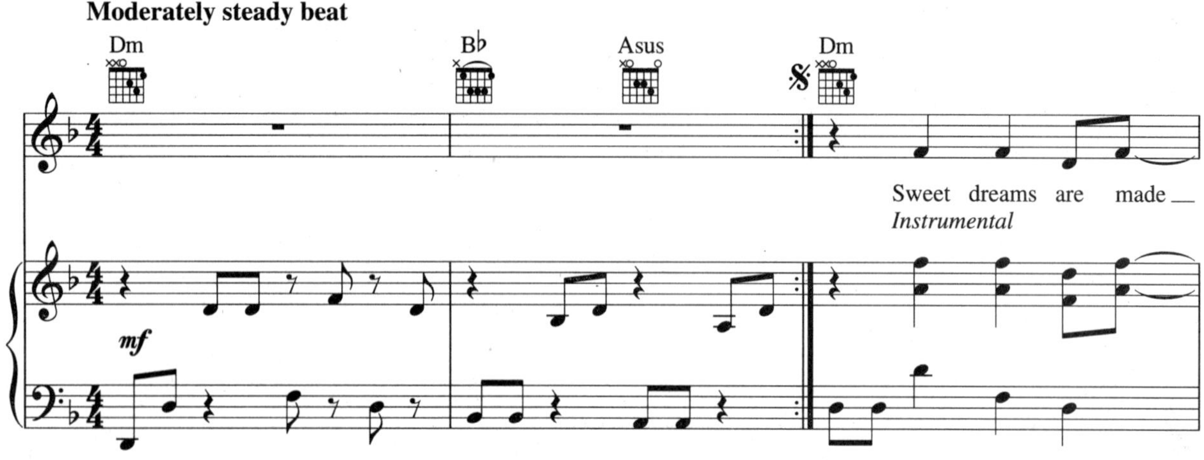

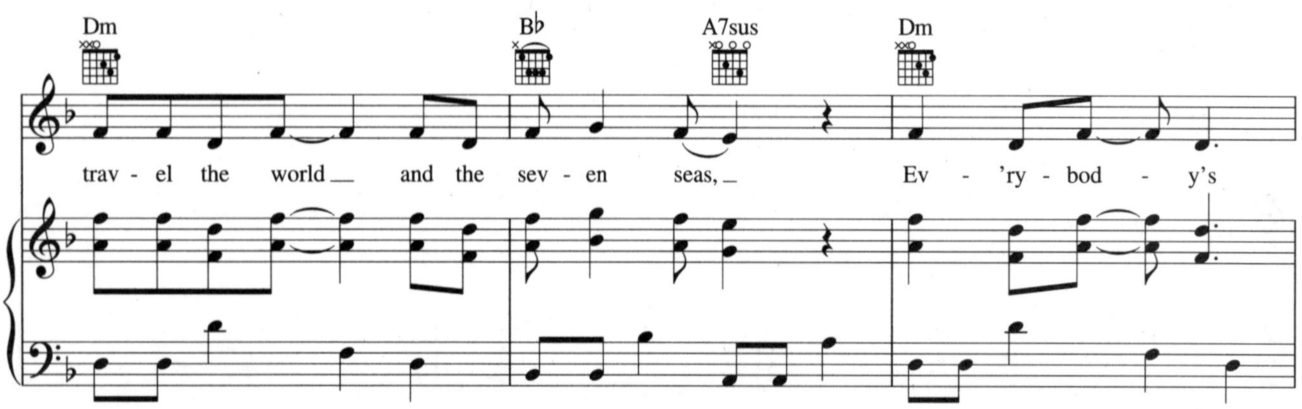

B♭
A7sus
Dm
B♭
A7sus
look - ing for some - thing.
End Instrumental
Some of them want to use you.
Dm
B♭
A7sus
Some of them want to get used by you.
Dm
B♭
Asus
Dm
Some of them want to a - buse you.
Some of them want to be
B♭
A7sus
To Coda
B♭
A
a - bused.

Dm
Gm
3fr
B♭
A
Dm
B♭
A7sus
Sweet dreams are made of this.
Dm
B♭
A7sus
Who am I to dis - a - gree? I
Dm
B♭
A7sus
trav - el the world and the sev - en seas.

Dm
B♭
A7sus
Ev - 'ry - bod - y's look - ing for some - thing.

B♭
A
D

Gm
3fr
B♭
A

Dm
G
Hold your head up. Keep your head up, mov - in' on.

Dm
G
Hold your head up, mov - in' on.
Keep your head up, mov - in' on.

Dm
G
Hold your head up, mov - in' on.
Keep your head up, mov - in' on.

Dm7
G
D.S. al Coda
Hold your head up, mov - in' on.
Keep your head up.

CODA
B♭
A
Dm

Gm
3fr
B♭
A

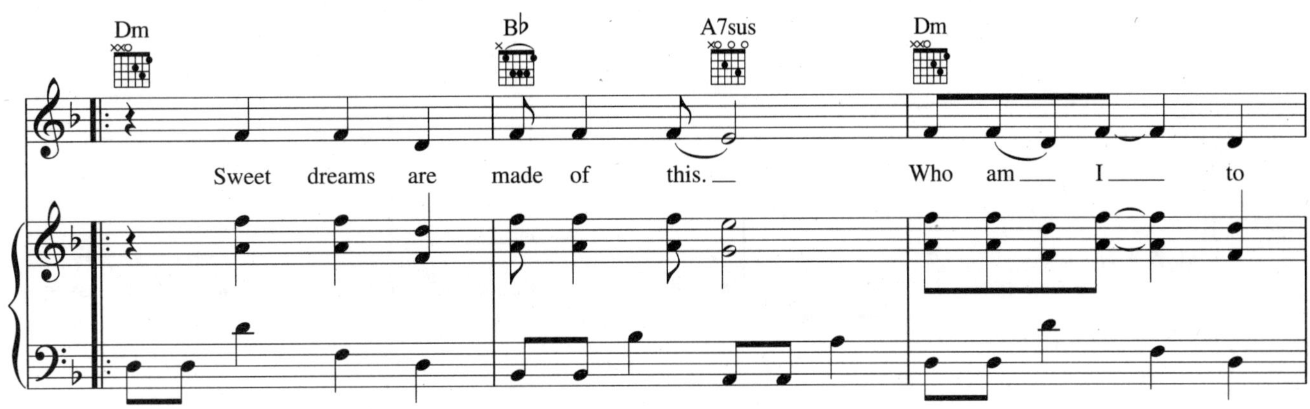
Dm
B♭
A7sus
Dm
Sweet dreams are made of this.
Who am I to

B♭
A7sus
Dm
dis - a - gree?
I trav - el the world and the

B♭
A7sus
Dm
B♭
A7sus
Repeat ad lib.
and Fade
sev - en seas.
Ev - 'ry - bod - y's look - ing for some - thing.

SWEET EMOTION

Words and Music by STEVEN TYLER
and TOM HAMILTON

sweet
e -
D/A
A
mo - tion.
You
I
A
talk a - bout things that no - bod - y cares,
sweet talk - in' ma - ma with a face like a gent,
pulled in - to town in a po - lice car;
Stand in the front just a - shak - in' your ass;
you're wear - in' out things that no - bod - y wears.
said my get - up - and - go must have got up and went.
your dad - dy said I took you just a lit - tle too far.
I'll take you back - stage, you can drink from my glass.

You're call - in' my name but I
Well, I got good news, she's a
You're tell - in' her things but your
I'm talk - in' 'bout some-thin' you can

got - ta make clear. I
real good li - ar, 'cause my
girl - friend lied; you
sure un - der - stand, 'cause a

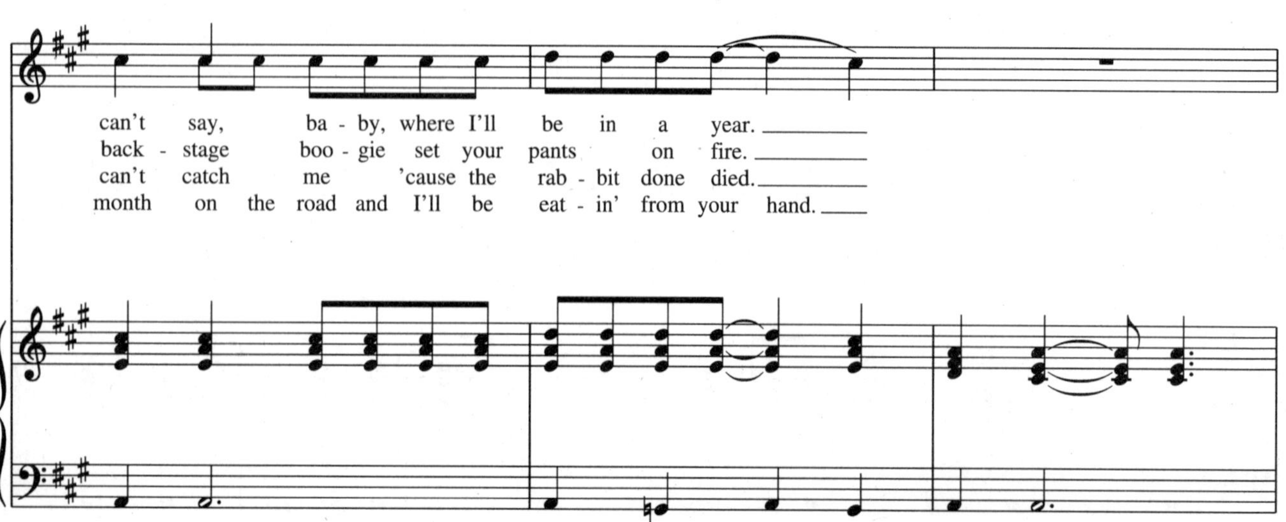
can't say, ba - by, where I'll be in a year.
back - stage boo - gie set your pants on fire.
can't catch me 'cause the rab - bit done died.
month on the road and I'll be eat - in' from your hand.

N.C.
To Coda
1,3
2
D.C. al Coda
(with repeats)
Some
CODA
E7
Repeat and Fade
Optional Ending

TAKE ME TO THE RIVER

Words and Music by AL GREEN
and MABON HODGES

E7
D
A
E7
You stole my mon - ey and my cig - a - rettes,
and I have - n't seen hide nor
Love is a no - tion that I won't for - get,
my sweet six - teen, now I
D
A
C
G
D
hair of you yet. I wan - na know.
Won't you tell me, am I
nev - er re - gret. I wan - na know.
Won't you tell me, am I
A7
in love to stay?
(Take me, take me.)
in love to stay?
Instrumental
E7
D
A
Take me to the riv - er, and wash me down.

E7
D
A
E7
Won't you cleanse my soul,
D
A
E7
To Coda
1
D
A
2
To Next Strain
get my feet on the ground?
Instrumental ends
3
D.S.S. al Coda
D
A
C♯m
A7
Hold me, love me,
C♯m
A7
G/D
squeeze me, tease me till I die,

B7
D.S.
(Take 3rd ending)
till I die.
Take me, ba - by, take me to the
CODA
D A E7
Yeah, yeah,
yeah, yeah,
E7
yeah.
D A E7
Dip me in the wa - ter,
D A
dip me in the
E7
wa - ter, ba - by.
1, 2
D A
Dip me in the
3
D A E7
rit.

TAKE MY BREATH AWAY
(Love Theme)
from the Paramount Picture TOP GUN

Words and Music by GIORGIO MORODER
and TOM WHITLOCK

Cm/G
3 fr
Fm
- n'lly lov - ers know no shame.
be - come the fa - ted ones.
- where there's a love in flames.
Cm/G
3 fr
B♭m
Turn - ing and re - turn - ing to
Turn - ing and re - turn - ing to
Turn - ing and re - turn - ing to
D♭/A♭
4 fr
E♭
3 fr
some se - cret place in - side;
some se - cret place to hide;
some se - cret place in - side;
A♭
4 fr
Cm/G
3 fr
watch - ing in slow mo - tion as you turn a - round and
watch - ing in slow mo - tion as you turn my way and
watch - ing in slow mo - tion as you turn to me and

Db
Eb
3 fr
Ab
4 fr
say,
say,
say,
"Take my breath a - way."
Cm/G
3 fr
To Coda
1 Db
Eb
3 fr
"Take my breath a -
Ab
4 fr
Cm/G
3 fr
Db
way."
Eb
3 fr
2 Fm
Cm/G
3 fr
Ab
4 fr

Bb
Eb/G
3 fr
Db
Through the hour - glass I saw you. In time, you slipped a - way.
Ab
4 fr
Bb
When the mir - ror crashed, I called
Eb/G
3 fr
Db
Ab
4 fr
you and turned to hear you say, "If on - ly for to -
Bb
Eb
3 fr
day I am un - a - fraid.

Ab
4 fr
Cm/G
3 fr
Take my breath a - way."
Fm
1
Cm/G
3 fr
2
Cm/G
3 fr
D.S. al Coda
"Take my breath a -
CODA
Db
Eb
3 fr
Ab
4 fr
My love, take my breath a - way.
Cm/G
3 fr
Db
Eb
3 fr
Repeat and Fade
My love, take my breath a -

TEACH YOUR CHILDREN

Words and Music by
GRAHAM NASH

D
must have a code
that you can
A
live by,
D
and so
G7
be - come your - self,
be - cause the past
D
A
is just a good - bye.

D
Teach your chil - dren
Teach your par - ents
G7
well; their fa - ther's
well; their chil - dren's
D
hell
hell
did slow - ly go by.
will slow - ly go by.
A
And
D
feed then on your dreams,
G7

D
the one they picks,
the one you'll know
A
by.
D
Don't you ev-
er ask them why;
G
if they told you, you would
D
cry,
so just look at them and
Bm
sigh

A
G
A
To Coda
and know they
D
G
love you.
D
A
D
(Can you
And you

G
hear and do you care?
of ten - der years can't know the
D
A
Do you see, you must be
fears that your el - ders grew by,
D
free to teach your chil - dren?
and so please help them with your
G7
D
You'll be - lieve they'll make a
youth. They seek the truth

A
D.S. al Coda
world that we can live in.)
be - fore they can die.
CODA
D
love you.
G
D
A
D
A5
5 fr
D

TEARS IN HEAVEN

Words and Music by ERIC CLAPTON
and WILL JENNINGS

D/F♯
A/E
E
if I saw you in heav - en?
if I saw you in heav - en?
if I saw you in heav - en?
F♯m
C♯/E♯
Em6
(1.,3.) I must be strong
and car - ry on
(2.) I'll find my way
through night and day
F♯
Bm
'cause I know
I don't be - long
'cause I know
I just can't stay
E7sus
To Coda
A
E/G♯
F♯m
A/E
here in heav - en.
here in heav - en.

1
D/F#
E7sus
E7
A
2
D/F#
E7sus
E7
A
C
Bm
Time can bring you down, __
Am
D/F#
G
D/F#
Em
D/F#
G
__ time can bend your knees. __
C
Bm
Am
D/F#
G
D/F#
Time can break the heart, __ have you beg - gin' please, _ beg - gin' please. _

E
A
E/G♯
F♯m
F♯m/E
D/F♯
A/E
E
A
E/G♯
F♯m
F♯m/E
D/F♯
A/E
E
F♯m
C♯/E♯
Em6
Be-yond the door
there's peace, I'm sure,

F#
Bm
E7sus
and I know there'll be no more tears in heav -
A
E/G#
F#m
A/E
D/F#
E7sus
E7
en.
A
D.S. al Coda
CODA
A
E/G#
F#m
en.
A/E
D/F#
E7sus
E7
A
rall.

THESE BOOTS ARE MADE FOR WALKIN'

Words and Music by
LEE HAZLEWOOD

F
You been mess - in' where you should - n't been mess - in',
You keep "same - in'" when you ought - a be chang - in',
I just me a brand - new box of match - es,
C
C/G
and now some - one else is get - tin' all your
now what's right is right, but you ain't been right
and what he / she knows, you ain't got time to
C
Eb
best.
yet.
learn.
These boots are made for
C
Eb
C
walk - in' 'n' that's just what they'll do.

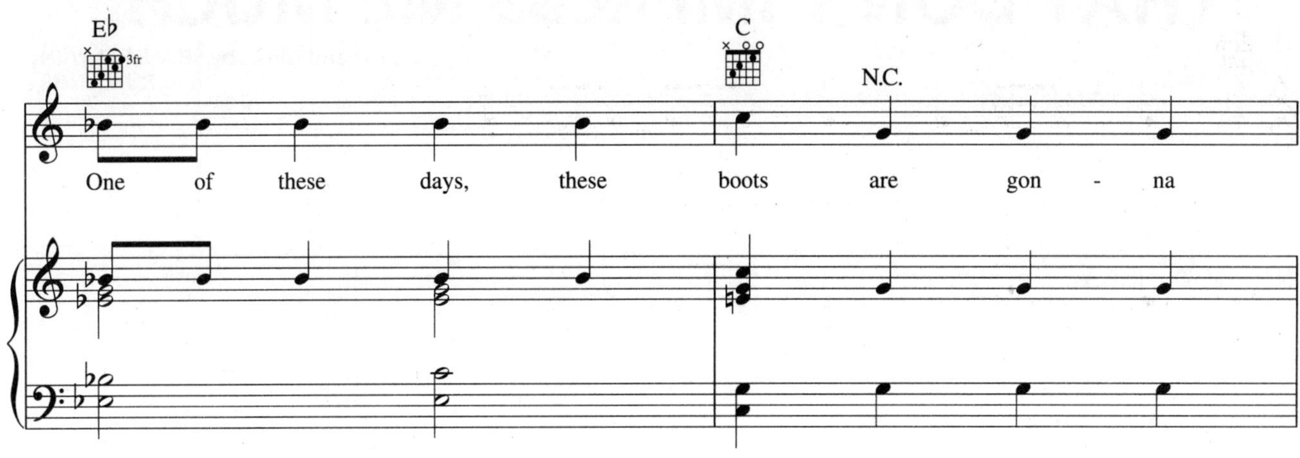
E♭
3fr
C
N.C.
One of these days, these boots are gon - na

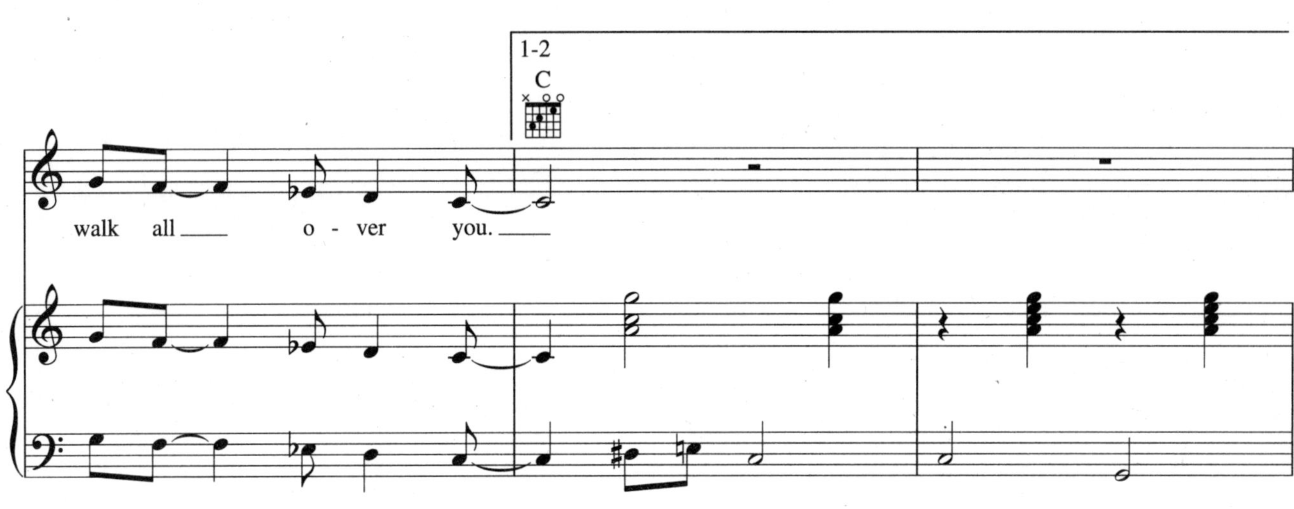
1-2
C
walk all o - ver you.

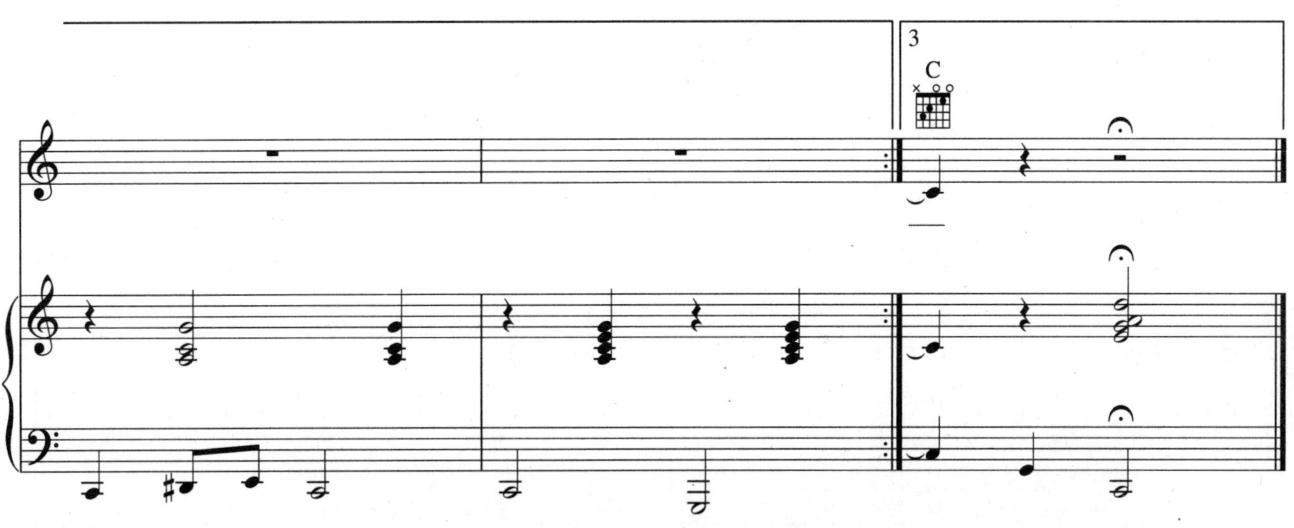
3
C

THAT DON'T IMPRESS ME MUCH

Words and Music by SHANIA TWAIN
and R.J. LANGE

Am
F
C
G
Bbm
Gb
Db
Ab
reg - u - lar o - rig - i - nal, a know - it - all.
heav - en for - bid it should fall out - ta place.
Come on, ba - by, tell me, you must be jok - in', right?
D
A
G
A
D
A
Eb
Bb
Ab
Bb
Eb
Bb
Oh, oh, you think you're spe - cial. Oh, oh, you think you're
G
Ab
N.C.
some - thing else.
(Spoken:) OK, so you're a rocket scientist.
(Spoken:) OK, so you're Brad Pitt.
(Spoken:) OK, so you've got a car.
(Sung:) That don't im -
F
C
G
Am
F
C
Gb
Db
Ab
Bbm
Gb
Db
press me much. So you got the brain, looks, moves, but have you

G
Am
F
C
G
Am
Ab
Bbm
Gb
Db
Ab
Bbm
got the touch? Now don't get me wrong, yeah, I think you're al - right, but
F
C
G
To Coda
Gb
Db
Ab
that won't keep me warm in the mid - dle of the night.
1
N.C.
Am
F
C
G
Bbm
Gb
Db
Ab
That don't im - press me much.
Am
F
C
G
Bbm
Gb
Db
Ab
2
N.C.
I That don't im - press me

Am
F
C
G
Am
F
Bbm
Gb
Db
Ab
Bbm
Gb
much.
Instrumental solo
C
G
Am
F
C
G
Db
Ab
Bbm
Gb
Db
Ab
Am
F
C
G
Bbm
Gb
Db
Ab
D.S. al Coda
Solo ends
You're
CODA
G
F
C
Ab
Gb
Db
- dle of the night. That don't im - press me much.

G
Am
F
C
G
Am
Ab
Bbm
Gb
Db
Ab
Bbm
You think you're cool, _ but have you got the touch? _ Now, now
F
C
G
Am
F
C
Gb
Db
Ab
Bbm
Gb
Db
don't get me wrong, _ yeah, I think you're al - right, but that won't keep me warm on the long, _
G
Ab
cold, _ lone - ly nights. _
Am
F
C
G
Bbm
Gb
Db
Ab
That don't im - press _ me much.

Am
F
C
G
Bbm
Gb
Db
Ab
(Spoken): OK, so what do you
think, you're Elvis or something?
Whatever.
(Sung:) That don't im - press __ me.

THESE DREAMS

Words and Music by MARTIN GEORGE PAGE
and BERNIE TAUPIN

Fadd9
A7sus4
skin in lin - en, per - fume on my wrist, and a
weak - er in my eye - sight, can - dle in my grip, and
wood full of princ - es free - dom is a kiss, but the
Fadd9
C/E
Dm7
full moon that hangs o - ver these dreams in the mist.
words that have no form are fall - ing from my lips.
prince hides his face from dreams in the mist.
Am7
C/E
G/B
F/A
These dreams go on when I close my
mf

C/G
Dm7
C/E
G/B
F/A
eyes. Ev - 'ry sec - ond of the night I
live an - oth - er life. These dreams that sleep when it's cold out -
side; ev - 'ry mo - ment I'm a - wake, the
To Coda
fur - ther I'm a - way.
1
Fadd9

2
Fadd9
G7sus4
There's some - thing out there I can't re - sist.
F/C
C
G/B
I need to hide a - way from the pain.
F/A
C
G7sus4
There's some - thing out there I can't re - sist.
F
C/E
Dm7
C
D.S. al Coda
CODA
C/G
D.S.S. and Fade
F
C/E
fur - ther I'm a - way. These

THIS LOVE

Words and Music by ADAM LEVINE
and JESSE CARMICHAEL

G7/B
Cm
I was so high I did not rec-og-nize the fire burn-ing in
I tried my best to feed her ap-pe-tite, keep her com-ing ev-
Fm
Ddim7
her eyes. The cha-os that con-trolled my mind.
'ry night. So hard to keep her sat-is-fied.
G7/B
Cm
I whis-pered good-bye, she got on a plane nev-er to re-turn
Kept play-ing love like it was just a game. Pre-tend-ing to feel
Fm
Ddim7
a-gain. But al-ways in my heart, oh.
the same then turn a-round and leave a-gain, but oh.

Cm7 Fm Bb7 Eb Cm7 Fm
This love has tak - en its toll on me. She said good - bye too
Bb7 Eb Cm7 Fm Bb7 Eb
man - y times be - fore. And her heart is break - ing in front of me. And
Cm7 F7 Ab G7 G7/B
I have no choice 'cause I won't say good - bye an - y - more, woah,
Cm Fm
1
Ddim7
woah, woah.

2
Ddim7
Fm7
I'll fix these bro - ken things.
E♭maj7
Bdim7
Re - pair your bro - ken wings
and make sure ev - 'ry - thing's al -
Cm
Fm7
- right. It's al - right.
My pres - sure on your hips.
E♭maj7
G7
Sink - ing my fin - ger - tips to ev - 'ry inch of you be - cause I know
3fr

Cm7
3fr
Fm
that's what you want me to do.
This love has
Bb7
Eb
3fr
Cm7
3fr
Fm
tak - en its toll on me.
She said good - bye too
Bb7
Eb
3fr
Cm7
3fr
Fm
man - y times be - fore.
Her heart is
Bb7
Eb
3fr
Cm7
3fr
F7
break - ing in front of me.
And I have no choice 'cause

A♭
G7/B
Cm7
Fm
I won't say good - bye an - y - more.
This love has
B♭7
E♭
Cm7
Fm
tak - en its toll on me.
She said good - bye too
B♭7
E♭
Cm7
Fm
B♭7
E♭
man - y times be - fore.
(1.) And my heart is break - ing in front of me.
(2., 3.) Her heart is break - ing in front of me.
Cm7
F7
A♭
G7
Play 3 times
She said good - bye too man - y times be - fore.
I have no choice 'cause I won't say good - bye an - y - more.

Cm7
Fm
B♭7
E♭
Cm7
Fm
B♭7
E♭
Cm7
Fm
B♭7
E♭
Cm7
F7
A♭
G7
Repeat and Fade
Cm7
Fm7
B♭7
E♭
Optional Ending
Cm

TO LOVE YOU MORE

Words and Music by DAVID FOSTER
and JUNIOR MILES

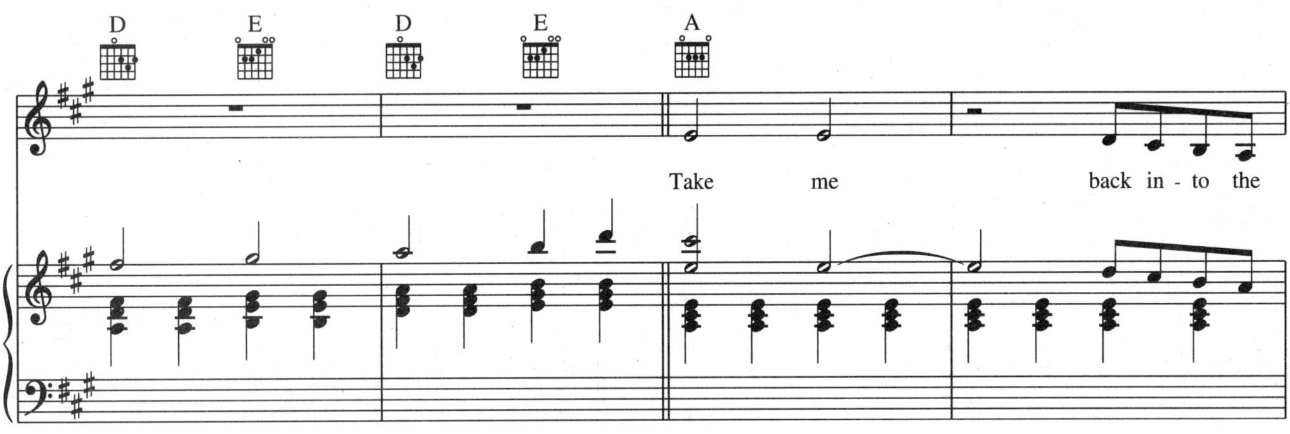

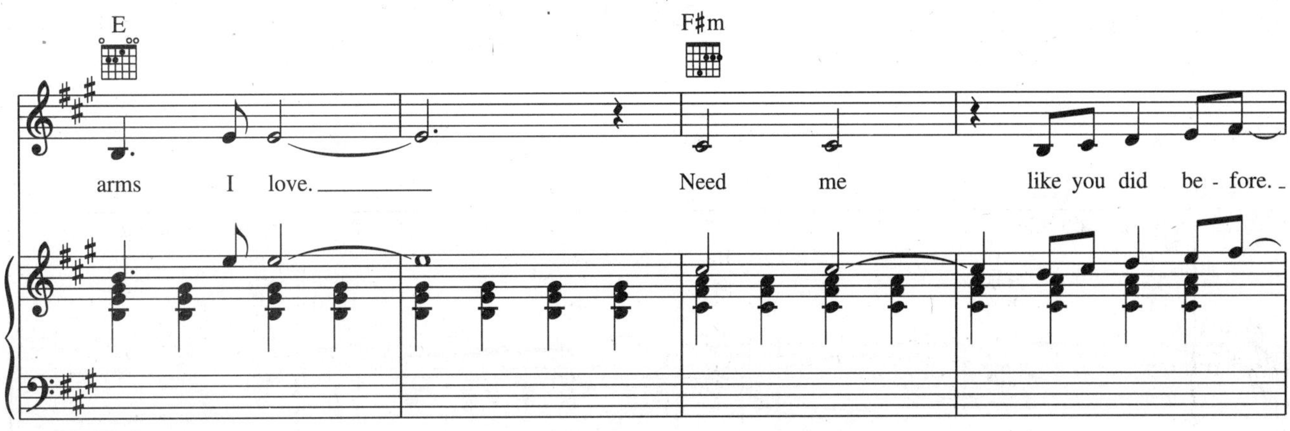

D
E
A
Am
Touch me once a - gain and re -
G
Gm
3 fr
Dm
A
mem - ber when there was no one that you want - ed
Esus
E
A
more.
Don't go, you know you'll
See me as if you
E
F♯m
break my heart.
nev - er know.
She won't
Hold me

D
E/D
love you like I will. I'm the
so you can't let go. Just be -
A/C#
Am/C
G/B
one who'll stay when she walks a - way,
lieve in me. I will make you see
Gm/B♭
Dm
A
Esus
and you know I'll be stand - ing here still.
all the things that your heart needs to know.
E
A
E
F#m
I'll be wait - ing for you here in - side my heart.

C♯m
D
A/E
E
I'm the one who wants to love you more.
A
Esus
E
A
E
(1., 2.) You will
(D.S.) Can't you
see I can give you
F♯m
C♯m
D
ev - 'ry - thing you need. Let me be the one to love
A/E
E
To Coda
A
you more.
2
A
4fr

F
Dm
And some way, all the love that we
A
Dmaj7
F
had can be saved. Whatever it takes,
Dm
Esus
E
we'll find a way.
A
B/A
E/G♯
Em/G

D/F♯
C/E
G/D
C6
F/A
E/G♯
A
Be - lieve in me.
Am
G
Gm
3 fr
Dm
I will make you see all the things that your heart
A
E
Esus
N.C.
D.S. al Coda
needs to know.
I'll be
CODA
A

A
E
F♯m
Oh.
C♯m
4fr
D
A/E
E
Oh.
A
1, 3
Esus
2
4
Dmaj7
A

A THOUSAND MILES

Words and Music by
VANESSA CARLTON

* *Recorded a half step higher.*

E♭5
F
B♭/D
E♭
6fr
3fr
Star-ing blank - ly a - head, just mak - ing my way, mak - ing a way through the
crowd.
E♭sus2
B♭/F
And I need you
'Cause I need you
And I still need you
and I'll miss you,
and I'll miss you,
and I still miss you,
To Coda
E♭(add9)
and now I won - der, if

F/E♭ E♭sus2 F Fsus Dm B♭/D F/E♭ E♭sus2
6fr
I could fall into the sky, do
you think time would pass me by? 'Cause
you know I'd walk a thousand miles if I could
Gm7 Dm7/A F
just see you to-night.

Eb5
F
Bb/D
Eb5
F
Bb/D
Eb5
(1.) It's
1
F
Bb/D
Eb5
F
Bb/D
Eb5
al-ways times like these when I think of you and I won-der if you ev-er
F
Bb/D
Eb5
F
Bb/D
Eb5
think of me.
'Cause
F
Bb/D
Eb5
F
Bb/D
Eb5
ev-'ry-thing's so wrong and I don't be-long liv-ing in your pre-cious

F
B♭/D
E♭5
6fr
F
B♭/D
E♭5
6fr
mem - o - ry.
2
F
B♭/D
E♭5
6fr
F
B♭/D
E♭5
6fr
And
Gm7
F/A
F/B♭
Cm6
3fr
Gm7
F/A
I, I don't want to let you know. I, I
F/B♭
Cm6
3fr
Gm7
F/A
F/B♭
Cm6
3fr
drown in your mem - o - ry. I, I don't want to let this go.

Gm7
F/A
F7sus
D.S. al Coda
CODA
E♭(add9)
F
I, I don't.
won - der,
F/E♭
E♭sus2
F
Fsus
Dm
B♭/D
if I could fall into the sky, do
you think time would pass us by? 'Cause
you know I'd walk a thou - sand miles if I could

Gm7
Dm7/A
F
just see you. If
F/E♭
E♭sus2
F
Fsus
Dm
B♭/D
F/E♭
E♭sus2
I could fall in - to the sky, do
you think time would pass me by? 'Cause
you know I'd walk a thou - sand miles if I could
6fr

Gm7
Dm7/A
F
just see you, if I could
Gm7
F/A
F
just hold you to -
B♭sus
B♭maj7(no3rd)
B♭
E♭5
6fr
night.
B♭sus
B♭maj7(no3rd)
B♭
E♭5
B♭sus
B♭
B♭sus

TIGHTER AND TIGHTER

Words and Music by TOMMY JAMES
and ROBERT KING

Bm7
A
ev - er gave me such a beau - ti - ful feel - ing.
A
D/A
Wo - man you touch my soul, now. Hon - ey, don't let go now.
Bm7
A
Hold on, ba - by, just a lit - tle bit tight - er. Just
D
E
hold on a lit - tle bit tight - er, babe.

D
E
I love you so much and I can't let go.
G
A
Hold on just a lit-tle bit tight-er, ba - by.
To Coda
A
D/A
N.C.
A
D/A

A
D/A
Love is so sur-pris - ing. I o-pened up my eyes and
Bm7
A
D.S. al Coda
you reached out and you took my hand.
CODA
N.C.
A
D/A
Bm7

A
D
Hold on a lit - tle bit
E
D
tight - er, babe. I love you so much and I
E
G
can't let go. Hold on just a lit - tle bit
A
N.C.
tight - er, ba - by.

A
D/A
Just a lit - tle, just a lit - tle, just a lit - tle bit tight - er, now, ba - by.
A
D/A
Just a lit - tle, just a lit - tle, just a lit - tle bit tight - er, now babe.
A
D/A
Just a lit - tle, just a lit - tle, just a lit - tle bit tight - er, now, ba - by.
E
F♯
hold on a lit - tle bit tight - er, babe.

E
F♯
I love you so much and I can't let go.
A
B
Hold on just a lit - tle bit tight - er, ba - by.
N.C.
B
E/B
Just a lit - tle bit,
just a lit - tle bit.

C#m
4fr
B
Come on, ba - by, lit - tle bit tight - er.
E/B
Just a lit - tle bit,
just a lit - tle bit.
Repeat and Fade
C#m
4fr
B
Come on, ba - by, lit - tle bit tight - er.
Optional Ending
C#m
4fr
B
Come on, ba - by, lit - tle bit tight - er.

TIME AFTER TIME

Words and Music by CYNDI LAUPER
and ROB HYMAN

F G Em F G Em
Flash back warm nights, al-most left be-hind.
F G Em F F/G Dm/C C
Suit - case of mem - o - ries time af - ter. Some - times you
Af - ter my
p
Dm/C C Dm/C C Dm/C C Dm/C C
pic - ture me. I'm walk - ing too far a - head. You're call - ing
pic - ture fades and dark - ness has turned to gray, watch - ing through
Dm/C C Dm/C C Dm/C C F G
to me, I can't hear what you've said. Then (1., 3.) you say
win - dows, you're won - der - ing if I'm O. K. Se - crets

Em
F
G
Em
F
G
go slow. I fall be - hind. The sec - ond hand
sto - len from deep in - side. The drum beats out
Em
F
G
Am
un - winds.
of time.
If you're lost, you can look and you will find me,
mf
F
G
C
G
time af - ter time. If you fall, I will catch you; I'll be
Am
F
G
C
wait - ing, time af - ter time.
If you're lost,
(Instrumental)

G
Am
F
G
you can look and you will find me,
time af - ter time.
C
G
Am
If you fall, I will catch you; I'll be wait - ing,
F
G
To Coda
1
C
2
C
D.S. al Coda
time af - ter time.
(End instrumental)
CODA
C
F
G
C
Repeat and Fade
Time af - ter time.
p

TRAIN IN VAIN

Words and Music by MICK JONES
and JOE STRUMMER

D
A
Bm
D
things you can ex - plain a - way,
but the heart-ache's in me 'til this
D
A/C♯
A
D
A/C♯
A
day.
You did-n't stand by me?
No, not at all!
You did-n't stand by
D
A/C♯
A
D
A/C♯
A
D
A/C♯
A
me?
No way!
All the times
when we were
job
but it don't
D
A/C♯
A
D
A/C♯
A
D
A/C♯
A
close.
I'll re-mem - ber these things the most.
I see
pay.
I need new clothes,
I need some-where to stay.
But, with

D Bm D A/C♯ A
all my dreams come tum-bl-ing down. I can't be hap-py with-out you a-
out all these things I can do But with-out your love I won't make it
D A/C♯ A D A
round. So a-lone I keep the wolves at bay. And there's
through. But you don't un-der stand my point of view. I sup-
Bm D D A/C♯ A
on-ly one thing I can say. You did-n't stand by me? No, not at all!
pose there's noth-ing I can do.
D A/C♯ A D A/C♯ A D A/C♯ A
To Coda
You did-n't stand by me? No way! You must ex-

F♯m
Bm
A
D
A/C♯
A
plain
why this must be.
D
A/C♯
A
F♯m
Bm
A
Did you lie
when you spoke to
D
A/C♯
A
D
A/C♯
A
D
A/C♯
A
me?
Did you stand by
me?
No, not at all!
D
A/C♯
A
D.S. al Coda
Now I got a
CODA
D
A/C♯
A
way!
You did-n't stand by

D
A/C♯
A
F♯m
Bm
me? No, not at all! You did-n't stand by me? No
way! You must ex - plain why this must be.
Did you lie
when you spoke to me? Did you stand by

D
A/C♯
A
me?
Did you stand by
me?
No, not at all!
Did you stand by
me?
No
way!
Repeat and Fade
Optional Ending

TROUBLE

Words and Music by GUY BERRYMAN,
JON BUCKLAND, WILL CHAMPION
and CHRIS MARTIN

Bm7
F
Am
G
and thought of all the stu - pid things I'd said.
G
Em7
Bm
G
Em7
Bm7
G
Em9
Bm*
F6
Amadd11
2. Oh no, what's this? A spi - der web and I'm caught in the mid - dle.
(Verse 3 see block lyric)
G
Em9
Bm*
F6
Amadd11
So I turned to run, and thought of all the stu - pid things I'd

G
Aadd11
Em7
done. And ah, I nev - er meant to cause you trou - ble. And
Aadd11
Em7
ah, I nev - er meant to do you wrong. And
Aadd11
Em7
ah, well if I ev - er caused you trou - ble, then
To Coda
Aadd11
Em7
G
Em7
oh no, I nev - er meant to do you harm.

Bm
G
Em7
Bm7
7fr
D.𝄋 al Coda
CODA
Em7
G
Em9
Bm*
7fr
G
Em9
Bm*
7fr
G
Em9
Bm*
7fr
G
Em9
Bm*
7fr
Em
F♯m
2fr
They spun a web
G*
3fr
F♯m
2fr
Em
F♯m
2fr
G*
3fr
F♯m
2fr
Em
F♯m
2fr
for me, and they spun a web for me, and they spun a web

Verse 3:
Oh no, I see a spider web and it's me in the middle.
So I twist and turn, but here am I in my little bubble.

Singing out ah, I never meant to cause you trouble,
Ah, I never meant to do you wrong.
And ah, well if I ever caused you trouble,
Then oh no, I never meant to do you harm.

TULSA TIME

Words and Music by
DANNY FLOWERS

F
peo - ple all live so fine. My
guess I'm just - a wast - in time. Well,
ba - by said I's cra - zy, my Mom - ma called me la - zy, I was
then I got to think - in', man, I'm real - ly sink - in' and I
C
goin' to show 'em all this time, 'Cause you
real - ly had a flash this time, I
know I ain't no fool - in', I don't need no more school - in', I was
had no bus - 'ness leav - in' and no - bod - y would be griev - in' if I

F
born to just walk the line.
went on back to Tulsa time.
Liv-in' on Tul-sa time.
Liv-in' on Tul-sa time.
Liv-in' on Tul-sa time.
Liv-in' on Tul-sa time.
C
Well, you know I been thru it when I set my watch back to it,
Gon-na set my watch back to it, cause you know I've been thru it,
1 F
2 F
D.S. and Fade
Liv-in' on Tul-sa time.
Well,

TRUE COMPANION

Words and Music by
MARC COHN

D
A
E
A
when it comes to love, I'm just an - oth - er fool. Yes, I'll
E
A
D
A
E
A
climb a moun - tain, I'm gon - na swim the sea.
D
A
E
A
There ain't no act of God, girl,
D
A
E
A
could keep you safe from me,

D
A
Bm/F♯
F♯m
My arms are reach - ing out,
Bm/F♯
F♯m
A
D9/A
4fr
out a - cross this can - yon.
A
D9/A
4fr
D
A
I'm ask - ing you to be my
E
A
D
A
true com - pan - ion, true

D
A
D
A
companion,
E
A
D
A
To Coda
true com - pan - ion.
1
E
A
D
A
E
D
D.S.
2
E
A
D
A
E
A
true com-pan - ion.

D A E D

A E A

D A E D

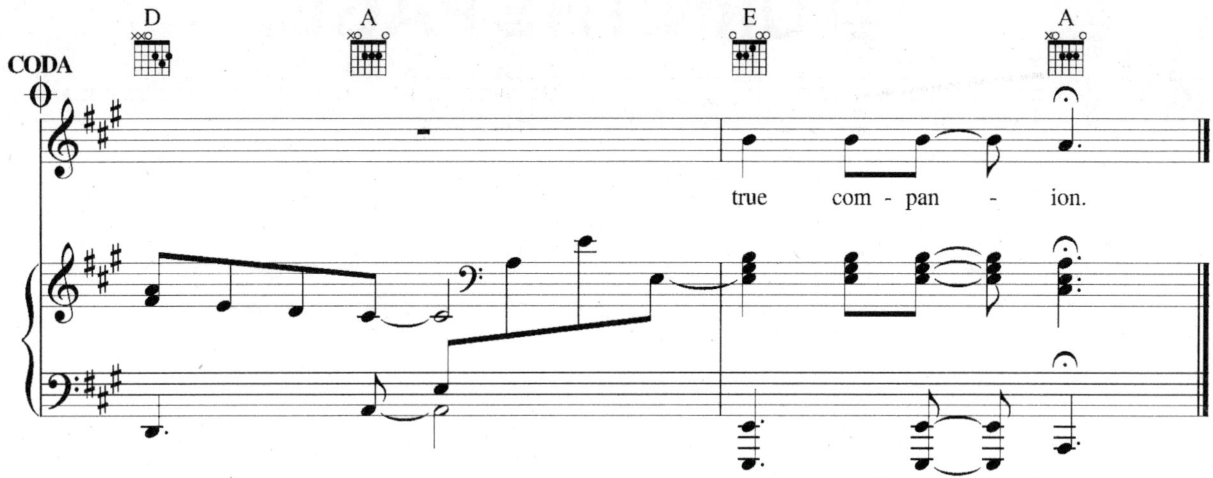

2. So don't you dare and try to walk away;
I've got my heart set on our wedding day.
I've got this vision of a girl in white,
Made my decision that it's you all right.
And when I take your hand,
I'll watch my heart set sail.
I'll take my trembling fingers
And I'll lift up your veil.
Then I'll take you home,
And with wild abandon
Make love to you just like a true companion.
You are my true companion.
I got a true companion,
Woah, a true companion.

3. When the years have done irreparable harm,
I can see us walking slowly arm in arm,
Just like that couple on the corner do,
'Cause girl I will always be in love with you.
And when I look in your eyes,
I'll still see that spark,
Until the shadows fall,
Until the room grows dark.
Then when I leave this earth,
I'll be with the angels standin';
I'll be out there waiting for my true companion,
Just for my true companion.
True companion,
True companion.

TURN THE PAGE

Words and Music by
BOB SEGER

Em
fore.
But your thoughts will soon be wan-der-in' the
D
way they al - ways do when you're rid - in' six - teen hours and there's
A
noth - in' much to do and you don't feel much like rid - in', you just
Em
Chorus
wish the trip was through.
Say, here I

D
Em
am on the road a - gain. There I
D
Em
am up on the stage. Here I
D
A
To Coda
go play - in' star a - gain. There I
C
D
1, 2
Em
go, turn the page.

Additional Lyrics

2. Well, you walk into a restaurant strung out from the road
And you feel the eyes upon you as you're shakin' off the cold;
You pretend it doesn't bother you but you just want to explode.
Most times you can't hear 'em talk, other times you can,
All the same old cliches, "Is that a woman or a man?"
And you always seem out numbered, you don't dare make a stand.
Chorus

3. Out there in the spotlight you're a million miles away.
Every ounce of energy you try to give away
As the sweat pours out your body like the music that you play.
Later in the evening as you lie awake in bed
With the echoes from the amplifiers ringing in your head,
You smoke the day's last cigarette remembering what she said.
Chorus

UNCHAIN MY HEART

Words and Music by BOBBY SHARP
and TEDDY POWELL

* Recorded a half step lower.

Dm6/F
Am6
Dm6/F
You got me sewn up like a pil - low - case,
but you let my love
Ev - 'ry time I call you on the phone,
some fel - la tells me that you're
Am6
F7
E7
go to waste.
not at home.
So un - chain
my heart, oh please, please, set me free.
Solo continues
Am
1
N.C.
2, 3
Un - chain my heart.
I'm un - der your spell,
Solo ends
I'm un - der your spell,
Dm6
Am6
like a man in a trance.

Dm6
F7
But I know darn well
that I don't stand a
E7
Am6
chance.
So un - chain my heart.
Let me go my way.
Un - chain my heart.
F9
Am6
You wor - ry me night and day.

Dm6/F
Am6
Why lead me through a life of mis - er - y,
Dm6/F
Am6
F7
when you don't care a bag of beans for me? So un - chain my heart, oh
E7
To Coda
Am
D.S. al Coda
(take 2nd ending)
please, please, set me free.
Instrumental solo
CODA
Am
Dm
Am
Repeat and Fade
Optional Ending
Dm
Am
(Vocal ad lib. on repeats)
Oh, won't you set me free?

VERTIGO

Music by U2
Lyrics by BONO

D5
E5
D5
E5
D5
E5
A5
G♯5
G5
5fr
7fr
5fr
7fr
5fr
7fr
5fr
4fr
3fr
N.C.
1.Lights go down, it's
dark, the jun - gle is your head, can't rule your heart. A feel - ing so much
strong - er than a thought, your eyes are wide and though your
soul it can't be bought your mind can wan - der.

E
7fr
D
5fr
G5*
Hel - lo, hel - lo, (Hola!)
I'm at a place called
A5*
2fr
Ver - ti - go. (Dónde está?)
It's ev - 'ry - thing I wish I
did - n't know except you
give me some - thing
I can feel.
D5
E5
To Coda
A5
G#5
G5
4fr
3fr
Feel.
2.The

N.C.
night is full of holes, as bul-lets rip the sky of ink with
gold.___ They twin-kle as the boys play rock and
roll.___ They know that they can't dance, at least they know... I___ can't stand the
beats, I'm ask-ing for the cheque, the girl___ with crim-son nails has Je-sus round her

neck, swing - ing to the mu - sic, swing - ing to the
D.S. al Coda
mu - sic. Oh. Oh. Oh.
Coda
D5 E5 D5 E5 D5 E5 A5
5fr 7fr 5fr 7fr 5fr 7fr 5fr
A G5* D A
G5* D A G5*
Check mat - ed, hours of fun,

D
A
D5
E5
D5
E5
D5
E5
5fr
7fr
check_ mat - ed.
A5
G♯5
G5
4fr
3fr
Em
Em7
All of this, all of this can be yours. All of this,
all of this can be yours. All of this, all of this can be yours. Just

Em7
N.C.
E
7fr
give me what I want, and no one gets hurt...
Hel - lo,
hel - lo,
D
5fr
G5*
A5*
2fr
E
7fr
(Hola!)
we're at a place called Ver - ti - go.
(Dónde está?)
Lights go down and
D
5fr
G5*
A5*
2fr
E
7fr
all I know is that you
give me some - thing and
I can feel your love teach-
D
G5
3fr
A5
5fr
E5
7fr
- ing me how.
Your love is

D
5fr
G5*
A5*
2fr
teach - ing me how, how to kneel.
D5 E5 D5 E5 D5 E5 A5 G#5 G5 D5 E5 D5 E5 D5 E5
Kneel.
A5 G#5 G5 D5 E5 D5 E5 D5 E5 A5 G#5 G5
Yeah, yeah, yeah, yeah, yeah, yeah, yeah,
D5 E5 D5 E5 D5 E5 A5 G#5 G5 E*
yeah, yeah, yeah, yeah, yeah, yeah, yeah, yeah, yeah!
8vb

WALK AWAY

Words and Music by
JOE WALSH

Fm
Db
me
you don't
want to talk a - bout it. Seems to
me
we talk all
night; here comes the morn - ing. Seems to
Fm
Db
Eb
3fr
me
you just
turn your pret - ty head and walk a - way.
me
you just
for - get what we said and greet the day.
Ab
4fr
Bbm
Cb
Bbm

A♭
D♭/A♭
A♭
D♭/A♭
4fr
Instrumental
cool my-self down; _
stomp-in' a - round. _
Think in' some words _ I can't name _ ya.
Meet you half way; _ got noth- in' to say. _
Still, I don't s'pose _ I can blame _
_ ya.
N.C.
Fm
Seems to me _ you don't

D♭
Fm
wan - na talk a - bout it. Seems to me you just
D♭
E♭
3fr
A♭
4fr
turn your pret - ty head and walk a - way.
B♭m
C♭
1
B♭m
A♭
4fr
D♭/A♭
4fr
A♭
4fr
D♭/A♭
4fr
I've got to

2
B♭m
A♭
4fr
Walk a - way.
Repeat and Fade
B♭m
C♭
B♭m
A♭
4fr
Optional Ending
B♭m
A♭
4fr
Walk a - way.

WALKING ON BROKEN GLASS

Words and Music by
ANNIE LENNOX

F
C
C/E
F
C/E
F
but I don't care for sug - ar, hon - ey,
but we've been hurt - ing one an - oth - er.
if I can't have you.
Now the pain has cut
C/E
F
G
Am
C
too deep.
Since you a - ban - doned me,
So, take me from the wreck - age,
To Coda
F
C
G/B
Am
my whole life has crashed.
save me from the blast.
Won't you pick the
Em
F
Gsus
3fr
piec - es up 'cause it feels just like I'm walk - ing on bro - ken

C C/E F C/E F C/E G C C/E F C/E F
glass.
Walk-ing on, walk-ing on bro - ken glass. Whoo,
C/E G C C/E F C/E F C/E G
hoo, yeah. Walk-ing on, walk-ing on bro - ken glass.
C C/E F C/E F C/E G Am
The sun's still shin - ing in the
G/B C C/E F C/E F C/E F G
deep blue sky, but it don't mean noth - ing to me.

F(add2)
Gsus
3fr
Whoa, let the rain come down,
C/E
F
C/E
F
C/E
F
G
Am
let the wind blow through me.
I'm liv-ing in an
C
F
C
G/B
emp - ty room
with all the win-dows smashed,
Am
C
Gsus
3fr
and I've got so lit-tle left to lose that it feels just like I'm

G
N.C.
C
C/E
F
C/E
F
C/E
G
walk - ing on bro - ken glass.
Walk - ing on, walk - ing on bro - ken glass.
C
C/E
F
C/E
F
C/E
G
Dm11
5fr
B♭
And if you're try - ing to cut me down,
And if you want to hurt me,
F
you know that I might leave
there's noth - ing left to fear

Dm9
B♭
'cause if you try to cut me down,
'cause if you want to hurt me,
1
F
I know that you'll suc - ceed.
2
Gsus
3 fr
you're do - ing real - ly well by me.
C
C/E
F
C/E
F
C/E
F
G
C
C/E
F
C/E
F
C/E
G
D.S. al Coda

CODA
Am
C
Lift me up and take me back. Don't let me
F
Gsus
3fr
keep on walk - ing. I can't keep on walk - ing on,
G/B
C
C/E
F
C/E
F
I can't keep on walk-ing on bro - ken glass.
Walk-ing on, walk-ing on
Repeat and Fade
Optional Ending
C/E
G
C
C/E
F
C/E
F
C/E
G
C
bro - ken glass.

WALK ON BY

Lyric by HAL DAVID
Music by BURT BACHARACH

Bb
C
Fmaj7
pri - vate 'cause each time I see you, I break down and cry.
tears and the sad - ness you gave me when you said good - bye.
Bb
Fmaj7
Bb
Walk on by. Don't stop! Walk on by.
Fmaj7
Bb
1
Fmaj7
Don't stop! Walk on by.
Bb
2
Fmaj7

WALKING IN MEMPHIS

Words and Music by
MARC COHN

G5
C5
A5
F5
3fr
5fr
W. C. Han - dy, won't you look down o - ver me?
(dou - ble - u)
Yeah, I've got a first - class tick - et but I'm as
blue as a boy can be. Then I'm walk - ing in Mem - phis.
Am
F
G
C
Was walk - ing with my feet ten feet off of Beale. Walk - ing in Mem -

F
G
C
Am
F
G
- phis,
but do I real - ly feel the way _ I feel? _
F5
Gsus
F5
C/E
Dm
F5
Gsus
F5
Saw the ghost of El -
C/E
Dm
F5
Gsus
F5
C/E
Dm
F5
- vis on Un - ion Av - e - nue, fol - lowed him up
Gsus
F5
C/E
Dm
F5
Gsus
F5
to the gates of Grace - land, then I watched him walk _ right through. _
3fr

C/E
Dm
C/E
F5
Gsus
3fr
C
Am
F5
Now se - cur - i - ty, they did not__ see him; they just
Gsus
C
Am
F5
Gsus
hov - ered 'round his__ tomb, but there's a pret - ty lit - tle thing_ wait -
C
Am
F5
C
ing for the King_ down in the Jun - gle Room. When I was walk - ing in Mem -
F
G
C
Am
F
G
Am7
- phis I was walk - ing with my feet ten feet off of Beale._

F
G
C
Am7
Walk - ing in Mem - phis
but do I real - ly
F
G
C7sus
C7
feel the way I feel?
3
C7sus
C7
C7sus
They've got cat - fish on the ta -
C7
C7sus
C7
- ble;
they've got
3

C7sus
C7
gos - pel in the air,
Suddenly slowly, freely
C
E7
F7
and Rev - er - end Green be glad to see you when you
F♯dim
9fr
G7
have - n't got a prayer, but
F5
G5
3fr
C5
3fr
A5
5fr
F5
boy, you've got a prayer in Mem - phis.
a tempo

G5
C5
A5
F5
G5
C5
Now Mu - ri - el plays pi - an - o
A5
F5
G5
C5
A5
F5
ev - 'ry Fri - day at the Hol - ly - wood,
and they
G5
C5
A5
F5
G5
C5
brought me down
to see her
and they asked me if I would,
A5
F
G7sus
C
Am
well, do a lit - tle num - ber,
and I

F G7sus C Am F G
sang with all my might. She said, "Tell me, are you a Chris-
C Am7 F5 C
- tian, child?" and I said, "Ma'am I am to - night." Walk - ing in Mem-
F G C Am7 F G
- phis. I was walk - ing with my feet ten feet off of Beale.
Am F G C Am7
Walk - ing in Mem - phis, but do I real - ly

1
F
C/E
Dm
C
Am7
2
F
G
F5
feel the way I feel?
Walk - ing in Mem -
feel the way I feel?
G5
C5
A5
F5
3fr
5fr
Put on my blue suede shoes and I board - ed the plane.
Touched down in the land of the Del - ta Blues in the

G5
C5
A5
F5
G5
C
mid - dle of the pour - ing rain.
Touched down in the land of the
rit.
Am
F
G
F5
G5
C5
Del - ta Blues in the mid - dle of the pour - ing rain.
a tempo
A5
F5
G5
C5
A5
F5
G5
C5
A5
F5
Gsus
G
C

WALTZ #2
(XO)

Words and Music by
ELLIOTT SMITH

F/C
B♭
N.C.
Gm
3fr
B♭
Em7♭5
1. First the mike, then a half ci - gar - ette,
2. Now she's done and they're call - ing some - one
3. Look - ing out on the sub - sti - tute scene,
E♭
C9/E
F
F7
sing - ing "Ca - thy's Clown": that's the man
such a fa - mi - liar name. I'm so glad
still go - ing strong! And it's oh,
Cm
3fr
Gm
3fr
she's mar - ried to now,
that my mem - 'ry's re - mote, 'cause I'm
mom,

Am7b5
D7
that's the girl that he takes a-round town. She ap-pears
do-ing just fine hour to hour, note to note.
it's o-kay, it's al-right, no-thing's wrong.
Gm
3fr
Bb
Em7b5
composed, so she is, I sup-pose;
Here it is, the re-venge to the tune:
Tell mis-ter man with im-pos-si-ble plans to just
Eb
C9/E
F
F7
F7/Bb
3
who can real-ly tell? She shows
"You're no good. You're no good,
leave me a-lone in the place

Cm
Gm
3fr
no e - mo - tion at all,
you're no good, you're no good."
where I make no mis - takes,
Am7♭5
Cm6
D7
D7/F♯
stares in - to space like a dead chi - na doll.
Can't you tell that it's well un - der - stood?
in the place where I have what it takes.
Gm
Cm
Gm
E♭m
I'm nev - er gon - na know you now, but I'm
B♭
F7
To Coda
Gm
gon - na love you a - ny - how.

B♭
E♭
B♭/D
E♭
B♭/D
F/C
1.
B♭
N.C.
2.
B♭
Bdim
Cm
3fr
I'm here to - day, ex - pect -
E♭maj9
E♭maj7
B♭
F/A
- ed to stay on and on and on.

Gm
Cm
I'm tired,
I'm tired.
E♭
D.S. al Coda
Coda
Gm
B♭
E♭
B♭/D
I'm nev - er gon - na know you now, but I'm
(Vocal tacet 3°)
E♭
B♭/D
1, 2.
F/C
3.
F/C
B♭
gon - na love you a - ny - how.

THE WARRIOR

Words and Music by NICK GILDER
and HOLLY KNIGHT

A
Bm
Well, is - n't love
prim - i - tive,
A
G
A
a wild gift that you wan - na give?
Break out of cap -
Bm
G
A
tiv - i - ty
and fol - low me, ster - e - o jun - gle child.
G
D
Love is the kill,
your heart's still wild.

Chorus

D
G
A
Bm
Shoot-ing at the walls of heart - ache, bang, bang. I am the
war - ri - or. Well, I am the war - ri - or, and
D/A
D/F♯
heart to heart you'll win, if you sur - vive
the war - ri - or, the war - ri - or.
1

2
A
Bm
D
G
A
Bm
war - ri - or.
I am
the war - ri - or.
G
A7/G
Instrumental solo ad lib.
Play 4 times
G
A7/G
D
G
A
Bm
Shoot - ing at the walls of heart - ache,

D
G
A
Bm
the war - ri - or,
(Shoot - ing at the walls of heart - ache.)
D
G
A
Bm
I am the war - ri - or, and
D/A
A
D/F#
G
heart to heart you'll win,
D/A
A
D/F#
G
heart to heart you win, if you sur - vive

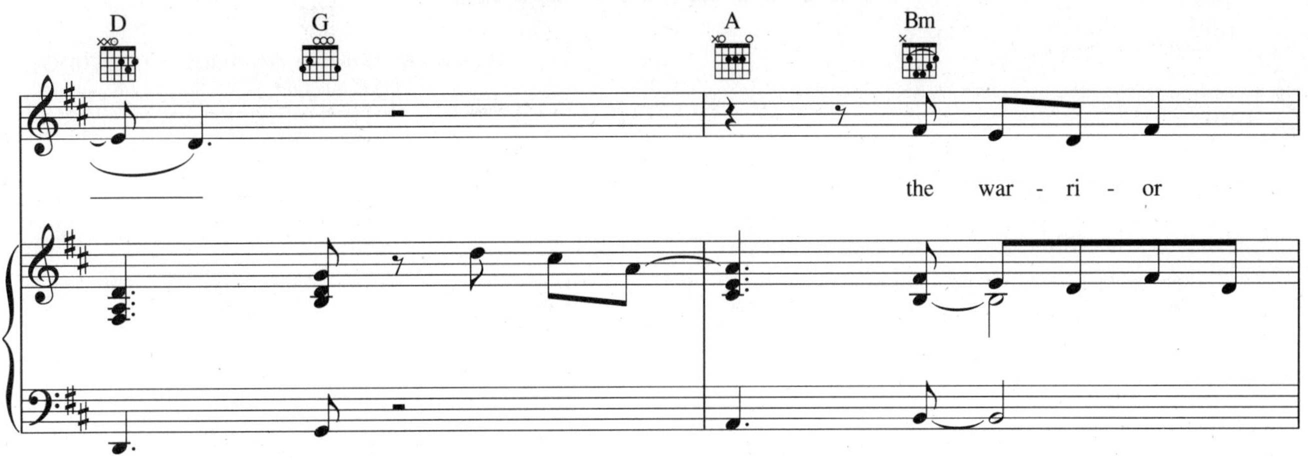

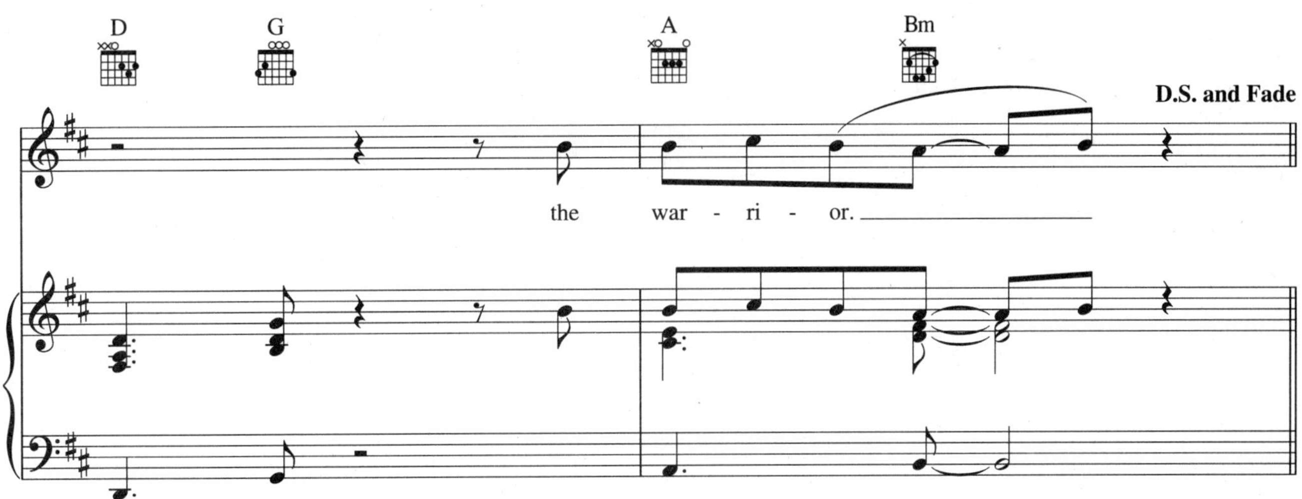

Additional Lyrics

2. You talk, talk, you talk to me,
Your eyes touch me physically.
Stay with me, we'll take the night
As passion takes another bite.
Who's the hunter, who's the game?
I feel the beat, call your name.
I hold you close in victory.
I don't wanna tame your animal style;
You won't be caged in the call of the wild.
Chorus

WATERFALLS

Words and Music by MARQUEZE ETHERIDGE,
LISA NICOLE LOPES, RICO R. WADE,
PAT BROWN and RAMON MURRAY

D♭maj7
A♭(add9)
3fr
B♭
at a son that she just can't touch.
ta - tion, but he just can't ___ see.
If at an - y
E♭
3fr
B♭(add9)
6fr
time he's in a jam she'll be by his side, but he does - n't
She gives him lov - ing that his bod - y can't han - dle, but all
D♭maj7
A♭(add9)/E♭
6fr
re - al - ize he hurts her so much.
he can say is, "Ba - by, it's good to me."
E♭maj7
3fr
B♭(add9)
6fr
But all the pray - ing just ain't help - ing at all, 'cause he can't
One day he goes and takes a glimpse in the mir - ror, but he

D♭maj7
A♭(add9)
3fr
seem to keep his self out of trou - ble. So, he goes out
does - n't rec - og - nize his own face.
E♭maj7
3fr
B♭(add9)
6fr
and he makes his mon - ey the best way he knows how, an - oth - er
His health is fad - ing and he does - n't know why. Three let - ters
D♭maj7
A♭(add9)
3fr
bod - y lay - ing cold in the gut - ter. Lis - ten to me.
took him to his fi - nal rest - ing place. Y'all don't hear me.
E♭
3fr
B♭(add9)
6fr
Don't go chas - ing wa - ter - falls. Please stick to the

D♭maj7
A♭(add9)
3fr
riv - ers and the lakes that you're used to. I know that you're
E♭
3fr
B♭(add9)
6fr
gon - na have it your way or noth - ing at all, but I think you're
D♭maj7
A♭(add9)/E♭
6fr
1.
2.
mov-ing too fast.
Come on.
E♭maj7
3fr
B♭(add9)
6fr
D♭maj7
A♭
4fr
Rap (See additional lyrics)

E♭maj7
3fr
B♭(add9)
6fr
D♭maj7
A♭(add9)/E♭
6fr
1.
N.C.
2.
Rap ends
E♭
3fr
B♭(add9)
6fr
Don't go chas - ing wa - ter - falls. Please stick to the
D♭maj7
A♭(add9)
3fr
riv - ers and the lakes that you're used to. I know that you're

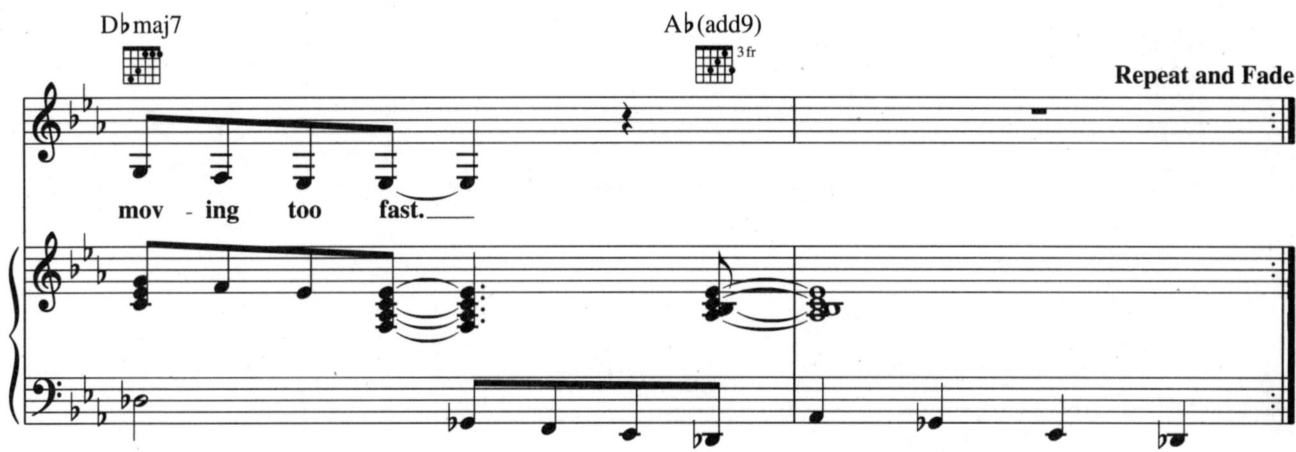

Additional Lyrics

Rap: I seen a rainbow yesterday
But too many storms have come and gone
Leavin' a trace of not one God-given ray
Is it because my life is ten shades of gray
I pray all ten fade away
Seldom praise Him for the sunny days
And like His promise is true
Only my faith can undo
The many chances I blew
To bring my life to anew
Clear blue and unconditional skies
Have dried the tears from my eyes
No more lonely cries
My only bleedin' hope
Is for the folk who can't cope
Wit such an endurin' pain
That it keeps 'em in the pourin' rain
Who's to blame
For tootin' caine in your own vein
What a shame
You shoot and aim for someone else's brain
You claim the insane
And name this day in time
For fallin' prey to crime
I say the system got you victim to your own mind
Dreams are hopeless aspirations
In hopes of comin' true
Believe in yourself
The rest is up to me and you

THE WAY YOU MOVE

Words and Music by ANTWAN PATTON,
PATRICK BROWN and CARLTON MAHONE

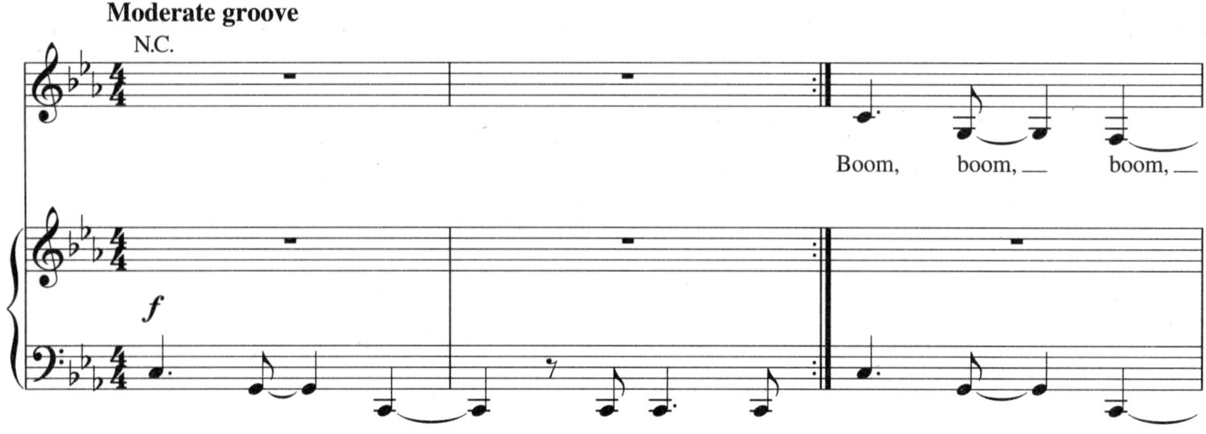

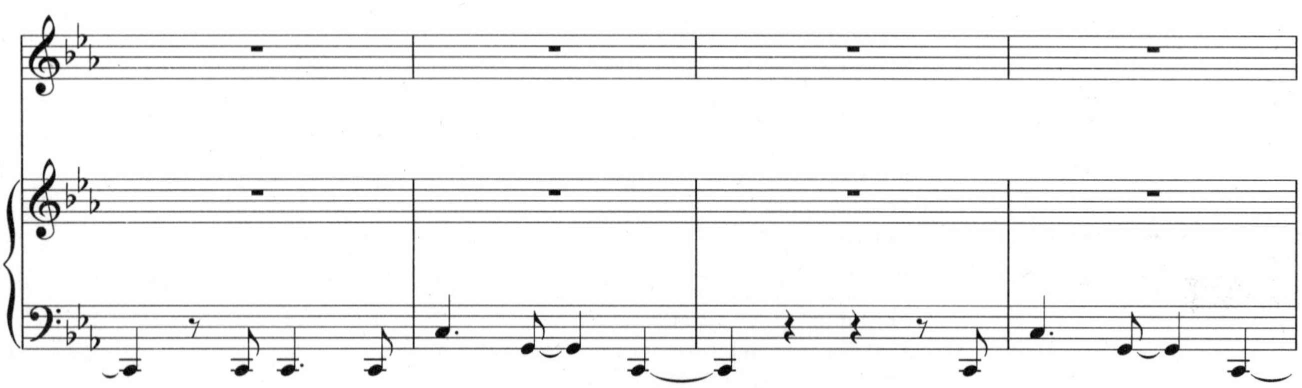

(Rap continues)

Cm7
3fr
I like the way you move.
I like the way you move.

A♭/C
3fr
Woo,
I love the way you move.
G7
Cm7
3fr
I love the way.
I love the way.
I love the way you move.
I love the way you move.
Woo,
A♭/C
3fr
I love the way you move.
I love the way.

1
2
G7
G7
Cm7
3fr
I love the way.
I love the way.
Hey ba - by, girl
don't you stop it. Come on la - dy, dance all a - round me. You
Ab/C
3fr
look so fine, look so fine. Look so fine, driv - in' me out of my mind,
G7
Cm7
3fr
out of my mind.
If I could, I would just leave with you

A♭/C
3fr
ba - by. Ooh, 'cause you light me, and ex - cite
me. And you know you got me ba - by.
G7
Cm7
3fr
I like the way you move. I like the way you move.
A♭/C
3fr
Woo, I love the way you move.

Rap Lyrics

Rap 1: Ready for action, nip it in the bud.
We never relaxin'. OutKast is everlastin'.
Not clashin', not at all.
But see, my nigga went up to do a little actin'.
Now that's for anyone askin'.
Give me one, pass 'em.
Drip, drip, drop, there goes an eargasm.
Now you comin' out the side of your face.
We tappin' right into your memory banks, thanks.
So click it or ticket, let's see your seatbelt fastened.
Trunk rattlin' like two midgets in the back seat wrestlin'
Speakerboxxx vibrate the tag.
Make it sound like aluminum cans in the bag.
But I know y'all wanted that eight-o-eight.
Can you feel that B-A-S-S, bass?
But I know y'all wanted that eight-o-eight.
Can you feel that B-A-S-S, bass?

Rap 2: The whole room fell silent. The girls all paused with glee.
Turnin' left, turnin' right, are they lookin' at me?
Well I was lookin' at them, there, there on the dance floor.
Now they got me in the middle feelin' like a man whore.
Especially the big girl. Big girls need love too.
No discrimination here, squirrel. So keep your hands off my cheeks.
Let me study how you ride the beat, you big freak.
Skinny slim women got the the camel-toe within' 'em.
You can hump them, lift them, bend them,
Give them something to remember.
Yell out "timber" when you fall through the chop shop.
Take a deep breath and exhale.
Your ex-male friend, boyfriend was boring as hell.
Well let me listen to the story you tell.
And we can make moves like a person in jail....
On the low, hoe!

WE ARE THE WORLD

Words and Music by LIONEL RICHIE
and MICHAEL JACKSON

Bsus B E A/E B/E E
We can't go on pre - tend - ing day by day that some -
Send them your heart so they'll know that some - one cares and their
A B7 E A/E E C♯m
one, some - where will soon make a change. We are all a part of God's
lives will be strong - er and free. As God has shown us by
G♯m F♯m7 F♯m7/A
great big fam - i - ly and the truth, you know, love is all we need.
turn - ing stone to bread, so we all must lend a help - ing hand.
Bsus B E/G♯ A B E
We are the world, we are the chil - dren, we are the ones

A
B
E
to make a bright - er day, so let's start giv - ing.
There's a
C♯m
4fr
G♯m
4fr
choice we're mak - ing,
we're sav - ing our own lives,
it's true;
F♯m7
A/B
1
E
A/E
B/E
A/E
we make bet - ter days, just you and me.
E
A/E
B/E
A/E
2
E
When you're

C
D
E
A/E
E
down and out, there seems no hope at all, but if you
C
D
E
just be - lieve, there's no way we can fall. Let us
C♯m
4fr
G♯m
4fr
re - al - ize that a change will on - ly come when
F♯m7
F♯m7/A
Bsus
B
we stand to - geth - er as one. We are the world,

A
B
E
we are the chil - dren, we are the ones
A
B
E
to make a bright - er day, so let's start giv - ing. There's a
C♯m
4fr
G♯m
4fr
choice we're mak - ing, we're sav - ing our own lives, it's true;
F♯m7
A/B
1
E
E/G♯
we make bet - ter days, just you and me. We are the world,

2
E
F
B♭
C
F
We are the world, we are the chil - dren, we are the ones
B♭
C
F
to make a bright - er day, so let's start giv - ing. There's a
Dm
Am
choice we're mak - ing, we're sav - ing our own lives, it's true;
Gm7
B♭/C
F
E♭/G
3fr
F/A
Repeat and Fade
we make bet - ter days, just you and me. We are the world,

THE WEIGHT

By J.R. ROBERTSON

A
C#m
4fr
D
A
Asus4
"Hey, mis-ter can you tell me where a man might find a bed?"
He just grinned and shook my hand, "No" was all he said.
E
D
Take a load off Fan-ny, take a load for free.
Dmaj7
Take a load off Fan - ny
and
and
and
you

Verse 2:
I picked up my bag, I went looking for a place to hide
When I saw Carmen and the Devil walking side by side
I said "Hey, Carmen, come on, let's go down town."
She said, "I gotta go but my friend can stick around."

Take a load off Fanny etc.

Verse 3:
Go down, Miss Moses, there's nothing you can say
It's just ol' Luke and Luke's waiting on the judgement day
"Well, Luke my friend, what about young Anna Lee?"
He said "Do me a favour son, won't you stay
and keep Anna Lee Company?"

Take a load off Fanny etc.

Verse 4:
Crazy Chester followed me and he caught me in the fog
He said "I will fix your rack if you'll take Jack, my dog."
I said "Wait a minute Chester, you know a peaceful man."
He said "That's O.K. boy, won't you feed him when you can."

Take a load off Fanny etc.

Verse 5:
Catch a cannonball now, to take me down the line
My bag is sinking low and I do believe it's time
To get back to Miss Fanny, you know she's the only one
Who sent me here with her regards for everyone.

Take a load off Fanny etc.

WEREWOLVES OF LONDON

Words and Music by WARREN ZEVON,
ROBERT WACHTEL and LeROY MARINEL

D5
5fr
C5
3fr
G5
3fr
for to get a big dish of beef chow mein.
Ow-ooh! Were - wolves of Lon - don.
Ow - ooh!
Ow-ooh! Were - wolves of Lon - don.
Ow - ooh!
You hear him howl - in' a-round your

G5
3fr
D5
5fr
C5
3fr
kitch - en door.
You bet - ter not let him in!
Lit - tle old la - dy got mu - ti - la - ted
late last night;
were - wolves of Lon - don a - gain.
Ow - ooh! Were - wolves of Lon - don.
Instrumental solo

D5
5fr
C5
3fr
G5
3fr
Ow - ooh!
Ow - ooh!
Were - wolves of Lon - don.
Ow - ooh!
1
2
Solo ends
He's the hair - y - hand - ed gent who
ran a - muck in Kent;
late - ly, he's been o - ver - heard in May-

G5
D5
C5
G5
- fair.
You bet-ter stay a-way from him!
He'll rip your lungs out, Jim!
D5
C5
G5
Huh! I'd like to meet his tai - lor.
D5
C5
G5
D5
C5
Ow-ooh! Were - wolves of Lon - don.
Ow - ooh!
G5
D5
C5
G5
Ow-ooh! Were - wolves of Lon - don.
3fr
5fr

D5
C5
G5
5fr
3fr
Ow - ooh!
Well, I saw Lon Cha - ney walk -
- ing with the Queen,
do - in' the were - wolves of Lon - don.
I saw Lon Cha - ney Ju - nior walk -
- ing with the Queen,
do - in' the were - wolves of Lon - don.

G5
3fr
D5
5fr
C5
6
I saw a were - wolf drink in' a pi - ña co -
la - da at Trad - er Vick's;
and his hair was per - fect.
Ow - ooh!
Repeat and Fade
Optional Ending
(1st time only)
Were - wolves of Lon - don.
Huh! Draw blood.
- don.

WHAT THE WORLD NEEDS NOW IS LOVE

Lyric by HAL DAVID
Music by BURT BACHARACH

Bm7
Em7
Bm7
Em7
world needs now is love, sweet love.
C
To Coda
B
B7
No, not just for some, but for ev - 'ry - one.
Em7
Lord, we don't need an - oth - er moun - tain. There are
Lord, we don't need an - oth - er mead - ow. There are
Dm9
3fr
G6/9
Cmaj7
C6
moun - tains and hill - sides e - nough to climb. There are
corn - fields and wheat - fields e - nough to grow. There are

Dm7
G13
3fr
Cmaj7
Em7
o - ceans and riv - ers e - nough to cross, e - nough to last
sun - beams and moon - beams e - nough to shine, oh, lis - ten, Lord,
A7
Am7/D
1
D9
4fr
Am7/D
2
D9
4fr
Am7/D
D.S. al Coda
till the end of time. What the
if you want to know. What the
CODA
B
B7
E7
C
ev - 'ry - one. No, not just for some, oh, but
Bm7
Cmaj7
D7
G
just for ev - 'ry - one.

WHEN I NEED YOU

Words by CAROLE BAYER SAGER
Music by ALBERT HAMMOND

D
A
need love, I hold out my hands and I touch
need you, I just close my eyes and I'm with
A♯dim
Bm
love, I nev - er knew there was so much love
you, and all that I so wan - na give you babe. It's
A
keep - ing me warm night and day.
on - ly a heart - beat a - way.
Bm
A
Miles and miles of emp - ty space in be - tween us, A
It's not eas - y when the road is good - bye love,

Bm
A
tel - e - phone can't take the place of your smile. ___ But you
hon - ey, that's a heav - y load that we bear. ___ But you
D
Bm
Em
know I won't _ be trav - el - ing ___ for - ev - er. ___
know I won't _ be trav - el - ing ___ a life - time. _
It's
Em7
1
A7
cold out, but hold out and do like I do. When I
2
A11
D
A G A
D.S. and Fade
Optional Ending
D
do. When I need you. When I need you.

WHEN I'M GONE

Words and Music by MATT ROBERTS,
BRAD ARNOLD, CHRISTOPHER HENDERSON
and ROBERT HARRELL

Slow Rock ♩ = 76

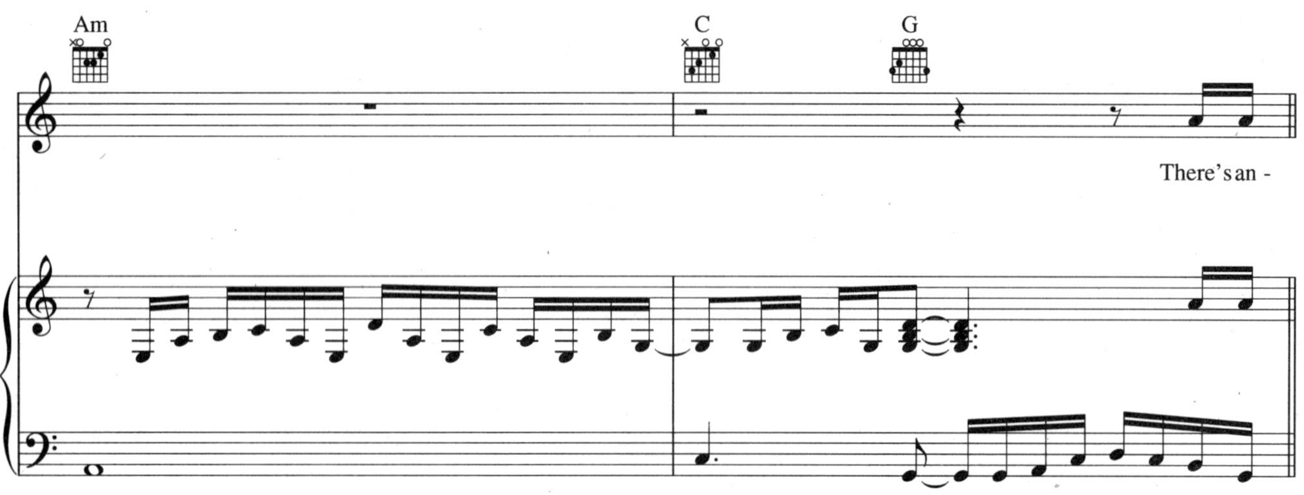

Am
C
G
3
se-crets in this life that I can't hide. Well,
Am
C
G
some-where in this dark - ness, there's a light that I can't find. Well,
Am
C
G
may-be it's too far a - way, yeah, or may - be I'm just blind.
Am
Yeah, may - be I'm just blind.

So, hold me when I'm
A5
5fr
D5
5fr
G5
3fr
here. Right me when I'm wrong. Hold me when I'm scared and love me when I'm gone. Ev-'ry-thing I
A5
5fr
D5
5fr
G5
3fr
am and ev-'ry thing in me wants to be the one you want-ed me to be. I'll nev-er let you
A5
5fr
D5
5fr
G5
3fr
down, e-ven if I could. I'd give up ev-'ry-thing if on-ly for your good. So, hold me when I'm

A5
5fr
D5
5fr
G5
3fr
To Coda
here. Right me when I'm wrong. You can hold me when I'm scared. You won't al-ways be there. So, love me when
3
3
A5
5fr
C5
3fr
G5
3fr
A5
5fr
I'm gone.
Love me when I'm gone.
3
3
C5
3fr
G5
3fr
Am
C
G
When your ed-u-ca-tion x-ray can-not see un-der my skin. I
Am
C
G
won't tell you a damn thing that I could not tell my friends.

Am
C
G
Roam - ing through this dark - ness, I'm a - live but I'm a - lone. And
Am
C
G
D.S. al Coda
part of me is fight - ing this, but part of me is gone. So, hold me when I'm
CODA
A5
B5
C5
D5
E5
D5
E5
A5
B5
C5
D5
G5
I'm gone.
A5
B5
C5
D5
E5
D5
E5
A5
B5
C5
D5
G5
A5

May-be I'm just blind.
So, hold me when I'm
A5
5fr
D5
5fr
G5
3fr
here. Right me when I'm wrong. Hold me when I'm scared and love me when I'm gone. Ev-'ry-thing I
A5
5fr
D5
5fr
G5
3fr
am and ev-'ry thing in me wants to be the one you want-ed me to be. I'll nev-er let you
A5
5fr
D5
5fr
G5
3fr
down, e-ven if I could. I'd give up ev-'ry-thing if on-ly for your good. So, hold me when I'm

A5
D5
G5
5fr
3fr
here. Right me when I'm wrong. You can hold me when I'm scared. You won't al-ways be there. So, love me when
3
A5
C5
G5
A5
I'm gone.
Love me when I'm gone.
C5
G5
Am
Cmaj7
G2
Love me when I'm gone, when I'm gone, when I'm
Am
Cmaj7
G2
A5
gone, when I'm gone.

WHERE DO BROKEN HEARTS GO

Words and Music by CHUCK JACKSON
and FRANK WILDHORN

D
A/B
Bm7
said we need - ed space, but all we found was an emp - ty place. And the
had was so much more than we ev - er had be - fore. And no
Em7
G/A
3fr
A
on - ly thing I learned is that I need you des - p'rate - ly.
mat - ter how I tried, you were al - ways on my mind.
So
F♯m7
Bm7
Em7
G/A
3fr
here I am, and can you please tell me, oh:
D
A/C♯
G/B
D/A
Where do bro - ken hearts go? Can they find their way home,

G D/F♯ Em7 G/A A

back to the o - pen arms of a love that's wait - ing there? And

D A/C♯ G/B D/A

if some - bod - y loves you, won't they al - ways love you?

G D/F♯ Em7 G/A A

3

I look in your eyes and I know that you still care for

1

D A/C♯ G/B F♯m/A G G/A A

me. I've been a -

2
D C/E D/F♯ G F♯m7 Em7 G/A A/D
3fr
me. And now that I am here with you, I'll nev-er let you go. I
B♭ F/A G G/A A♭/B♭
3fr 4fr
3
look in-to your eyes and now I know. Now I know.
E♭ B♭/D A♭/C E♭/B♭
3fr 3fr 6fr
Where do bro-ken hearts go? Can they find their way home,
A♭ E♭/G Fm7 A♭/B♭ B♭
4fr 3fr 4fr
back to the o-pen arms of a love that's wait-ing there? And

E♭
B♭/D
A♭/C
E♭/B♭
if some - bod - y loves you,
won't they al - ways love you?
A♭
E♭/G
Fm7
A♭/B♭
B♭
I look in your eyes and I know that you still care.
Fm7
A♭/B♭
B♭
E♭
B♭/D
know that you still care for me, for
A♭/C
Gm/B♭
A♭
A♭/B♭
B♭
E♭
me. You still care for me.

WHITE RABBIT

Words and Music by
GRACE SLICK

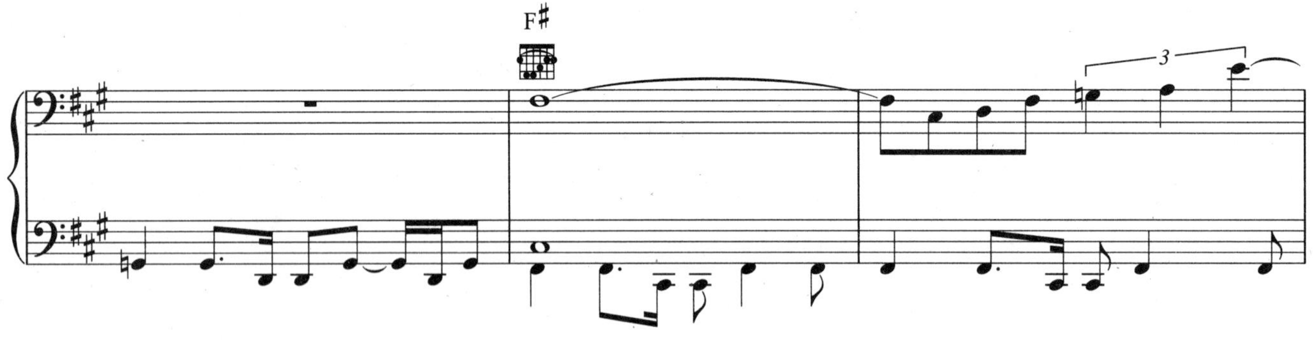

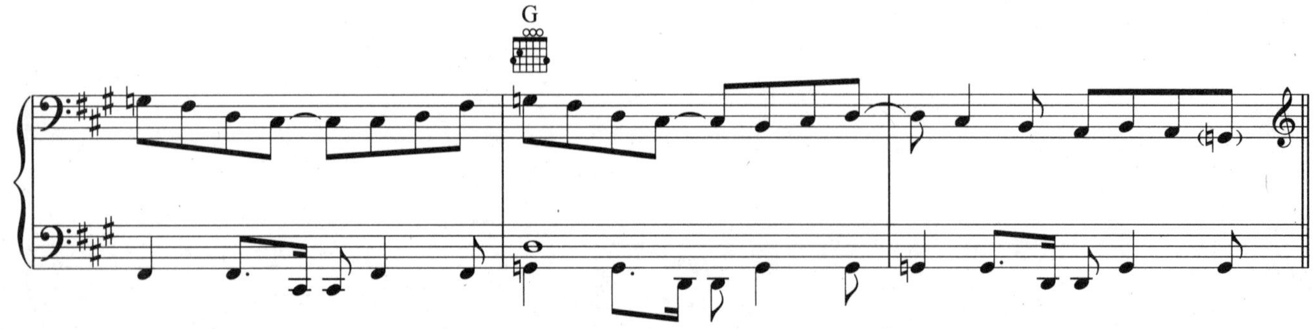

Psychedelic Stomp
F♯
G
mf
One pill makes you larg - er and one pill makes you
you go chas - ing rab - bits and you know you're going to
small. And the ones that moth - er gives you don't
fall, tell 'em all who got a smok - in' cat - er - pil - lar has
A
C
D
do an - y - thing at all. Go ask A - lice when she's ten feet tall.
giv - en you the call. Call A - lice when she was just small.
1
2
E
And if
When the men on the

A
chess - board get up and tell you where to go. And you've
E
A
just had some kind of mush - room, and your mind is mov - ing low,
F♯
go ask A - lice, I think she'll know.
G
When log - ic and pro - por - tion have fall - en slop - py

F♯
dead, and the white knight is talk - ing back - wards, and the
G
A
red queen's lost her head, re - mem - ber
C
A
E
A
what the dor - mouse said. Feed your head,
E
A
feed your head.

WILD WORLD

Words and Music by
CAT STEVENS

Am
D7
G
Cmaj7
But if you want to leave take good care, hope you have a lot of nice things to wear;
But if you want to leave take good care, hope you make a lot of nice friends out there.
F
Dm
E
G7
but then a lot of nice things turn bad out there.
But just re-mem-ber there's a lot of bad and be - ware.
C
G
Oh ba - by, ba - by it's a
F
G
F
wild world.
It's hard to get by just up-on a

C
G
smile.
Oh, ba - by, ba - by it's a
F
G
F
To Coda
wild world.
I'll al-ways re-mem - ber you ___ like a
1
C
Dm
E
2
C
Dm
E
child, girl. ___
child, girl. ___
Am
D7
G
Cmaj7

F
Dm7
E
Ba - by I love _ you,
Am
D7
G
C
but if you want to leave ___ take good care, hope you make a lot of nice friends_ out
F
Dm
E
G7
there. But just re - mem - ber there's a lot of bad and be - ware. ___
D.S. al Coda
CODA
C
child, girl. ___

WITH OR WITHOUT YOU

Words by BONO and THE EDGE
Music by U2

E♭
E♭/B♭
Cm7
Sleight of hand and twist of fate, on a bed of nails
Through the storm we reach the shore. You give it all
E♭/A♭
E♭
E♭/B♭
she makes me wait. And I wait with-out
but I want more. And I'm wait - ing for
Cm7
A♭
E♭
you, with or with-out you,
you, with or with-out you,
1
E♭/B♭
Cm7
A♭(add9)
with or with - out you.

Eb/Bb
Cm7
Ab(add9)
with or with - out you, uh, huh. I can't live
Eb
Eb/Bb
Cm7
with or with - out you.
Ab(add9)
Eb
Eb/Bb
Cm
Ab
Eb
Bb7sus
And you give your-self a - way. And you

Cm7
Ab
Eb
give your-self a - way.
And you give,
and you give,
Bb7sus
Cm7
To Coda
Ab
and you give your-self a - way.
Eb
Bb7sus
Cm7
My hands are tied,
the bod - y bruised.
Ab
Eb
Bb7sus
You got me with
noth-ing to win
and

Cm7
3fr
A♭
4fr
D.S. al Coda
CODA
A♭
4fr
noth-ing left to lose. And you
Wth or with-out
E♭
3fr
B♭7sus
Cm7
3fr
you, with or with - out you, oh.
A♭
4fr
E♭
3fr
B♭7sus
I can't live with or with-
Cm
3fr
A♭
4fr
E♭
3fr
out you. Oh.

B♭7sus
Cm7
3fr
A♭
4fr
Oh.
E♭
3fr
B♭7sus
Cm
3fr
Oh,
oh,
oh.
A♭
4fr
E♭
3fr
B♭7sus
With or with-out you,
with or with-
Cm7
3fr
A♭
4fr
E♭
3fr
- out you, uh, huh.
I can't live

B♭7sus Cm A♭

with or with - out you, with or with-

E♭

out you.

Ah. Ah.

E♭ B♭sus Cm A♭(no3)

Repeat and Fade

WOMAN

Words and Music by
JOHN LENNON

Fm
B♭sus
B♭
A♭
4fr
Fm7
Gm
3fr
thank - ful - ness
for show - ing me the mean - ing of suc -
keep us a - part.
Af - ter all, it is writ - ten in the
B♭sus
B♭
E♭maj9
Cm7
3fr
cess.
stars.
Ooh,
well,
Fm7
B♭6
E♭maj9
Cm7
3fr
well.
Doo doo doo doo doo.
Ooh,
well,
Fm7
1
B♭6
2
B♭6
well.
Doo doo doo doo doo.
doo doo.

E
F#m7
E/G#
F#m7
E
C#m
4fr
Wom - an, please let me ex - plain. __ I nev - er meant to cause you
F#m
Bsus
B
A
F#m7
G#m
4fr
sor - row or pain. __ So let me tell you a - gain and a - gain and a -
Bsus
B
Emaj9
C#m7
4fr
gain: __ I love __ you, yeah,
F#m7
Repeat and Fade
B6
Optional Ending
B6
E
yeah, now and for - ev - er. I ev - er.

WOO-HOO

Words and Music by
GEORGE DONALD McGRAW

B♭7
F
B Chorus
F
F7
Woo - Hoo Woo - Hoo - Hoo Woo - Hoo Woo-Hoo-Hoo
mf-f
B♭
F
Woo - Hoo Woo - Hoo - Hoo Woo - Hoo Woo - Hoo - Hoo
C7
B♭
1.
F
Woo - Hoo Woo - Hoo Woo - Hoo - Hoo - Hoo
2.
F
Woo-Hoo-Hoo - Hoo!

YELLOW

Words and Music by GUY BERRYMAN,
JON BUCKLAND, WILL CHAMPION and CHRIS MARTIN

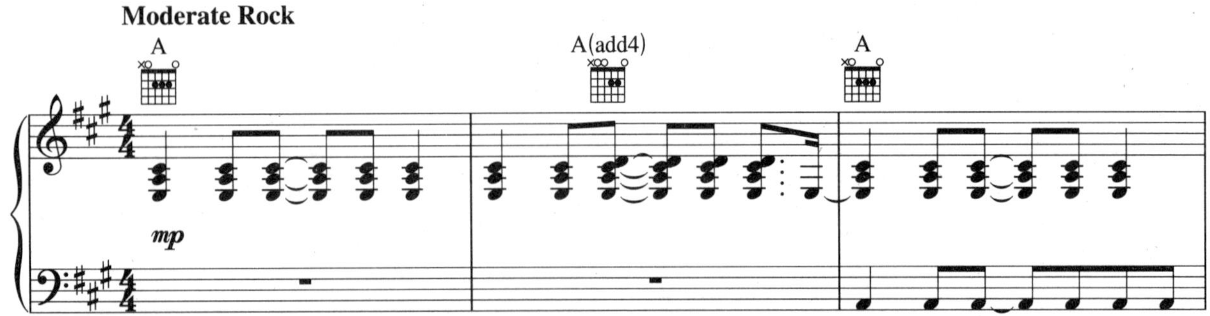

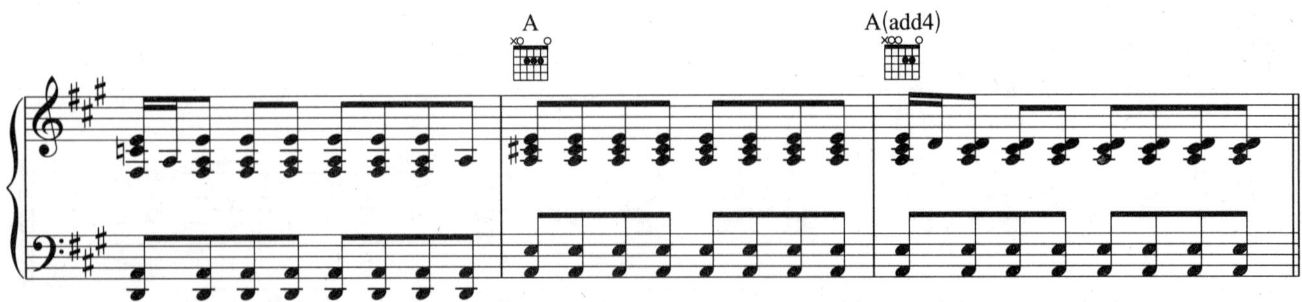

A
E6
Look at the stars; look how they shine for you,
mf
Dmaj7
and ev - 'ry - thing you do.
Yeah, they were all yel - low.
A
E6
I came a - long; I wrote a song for you,
I swam a - cross, I jumped a - cross for you.
mp
Dmaj7
and all the things you do,
Oh, what a thing to do,
and it was called "Yel - low."
'cause you were all yel - low.

A
E6
I drew a line, So then I took my turn.
I drew a line for you.
Dmaj7
Oh, what a thing to have done; and it was all yel-low.
Oh, what a thing to do; and they was all yel-low.
A
A(add4)
Dmaj7
Your skin.
F♯m7
E6
Dmaj7
F♯m7
E6
oh yeah, your skin and bones turn in - to some-thing beau - ti - ful.

Dmaj7
F♯m7
E6
And you know, you know I love you so,
for you I bleed my-self
Dmaj7
Dmaj9♯11
Dmaj7
Dmaj9♯11
Dmaj7
dry,
you know I love you so.
for you I bleed my-self
A
A(add4)
E7(add4)
dry.
f
D(add2)

A
1
A(add4)
2
A(add4)
It's
A
true;
look how they shine for
E7(add4)
you,
look how they shine for
D(add2)
you,
look how they shine for...
A
A(add4)
Look how they shine for

E7(add4)
you,
look how they shine for
D(add2)
you,
look how they shine.
A
Look at the stars;
look how they shine for
Em7(add4)
5fr
you,
and all the things that you do.
Dmaj7

YOU ARE NOT ALONE

Words and Music by
ROBERT KELLY

1, 3.
C♯m7
F♯7sus4
and leave my world so cold?
(1, 3.) Ev-'ry
A6
G♯7
E
day I sit and ask my-self how did this thing end?
C♯m7
F♯7sus4
Some-thing whis-pers in my ear and says.
(2. 4.) You are not a-lone
2.
F♯7sus4
B
Gmaj7
A/G
but you are not a-lone
lone,
lone,

B
Gmaj7
F#7sus4
why
lone.
(3.) Just the oth - er night
4.
F#7sus4
B
G
A/G
but you are not a-lone.
Whis-per three words then I'll come
Em7
Gmaj7
A/G
run-ning,
I
and girl you know that I'll be
F#7sus4
G7sus4
D♭
there,
I'll be
there.
You are not a-lone,

D♭
B♭m7
E♭m7
fr6
I am here with you, though you're far a-way, I am here to stay,
A♭7sus4
fr4
D♭
B♭m7
but you are not a-lone but I am here with you, though we're far a-part,
E♭m7
fr6
A♭7sus4
fr4
E♭/B♭
fr3
you're al-ways in my heart but you are not a-lone
E♭
fr3
Cm7
fr3
Fm7
I am here with you, though you're far a-way, I am here to stay

Verse 2:
You are not alone
I am here with you
Though you're far away
I am here to stay.
You are not alone
I am here with you
Though we're far apart
You're always in my heart.
But you are not alone.

Verse 3:
Just the other night
I thought I heard you cry
Asking me to go
And hold you in my arms.
I can hear your breaths
Your burdens I will bear
But first I need you here
Then forever can begin.

Verse 4:
You are not alone
I am here with you
Though you're far away
I am here to stay.
But you are not alone
I am here with you
Though we're far apart
You're always in my heart.
But you are not alone.

YOU BELONG TO ME

Words and Music by CARLY SIMON
and MICHAEL McDONALD

Fm9
G7sus
know? Don't you know I'll al - ways
me. Thought we'd closed the book; locked the
Cm9
be your girl?
door.
You don't have to
A♭maj7
G7sus
G+/B
prove to me you're beau - ti - ful to strang -
Cm7
E♭maj7
E♭7
E♭/F
F6
3fr
3fr
- ers. I've got lov - ing eyes

Eb/F
F6
Abmaj7/Bb
G7sus
C7#5
of my own.
(You be-long to
Bbm7
Fm7
me.) Tell her you were fool-ing. (You be-long to me.) You don't e-ven
Bbm7
know her. (You be-long to me.) Tell her that I love you. (You be-long to
C7sus
C7#5
1
2
D.S. and Fade
me.) You be-long to (You be-long to

YOU DO SOMETHING TO ME

Words and Music by
PAUL WELLER

D
Am7
Bm7
wonder - der - ful
then chase it all a - way
(Verse 3: Instrumental to chorus)
Em
mix - ing my e - mo -
D
Am7
Bm7
- tions,
that throws me back a - gain
Em
CHORUS
Hang - ing on the

C7/G
Am7
wi - re yeah.
I'm wait - ing for my
Em
C7
3fr
change
I'm danc - ing through the
1.
G
A
C
C/D
Em
fi - re just to catch a slame and feel real a - gain.
f
mf
2.
Em
D
Am7
Bm7
You do some - thing to me
some - where deep in -
mf

Em
D
-side,
I'm hop-ing to get close to
Am7
Bm7
Em
a peace I can-not find
Danc-ing though the
f
C7/G
Am7
C/D
fi-re yeah,
just to catch a flame
Em
C7
3fr
just to get close

G
A
C7
3fr
to.
just close e - nough to tell you that:
sf
Em
D
You do some - thing to me,
mf
Am7
Bm7
Em
3
some - thing deep in - side.
rall.

YOU MUST LOVE ME

from the Cinergi Motion Picture EVITA

Words by TIM RICE
Music by ANDREW LLOYD WEBBER

Flowing

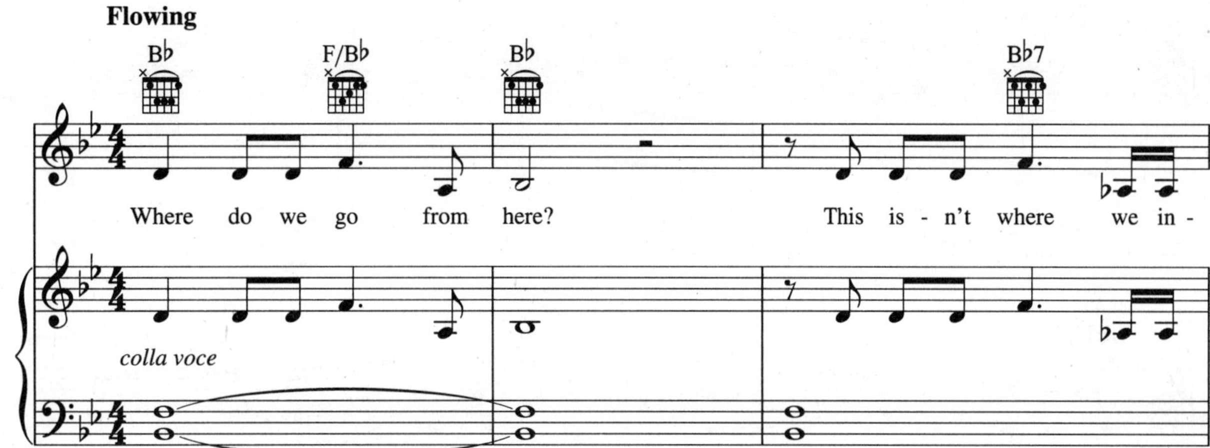

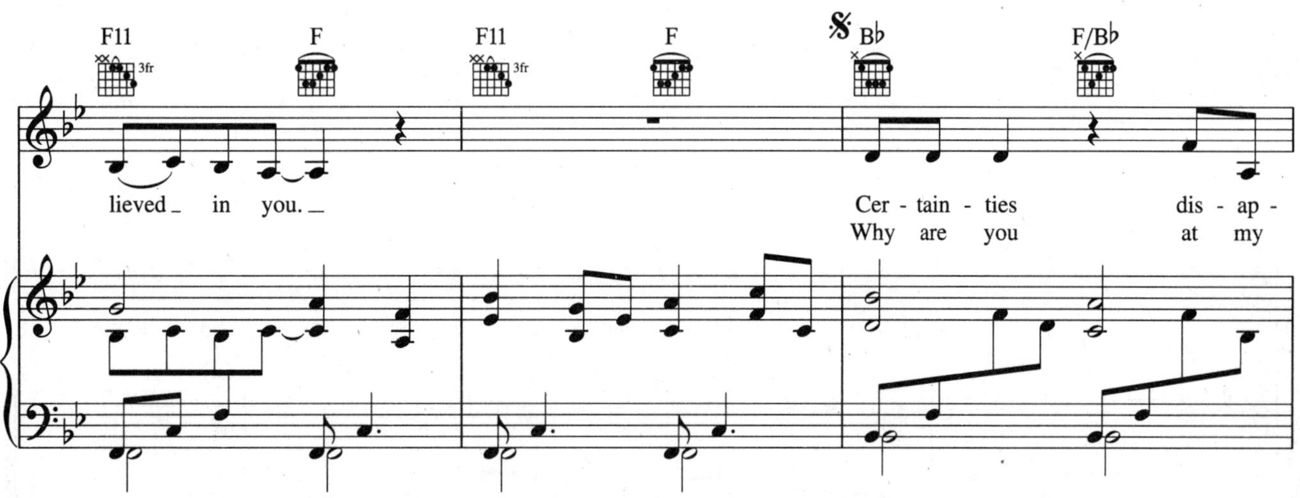

B♭
B♭7
E♭
3fr
pear
side?
what do we do
How can I be
for our dream to sur - vive,
an - y use to you now?
Cm7
F11
F
how do we keep
Give me a chance
all our pas - sions a - live
and I'll let you see how
as we used to do?
noth - ing has changed.
F11
F
D7
Gm
D7
3
Deep in my heart I'm con - ceal - ing
things that I'm long - ing to
Gm
D7
F/E♭
E♭
Cm7
Dm7
say,
scared to con - fess
what I'm feel - ing
fright - ened you'll slip a -
rit.

F
Bb
Eb/Bb
6fr
F/Bb
Bb
To Coda
way, you must love me,
you must love me.
a tempo
Eb/Bb
F/Bb
Bb
F/Bb
Bb
Bb7
Eb
3fr
Cm7
3fr
F11
3fr
F
F11
3fr
F
D.S. al Coda
CODA
Eb/Bb
6fr
F/Bb
Bb
You must love me.
rit.

YOU WERE MEANT FOR ME

Words and Music by JEWEL KILCHER
and STEVE POLTZ

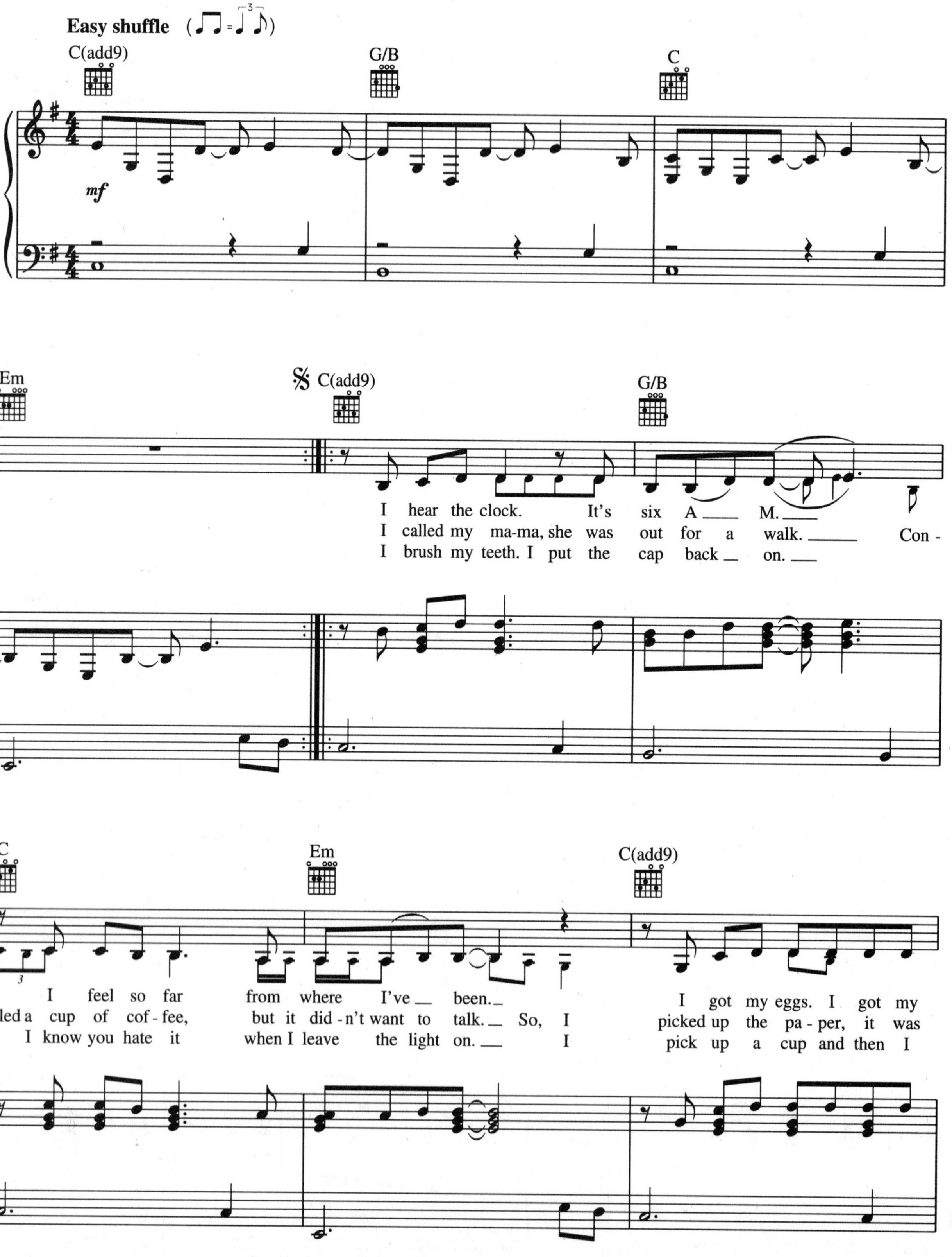

Easy shuffle

C(add9) G/B C

mf

Em C(add9) G/B

I hear the clock. It's six A___ M.___
I called my ma-ma, she was out for a walk.___ Con -
I brush my teeth. I put the cap back ___ on.___

G/B
C
D
pan-cakes, too. I got my ma-ple syr - up, ev-'ry-thing but you.
more bad news. My heart's be-ing bro-ken by peo-ple be-ing used.
turn the sheets down and then I take a deep breath, a good look a-round.
C(add9)
G/B
C
I break the yolks and make a smil - ey face. I kind - a like it in my
Put on my coat in the pour - ing rain. I saw a mov - ie, it just
Put on my p j's and hop in - to bed. I'm half a - live, but I feel
Em
C(add9)
G/B
brand new place. Wipe the spots up o - ver me, don't leave my keys in the door. I
was - n't the same 'cause it was hap - py or I was sad, and
most - ly dead. I try and tell my - self it'll be all right.

C
D
C
nev-er put wet towels on the floor an-y-more
it made me miss you, oh, so bad
I just should-n't think an-y-more to-night
'cause dreams last
D
G
D/F#
Em7
Em7/D
so long e-ven af-ter you're gone.
C
D
G
D/F#
I know that you love me, and soon you will see
Em
Em/D
C
D
you were meant for me and I was meant for
To Coda

Em
1
2
you.
I
Am7
D
Bm
D
go a-bout my bus - 'ness. I'm do-ing fine. Be-sides, what would I say if I had
C
G/D
Am7
D
you on the line? Same old sto-ry, not much to say.
Freely
Bm7
2fr
Em
Tempo Primo
C(add9)
Hearts are bro-ken ev-'ry - day.

G/B
C
1
Em
2
Em
D.S. al Coda
CODA
Em
you.
Yeah, _ you were
3
C
D
C(add9)
meant for me,
and I was meant for
you.
G/B
C
Em
rit.

YOU'RE SO VAIN

Words and Music by
CARLY SIMON

Am7
G/A
Am
F
C/F
te - gic - 'lly dipped be - low one eye, your scarf, it was ap - ri - cot.
said that we made such a pret - ty pair, and that you would nev - er leave.
flew your Lear jet up to No - va Sco - tia, to see the to - tal e - clipse of the sun.
Fmaj7
G
Em7
You had one eye in the mir - ror as you
But you gave a - way the things you loved and
Well, you're where you should be all the time and
C
watched your - self ga - votte and all the girls dreamed that they'd
one of them was me. I had some dreams, they were clouds
when you're not you're with some un - der - world spy or the wife
be your part - ner, they'd be your part - ner and
in my cof - fee, clouds in my cof - fee and
of a close friend, wife of a close friend and
you're so vain,

Dm7
C
you prob-'bly think this song is a - bout you, you're so vain.
Am7
Fmaj7
G13
2 fr
I'll bet you think this song is a - bout you. Don't you? Don't
1, 2
3
C
you? You you? Don't you? You're so vain,
Well, I
Dm7
C
Repeat and Fade
you prob-'bly think this song is a - bout you.

YOUR SONG

Words and Music by ELTON JOHN
and BERNIE TAUPIN

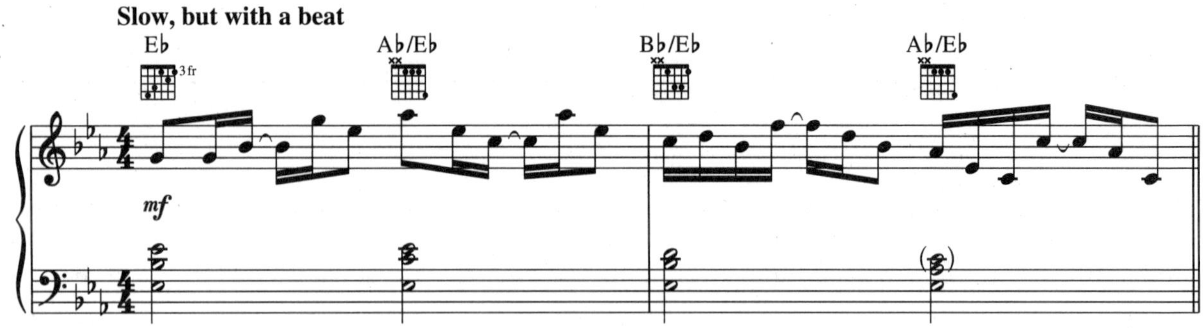

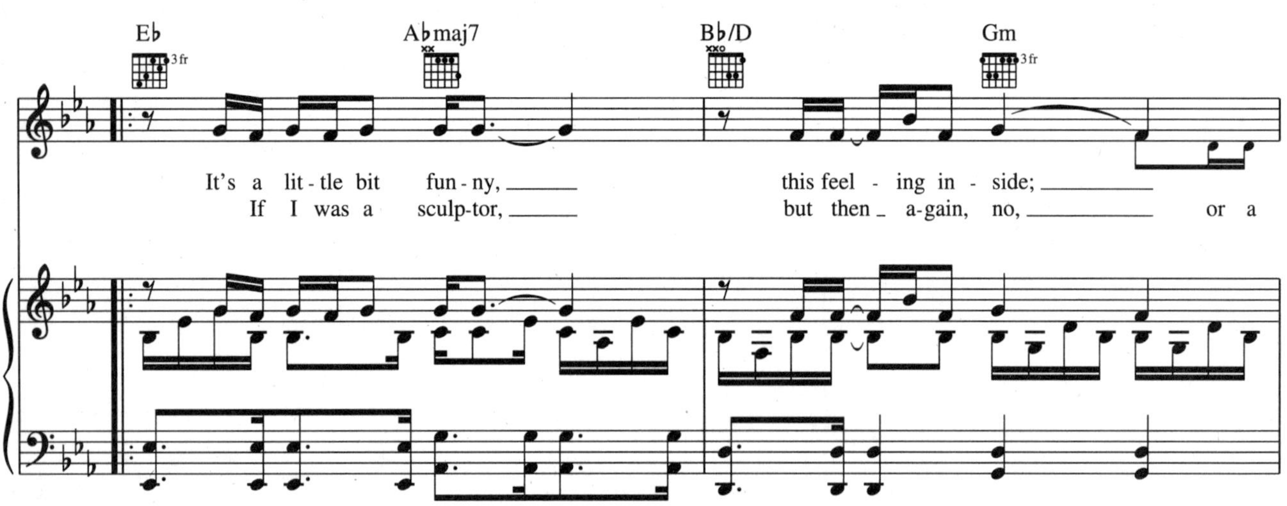

Eb/Bb
6fr
Bb
G/B
Cm
3fr
Don't have much mon - ey, but, boy, if I did,
know it's not much but it's the best I can do.
Eb
3fr
Fm7
1
Ab
4fr
Bb
I'd buy a big house where we both could live.
My gift is my song, and
Bbsus
Bb
2
Ab
4fr
Eb
3fr
this one's for you.
Ab/Eb
Eb
3fr
Bb/D
Cm
3fr
And you can tell ev - 'ry - bod - y

Fm7
Ab
Bb/D
Cm
this is your song.
It may be quite simple, but
Fm7
Ab
Cm
Cm/Bb
now that it's done,
I hope you don't mind,
I hope you don't mind
Cm/A
Ab6
Eb/G
Ab6
that I put down in words
how won - der - ful life is while
rit.
Ab
Bb
Bbsus
Bb
you're in the world.
a tempo

Eb
Abmaj7
Bb/D
Gm
I sat on the roof and kicked off the moss; well, a
So ex-cuse me for - get-ting, but these things I do;
Cm
Cm/Bb
Cm/A
Ab7
few of the vers - es, well, they've got me quite cross.
You see I've for-got-ten if they're green or they're blue.
Eb/Bb
Bb
G/B
Cm
But the sun's been quite kind while I wrote this song;
An-y - way, the thing is, what I real - ly mean,
Eb
Fm7
Ab
Bb
it's for peo-ple like you that keep it turned on.
yours are the sweet - est eyes

B♭sus
B♭
2
A♭
4fr
E♭
3fr
I've ev - er seen.
A♭/E♭
E♭
3fr
B♭/D
Cm
3fr
And you can tell ev - 'ry - bod - y
Fm7
A♭
4fr
B♭/D
Cm
3fr
this is your song.
It may be quite simp-le, but
Fm7
A♭
4fr
Cm
3fr
Cm/B♭
now that it's done,
I hope you don't mind, I hope you don't mind

Cm/A
Ab6
3 fr
Eb/G
3 fr
Ab6
3 fr
that I put down in words how won - der - ful life is while
rit.
1
Ab
4 fr
Bb
Bbsus
Bb
you're in the world.
a tempo
2
Ab
4 fr
Eb
3 fr
Ab/Eb
you're in the world.
a tempo
Bb/Eb
Ab/Eb
Eb
3 fr